To DEAR J
friend from
Kinder...
with my love Nina
x

Tealeaves Under The Bed

July 2010

Nina Sheeran

 en Press

First published in Great Britain by Pen Press
All paper used in the printing of this book has been made from wood
grown in managed, sustainable forests.

ISBN 978-1-907499-47-0

Pen Press is an imprint of
Indepenpress Publishing Ltd
25 Eastern Place
Brighton
BN2 1GJ

Printed and bound in the UK

A catalogue record of this book is available from
the British Library

Cover design by Jacqueline Abromeit

Acknowledgements

I want to thank my very dear friend Ebba Hribar for wonderfully spending so much time over 2 years printing my handwritten scripts. Ebba was our very first Danish au pair girl in 1957 aged 17. We have remained friends ever since. I am greatly indebted to her for her kindness and interest.

Tom and Alma Bryan
Nina's parents to whom the letters were written

Preface

"Tealeaves under the Bed"? Why on earth tealeaves under the bed?! What is that supposed to mean in connection with nursing? IT MEANS – ! that 60 years ago, when my peers and I were probationers, the first thing we had to do when we went on duty in the morning, was to collect the bucket of yesterday's used tealeaves from the kitchen (no teabags in those days you know!) and scatter them under all the beds in the ward in preparation for sweeping the ward floors. A very successful method it was, too, settling the dust before the sweeping. We had no cleaning machines then either.

What you are about to read is the true daily activities and honest opinions of an 18-year-old girl progressing in her training to be a nurse at the Middlesex Hospital, Mortimer St, London during three years 1950–1953.

She tells her reactions to her parents in almost daily letters, and she finally achieved her State Registration in July 1953. The rest will gradually unfold itself in what I hope you will find an interesting and enjoyable read! A lot of things happened as a result of this qualification, but that's another story! That girl of 18 is me – Nina – now 78!

Lieut. Ernest Sheeran
Sherwood Foresters 1940

**Ernest Sheeran (centre)
Senior Student at St Aidan's College, Birkenhead**

1936
Nina Bryan sets out to be a nurse!
Her sister Shirley and her dolls are her patients

THE MIDDLESEX HOSPITAL
W.1

Museum 8333

31. 12. 47.

The Lady Superintendent will
be pleased to give you an interview
on March 30th
at 10·30 AM

MATRON & LADY SUPERINTENDENT
OF NURSES:
MISS M. MARRIOTT.

THE MIDDLESEX HOSPITAL,
LONDON. W.1.
MUSEUM 8333. EXT. 309.

(And. 6-4-48)

March, 31st, 1948

Dear Madam,

I am pleased to inform you that
your application for nursing training is successful,
subject to a satisfactory medical examination and
to your sending satisfactory dental and vaccination
certificates and I can offer you a provisional
vacancy for May, 1950.

I should be glad to receive your birth and school
certificates, these will be returned to you.

You should attend for a medical examination during
January, 1950, on any day (except on a Saturday or
Sunday) at 12 noon, going direct to the Nurses' Home
Foley Street. At the same time would you please call
at Messrs Willmott Ltd. 15.c. Warren Street, W.1. to
be measured for your uniform.

You should send your dental and vaccination certificates
one month before your entry.

Kindly acknowledge this letter.

Yours faithfully,

M.J. Marriott
p.p. Slut.

Matron and Lady Superintendent of Nurses

Miss N.A. Bryan.

The Middlesex Hospital Preliminary Training School

3rd May 1950
There's such a lot to do for Monday – sewing on Cash's name tapes and so on. My vaccination has taken – so itching like fury. I have to have a Mantoux test when I get to the hospital and they are going to immunise me there as well. Mum has bought me some smashing cotton pyjamas today, blue ones and pink ones with spots! I've booked a hairdressing appointment. Have had a letter from Messrs Willmotts to say that they would supply the regulation stockings but they regret they do not stock the shoes. So now I have to hunt around for shoes in 2 or 3 days. I should think that I shall arrive at the hospital and find I have no uniform!

6th May
Six pairs of hospital stockings arrived today and we spent an hour walking around shoe shops – couldn't get exactly what the hospital ask for but they're quite nice, quite suitable and serviceable. Managed to get an umbrella and ran like the wind to Boots and then Woolworth's trying to get everything I needed. Some visitors today gave me a lovely manicure set as a farewell present – in a green leather case, with a zip, so it matches my writing case. I've got all my books. Now I'm in a flat spin over the packing. Mummy has been sewing on all the name tapes while I've been collecting all my bits and pieces together and put them in my trunk and case. I've had my name painted on the end of my trunk. Mum and Dad are going with me tomorrow on the 11.17 train from Loughborough, changing at Leicester. We get in about 1.15 I think. I can hardly believe I'm actually going to London at last and I'm wondering very much just what is in store for me. Our doctor (a good friend) says the most important thing is to make up my mind before I go that I'm going to <u>enjoy</u> it. I think I shall love it.

9th May

I have been so busy since I arrived here. The first day especially was rather hectic and I didn't really know whether I was standing on my head or my heels! Today has been a bit of a turmoil too but we are getting more settled now and have quite a lot of off-duty time, though we are already having to work jolly hard and having our first test at 2.30pm on Saturday.

This house was once a hotel so we have telephones in all the rooms. We are allowed to put calls through or receive calls at <u>any</u> time until 9.30pm. There are lectures till about 5pm but after 7.30pm we are always free. There is always a telephone operator down in our hall and he seems to be quite quick in putting our calls through. The number is Paddington 8883 and you should ask for NURSE BRYAN!! They will then get through to my room which is 56.

Incidentally we have a "long" holiday arranged for July 28th-Aug 4th and including the second weekend. Everything is marvellous here now that I've got over that first momentary feeling of loneliness. The only snag is that I'm rather too far from home and feel a bit cut off.

A lot of the girls live in or near London, and have gone home this evening – we've been off since 5pm. But one girl's parents are in South Africa, and Paddy Gee's parents live in Cyprus, so I suppose I must be thankful to have mine in England! Paddy Gee, by the way, is the girl with whom I share a room. She lives with her aunt in Edinburgh and is very nice. She's extremely tall (6ft) dark and attractive. Most of the girls have their own rooms, so we're rather unfortunate, though in a way it's an advantage, because we have great fun and are already very good friends. Our room is on the 5th (top) floor, and is really rather small for two people because there's not much cupboard space. We are especially depressed after seeing one of the other two double rooms, which in a hotel would be a very pleasant room. It's big and roomy and the beds are side by side with a table between. Ours is an attic room with a sloping ceiling. But still the beds are soft and though the heat and noise of traffic kept me awake last night, I'm sure we shall be very comfortable. I thought I should never go to sleep last night, but it <u>was</u> the first night and everything was somewhat strange. Moreover the church is just across the road from our window and the clock strikes terribly loudly on the hour!

Mummy and Daddy came with me yesterday by the 11.27 from Loughborough, changing at Leicester (where we waited 20 mins) and getting into St Pancras at 2.30. We queued for ages for a taxi and got to the hospital at 3.30. I was shown straight up to my room – with Mum and Dad – and then went for a walk round with them until I had to come back for tea at 4.30. It was horrible having to say goodbye to them but the girls are very friendly and we soon mixed together. It was a nice tea, followed by a lecture at 5.30 on what is expected of us as nurses. We were taken around the building and then had supper at 7.30. This consisted of tomato soup, roast beef, roast potatoes, cauliflower and Yorkshire pud, followed by rhubarb and ice-cream. We were free after that and went to bed (after fetching a cup of cocoa from the kitchen in our dressing gowns) at 10.30. Incidentally I had to serve at supper, and have to for this week because I'm one of the first four in the alphabet.

This morning the night porter rang the rising bell at 6.30 – the normal time – allowing nobody to oversleep. One couldn't fail to wake up! We dressed and stripped our beds, and were down for prayers in the nurses' sitting room (where I'm writing this) for 7.10. Nobody volunteered to play the hymn and Sister Slater seemed rather distressed, so I played! And now it seems I shall have to play and choose the hymns till I can work out a rota!!

10th May – Thursday
I'm afraid my off duty has been mucked about but I now have the weekend off.

14th May
I'm so pleased I came here. We seem to have settled into a routine quite quickly. Last Friday four of us went to hear a debate at the Houses of Parliament – it was on food, by Maurice Webb. We've just had lunch of chops, roast potatoes and haricot beans, plums and

junket. When I've finished this letter Paddy and I are going out into the Park, then coming back for tea and Evensong. My off duty times are: Mon, Wed, Thurs, Fri afternoons 1.30-5, Tuesday 4.30 to 11, Sat. 2.30-11 and Sunday all day. There's quite a lot of study to do after lecture time so we often stay in to work in our free time.

We have a little gang of 4 here – Paddy Gee, Anne Bishop (tall and plump with glasses, very amusing) and Mary Barnett (tall and slim and attractive and very dignified) and me. Mary has a young man of 25 called David. She says they are not serious and she likes to feel "free"! Anne Bishop is a scream. She says she's been out with thousands of boys – from the age of 10!

We've had quite a lot of lectures on Public Welfare and the other day we spent an hour on Child Welfare – and help to mothers before and after their babies' birth – the daily routine in a baby's life, times of sleeping, kicking, playing, eating etc and how to develop their minds by surrounding them with flowers and beautiful things.

To describe this place – the Bayswater Rd runs parallel with Lancaster Gate, and Middlesex House faces on to the street. There's an entrance hall with telephone switchboard by the door, and dining room on the right as you go in.

The stairs face the front door and the practical room is on the left. Over the hall (on the 1st floor) is Sister's Office. Over the dining room is the nurses' sitting room, looking out over Lancaster Gate and over the practical room is the classroom. There are 5 floors and Paddy and I sleep on the 5th. There's a lift up to the 3rd floor. After that we have to walk – it's killing!

Paddy and I are becoming prize chumps here! – we do everything wrong! We went for a walk in Kensington Gardens after supper the other evening and got locked in! We got lost, and when eventually we found the road again the gates were all locked. We just got back here by clocking in just in time, and Sister was waiting for us! She advised us not to go there again at that time of night – we'd already decided not to because we'd had several offers while strolling around, from chaps wanting a girl to sit with them. The same day the telephone rang for rather a long time and the operator had gone for his lunch. So Paddy and I decided to have a go! She put a plug in and I turned off the alarm switch and then Sister appeared. She kept saying "Hello, Hello" and then repeatedly to us – "They've forgotten to press button A so I can't hear them!" All the time of course it was Paddy and I who had cut them off by mistake!

In a lecture Sister asked what else was provided by the National Health scheme besides free dental and medical advice. Paddy shouted out "WIGS". The whole class plus Sister just roared!

We have three sisters who lecture us, and several doctors from the hospital. We had a talk on Fire Precautions by a fireman the other day and learnt how to rescue patients in blankets and on mattresses etc. We also let off a fire extinguisher! Tomorrow morning we have cookery and on Tuesday we go to the Medical School to see bodies being cut up!

Timetable beginning 15th May e.g:

Monday		Thursday	
6.30	Rising bell	8.30	Elementary Science
7.10	Prayers	10.15	Nursing Dem
7.15	Household duties	11.40	Bandaging
7.30	Breakfast	1.45	Dr. Ormorod
8	Household duties	5.50	Evensong
8.30	Nursing lecture	6.30	Physiology
9.30	Break		
10	Cookery		
12.50	Lunch		
1.30	Off duty		
5	First Aid lecture		
6.30	Anatomy lecture		
7.30	Supper		

17th May
It's now 8.30am and I'm supposed to be studying from 8-9am but I'm going with "our four" this afternoon to the Old Bailey and will not have another chance to write this letter. We went on Monday afternoon but No 1 Court (the murder court) was full and we had to

go on the back row of No 3. The policeman says that if we tell him we're there this afternoon (if there's a queue) and then dash into the "ladies", he'll cough when it's time to come out! We then follow him and he'll try to get us on to the front row of No 1!!

Yesterday we went to the Medical School at the hospital for anatomy. We had to wear long white gowns as we spent the afternoon in the medical students' dissecting room. Dr. Ormorod explained everything to us and it really was very interesting, though a bit gruesome – in fact one girl fainted. There were tables all round the room with human bodies on them, some whole, and some dissected arms and legs! Some of the bodies had the skin peeled off to expose the muscles – which we had to feel and pull apart to find out where they were attached. Another chappie had the front of his abdomen removed, and when we pulled out the cotton wool stuffing we could see all his innards lying there! There were heads lying about with chunks cut out of them, and some things were rather ghastly. There were premature babies in glass jars, cut down the midline to show their interior organs. It's all so fascinating, but I'm sure I shall see skeletons in my sleep!

We've been out for lots of walks. These warm days are lovely for Kensington Gardens. Young couples go there by the dozen with small children and babies. We have a baby in our practical room called "Baby Chase". We have to make up the baby's cot etc (a doll of course!).

19th May
Time is flying and has done ever since I came here. It seems no time since we were doing last Saturday's test, and now we're sweating on the top line for tomorrow's, which is at 8.30am. Sister Jackson is ill and our timetable has been rather messed up as a result. I have tons of notes to copy up and learn before tomorrow so I'm giving up all my free time today to catch up. It's nearly 3pm now and "our little four" have been out in Kensington Gardens for a little while, hoping to do some work there. Anne Bishop and I got cold and came back and now we're in one of the study rooms. Anne is talking her head off and nearly driving me mad and I'm trying to keep one ear sufficiently tuned in her direction to make suitable replies! We had a Confirmation service in the church here last Wednesday and Paddy

was confirmed at the last minute! – Ha! Ha! Paddy and Mary must have got cold now, they're just coming across from the park, having some difficulty crossing the busy road.

We had another visit to the Law Courts on Wednesday afternoon, but our policeman let us down and we had to go in No.3 Court after all.

Yesterday afternoon "we four" went shop gazing on Oxford Street. We had 2/- ice cream soufflés each and then spent ½ an hour trying hats on in a Sale in one of the Oxford Street shops (we didn't buy anything though!).

Last night we had our first choir practice in church with the organist. He says we do jolly well! We've got two parts in our choir too! It's just formed from the Prelim Training School and is jolly good fun! Also last night I had to read the lesson at the service at 6pm. We have Evensong every evening at 6pm except Tuesdays and Saturdays when we're off from lunch time. It's a lovely idea.

We've just got in Sister Byron's good books! She came in here to get two baskets of laundry and we offered to help her carry them out. She says "It is a pleasure to know nice helpful girls like you"!

21st May
It's a mouldy day today as far as weather goes – this morning we had a tremendous thunder storm about 10 o'clock, with thunder and lightning and spasms of downpours ever since.

Yesterday afternoon Paddy, Anne and I went to the Marble Arch News House for an hour or so and saw Charlie Chaplin. We went to Holy Communion at 8 this morning. Paddy took communion for the first time after her confirmation. There were 60 communicants!

Last night we had a bit of fun because one of the girls got herself locked in the 4th floor W.C. She was there from 10 to 6 till after 7 o'clock! The key broke when she tried to open the door and she couldn't make anyone hear when she called! The porter says he's had to break open at least 10 doors in the fortnight that we've been here!

22nd May
Sister complained of the mess in our bedroom yesterday (reported to her by the house-sister) so we took her up to show her just what we

have to put up with – no room to move or put our clothes. She was very nice and is going to look into the matter!

26th May

Last night a crowd of us from Lancaster House went to the Nurses Home Foley Street to hear the Stock Exchange male voice choir. The recital lasted for about an hour and was very good indeed. We went in the hospital bus and then had to find our own way home – we went absolutely mad walking along Oxford Street. We were laughing and singing and having a super time. It was very late when we got back so we had rather a late night. We had a good look in all the shop windows. The girls say they don't know why I've come here at all if I have the prospect of being married when I want to say the word. When I think of the <u>awful</u> Practical Nursing we had this morning I think how marvellous I am to endure it, because I think I ought not to be married at 18!!! but really I've never set a trolley before in my life and we get told off left and right for every little thing we miss out! Still it's jolly good fun and we laugh about it afterwards. It's a test of our powers of courtesy.

I must go and practise the organ in church now. I played for the service on Wednesday night and I'm playing again this evening. My arm is aching something <u>AWFUL</u> from the immunisation and I've got to have one in the other arm too!

I have time off next weekend to go home and I'm going to ask Sister if I can do my test on Friday afternoon in my free time and then catch the 12.15pm train from London. That would be so much better than messing about at Lancaster Gate till the 3.20 train.

At 9.30 every morning we dash out of the drawing room to see if there are any letters for us, and this morning as I was "dashing" Sister said, "There's a letter for you, Nurse Bryan." When Paddy gave it to me it was from Mummy. I said, "But surely there must be another one!" and Paddy and Anne Bishop just looked mischievous and said, "No there's only one today!" and dashed downstairs. When I got to the bottom of the stairs Paddy came running to me waving Ernest's (your) letter and said, "Oh look I've found another letter for you down here!" I could have strangled them – they'd obviously pinched it for a bit of fun!! By the way, 6 of us wrote to the "Much Bindingites" to ask if we could go to one of their programmes in the studio. They replied last week and sent one complimentary ticket for 2 people! We put our names in a hat and mine was one of the two to be drawn out. Aren't I <u>lucky</u>?! So we're going on Friday 2nd June at 9.55pm.

Today we had cookery from 10.30am to 12.30pm and we got a most awful fit of the giggles! During Mrs. Hall's demonstration, her assistant (Mrs. Griffiths) came marching in with an enormous fencing sword (or what you will) in her hand, and made straight for Mrs. Hall! I quite thought she was going to "do her in"! I burst out laughing and set Paddy off too. Next thing I saw Mrs. Griffiths plunging the wretched sword down the "plug-hole" of the sink and nearly disappearing with it! My tummy quaked and quaked with giggles and the tears were streaming down our faces. Paddy hadn't got a hanky so we had to keep passing mine backwards and forwards! Then Mrs. Hall said, "What's the joke, nurse?" I felt a bit taken aback then so managed to stop! I went to her afterwards to apologise! She said she was very pleased I'd gone to apologise and <u>she</u> couldn't help thinking that Mrs. Griffiths looked a bit like Richard Coeur de Lion!

Tomorrow we go for another Anatomy lecture at the hospital Medical School. On Wednesday afternoon we have to go to the hospital for mass radiography, so bang goes a free afternoon. By the way my Mantoux test worked the second time so I'm free from TB so to speak.

On Thursday we have a nursing test (i.e. bed making, blanket baths, care of head, mouth and pressure areas etc.) and then on Sat. we have another test – an hour each time. Last Sat's was fairly stiff but could have been worse. We haven't had the results yet. It's getting late now so I must go to bed. Heaven knows when I shall get my work done. I was so full after supper that Anne Bishop and I had to go for a walk around Kensington Gardens to shake it down!

Most of the nurses know that I'm going to marry a parson now and they're always asking if I've had a letter! Paddy and Mary and Anne are <u>longing</u> to meet you, so I shall have to look out! Fortunately they're all too tall for <u>you</u>!

I must go for lunch now. I've just been practising my bandaging and getting in a mess with the divergent spica of the elbow!

In Kensington Gardens

Bish and Nina

Paddy and Bish

Nina, Paddy and Mary

30th May

I'm beginning to wonder if I shall stick the three years before getting married. I shall soon be 19 and lots of people get married at 19 but it seems awfully young to me. Nobody could object to my being married at 21. It's nothing to do with finishing my nursing – it's just I feel too young to be married! Mummy says she's proud of me to be "keeping my head" over all this! Also I refuse to get married till I have a house to live in!

31st May

We had our test marks today. I got 66%. One girl who did anatomy and physiology in Higher got 86% but otherwise they were all 60s and 70s. A lot of girls did the pre-nursing course and have found it very useful. I wish I had done it now.

Mary Barnett says that when you come to London next time you're to bring a nice young man for her. She says she's "in love with love" and she wants to fall in love with somebody! He must be at least 6 ft, reasonably good-looking, wide interests, intelligent but not an intellectual snob!! – oh, and amusing!

1st June

Went to the hairdresser's yesterday and had my hair cut and styled. If you say you're from the Middlesex one girl does it free for you. I felt happy today to receive my cheque for £5.1.6! Now I can pay for my ticket home.

Paddy and I are going to the Much Binding programme now, and had to ask Sister for a late pass. Sister laughed and said she thinks we must have been to everything now! – Law courts, Houses of Parlt. Etc.!

5th June

The weather is jolly hot! – We don't know how to keep cool! I've been off duty this afternoon and Paddy and Bish and I went shopping but didn't buy anything! They are now writing a letter to you! This morning we had cookery and made macaroni cheese, junket and rhubarb! I had to leave this to go for tea, then a lecture at 5, church, another lecture, supper and now it's 8.45. Paddy is feeling sick and has a bad throat. I'm on top of the world – I was top of our nursing test with 82%. Can't believe it. One of the girls here – Jill Fletcher, who is 22 – is going to be engaged in August. She met her "young man" 7 weeks ago on the boat coming back from Africa. I think she's a bit daft to get engaged so soon, but apparently he's going back to Rhodesia in August. I shall be so jealous!

Bish is always talking about her father being a "big bug" in the Law Courts. She shows off a bit but she's really nice and doesn't <u>mean</u> to show off. Mary has gone home tonight as she's doing her exam tomorrow. She did the prelim nursing course before she came here and this is the exam. The three of them have started saving for a wedding present for us! The latest is a 2-seater car with diamond headlights and ruby rear light, pearl handles!!! Or if they can't get that they're going to get the engagement ring for you from Woolworths!! They've chosen a ring for me – diamonds and sapphires alternately! They want 1. to come to your ordination 2. to be bridesmaids and 3. to be godmothers to the babies!! They've now finished their letter to you and are looking out their most smashing photos to send with it, so I shall expect to see you here on the next train after receiving them! Paddy looks like a film star in hers.

8th June
So glad you enjoyed the girls' letter! No I don't snore! So they accused me of stertorous breathing or respiration due to cerebral catastrophe! Wait till I see them! Yesterday several of us went swimming. I had to borrow Paddy's bathing costume as she had 2 and I hadn't got mine here. We went to the Nurses' Home swimming pool.

9th June
Thank you for the reply to the girls' letter – they've been going crackers over it all morning. Paddy and I have changed our bedroom and have got a lovely one with a private bathroom on the 3rd floor, so the lift takes us all the way! Tonight will be our first night there. All four of us spent an hour moving our things and we're straight now. I'm reading the lesson in church again tonight so must go and practise. By the way the girls want you to christen their babies eventually (when they have them!) and you're going to be busy as Paddy wants 2, Mary 4 and Bish 3 or 4. Mary is definitely going to have twins she says! They can't believe that I dare to talk to you about such things as having babies!! They really have persuaded me

that I ought to get engaged SOON. I was quite resolved to wait till I was 20, but now I'm convinced I shouldn't! I wondered whether to put off telling you until I'd decided against it again in case my head had been turned temporarily – but no! I'm sure Mum and Dad will not agree to getting married sooner though. Perhaps I can alter my birth certificate or give the earth an extra push around so that 3 years go in ¼ hour!

13th June

We had anatomy again at the Medical School and did reproductive organs. We could actually put our hands inside and feel them! Sister told us a daft story which should amuse you! You know that in an incomplete miscarriage (or sometimes after a normal delivery) some of the foetal placenta gets left behind, so it has to be taken out with instruments. The instrument is called a curette. In a recent exam one of the nurses wrote on her paper that a CURATE was necessary instead of a curette!!! How about it?

Paddy and Bish and I went to the News Theatre straight after tea and then we went and put Bish's gloves on Mrs. Chase (the dummy patient) while Bish wasn't looking, for a bit of fun.

21st June

We had a party last night at Mary's home and it was good fun – about 8 males and 8 females and we played charades, murder, advertisements etc and had a lovely supper. It started at 6.30 and we left Mary's house at 10.45 – we had a late pass till 11.30pm. One of the boys who is training at Guy's hospital brought us back in his car, so it only took about 20 mins, instead of one and a quarter hours on the bus. Mary's parents are very nice, especially her father who is very jolly. I think her mother is a bit shy. Her sister Elizabeth is nearly 17 and looks older than Mary.

Yesterday afternoon we had our last lecture at the anatomy school – this time not amongst the bodies! It was jolly good fun. We were in the lecture room and had surface anatomy. Some poor chap with extra-specially wizard muscles had to sit in front of us all afternoon and be pushed and pulled and poked by Dr. Ormorod, so that we could learn about him. He seemed rather embarrassed in front of 39 silly females. Dr. Ormorod was drawing all over him with red and blue chalks. He looked quite patriotic by 3.15!

Yesterday morning we went in the hospital bus to the hospital laundry and spent an hour or so watching our dirty clothes being laundered! We ironed some sheets and things in the big ironing machines – but they didn't give us any tea like in the Dairy!

This morning we had quite a "to do" because one of the girls broke an enormous bottle of ink when she was cleaning the classroom. The ink went all over the floor and we had a dickens of a job to clean it all up.

Bish and I are going to Evensong at St Martins in the Fields on Sunday – haven't been there before.

Have had two more tests back. Yesterday I was on top of the world with 78% – today I'm fed up with only 62! There are only two more now before the exams.

I'm sorry you thought I looked tired and "like a shadow" last time I was home. I'm really OK. I know men like to be petted and soothed if they're under the weather, but I'm sure women don't! I hate it! By the way Bish wants to know if you remember a chap from the Queens Own Yorkshire Dragoons called Geoffrey Fletcher? He was a captain and is now about 30 and married to a girl called Judy Lloyd.

Last night we went absolutely mad! To begin with we had an explosion at supper time! Bish informed us that she'd discovered the cause of cancer so we drank her health. Then I decided I'd found a cure for over tiredness and we all drank each other's health again. I just touched Bish's glass with mine and her glass just exploded! The water went all over the table and the pieces of glass flew right across the room. It wasn't like ordinary broken glass, it was in tiny balls! Sister said that glasses sometimes explode on the shelf! We left the dining room and went upstairs, and lo and behold we saw Sister Burgess sitting alone in the lift on the first floor with the light on! She called to us and said that she'd been stuck there for ½ an hour! We managed to get her out but there's no lift in use today! At bedtime Mary and Bish came into our room in their dressing gowns while we were getting ready for bed. I'd got as far as my petticoat when they decided to have a "sing song"! I started to sing opera-fashion (like fat females sing you know!). They roared with laughter so of course I continued! Then I put my skirt over my head with one of the roses from our vase sticking out of the top and a leather belt round my waist, Paddy's winter boots and my black and white woolly gloves! Then they plonked a lampshade on my head and pushed some more roses into the top. We were howling with laughter all the time! Then Mary made me extra large lips with lipstick and dared me to go downstairs to the sitting room! I <u>did</u> go, believe it or not and we bumped into Sister Slater twice and Sister Jackson once! It really did us a lot of good to have a bit of fun. I continued my opera singing all the time of course! What are we? Prize idiots!!

We're going to the waterworks this afternoon.

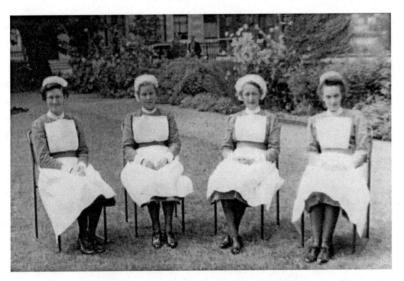

Sisters Byron, Slater, Burgess, and Jackson

25th June
I'm spending this weekend quietly in London for a change! I must catch up on the thousands of jobs I still have to do and try to copy up my notes to date. I must settle down to some learning for my cookery theory exam 10.30-12.30 tomorrow. I'm hoping the theory I did at school will help me.

Paddy has gone off to Kew today to see an elderly lady she knew in Cyprus. She won't be back till after 6pm so Bish and I are going to Westminster Abbey by ourselves. Mary has gone home for the weekend. I pity Paddy being so far from home – she's already wishing she'd gone to a hospital nearer home.

We went to the Waterworks at Hampton Court last Friday. We had 40 mins drive through London in the hospital bus, and then spent about an hour looking round the filter beds. It was quite interesting, but mostly outside and it was pouring with rain so we had to be wrapped up in macintoshes. They gave us cups of tea and cakes afterwards in the engine room!! It was super. We sat 6 at a table and listened to music!

We had an Anatomy and Physiology test yesterday – I didn't finish and only got 62% – Sister didn't seem very pleased after my 78% last time.

Time is flying. We've been here 7 weeks tomorrow. Soon it will be July 28 and I shall be going home for 10 days and there'll be no more swotting till the next study block in 6 months' time. That's if I get through my exams! I'm scared of the vivas and there are as many vivas as written exams.

Yesterday afternoon the vicar and churchwardens of Christ Church across the road, held an At Home for parishioners. Several of us went, and chatted to some of the people there. We had cakes and tea sitting at little card tables, and a chappie came round taking photos of each little group.

By the way I actually came back to Lancaster Gate from Marylebone station <u>by tube</u> instead of in a taxi! I was so pleased to have only spent 4d instead of 2/-!

Bish and I are reclining in our bedroom at present – Bish has been writing letters but now she's lying on Paddy's bed trying to go to sleep! She's had bad toothache for several nights and hasn't been able to sleep.

Last night Paddy and Bish and I had a long discussion about marriage! Now Paddy and Bish have decided to be spinsters for the rest of their lives because "there's more in marriage than meets the eye" and they don't like the thought of it! Bish has just remarked that it will have to be a "strong love" to change her mind! Really I used to feel just the same once. I used to be quite terrified of living with a man! What's more they (Paddy and Bish) have decided that if they do get dragged into being married they will order twin beds straight away! They're sure they could never be bothered to have to sleep in a double bed for the rest of their lives! We went on for over an hour – some of it constructive, but some of it utter rot!

Sister says that it has been worked out that 50% of the nurses at the Middlesex leave during the first year! Reasons – sore feet or <u>men</u>! In one way I wish I were going to one of the 50% but it wouldn't be sore feet!!

Bish, if you please, is now not sleeping but reading a love story! She keeps reading descriptions of kisses to me! The story is of a girl's first kiss – how "her bones seemed to melt away, a little thrill ran through her finger tips and down her arm until she totally yearned for him. The first stirrings of desire were translated by her immaturity into yearning. She wanted to cherish him, to comfort, to love him... The future stretched illimitable, shining with gossamer dreams and unborn hopes. A radiant world into which they could walk hand in hand loving each other..." I know how that girl felt!

2nd July
We went to Communion last Thursday at 7am so that we could have a lie-in today. It was wonderful to have more than 10 hours in bed for once, We were in bed for 10.15 last night and breakfast was at 9 this morning. Paddy, Bish and I dashed off to see the Changing of the Guard at Buckingham Palace for 10 o'clock but unfortunately they only do it every other week, so we shall have to go again next Sunday. We walked back to Westminster Abbey for 11 o'clock (10 to actually) only to discover that the service started at 10.30. But we crept into the crowded Abbey and stayed through to the end of the service. It was a lovely service and the singing was really beautiful. We were out by 12.10 and walked to Trafalgar Square to see the fountains and the pigeons! Then we dashed back here by tube for lunch at 12.45. On the way back from Westminster Abbey to Trafalgar Square we watched the changing of the Horse Guards at Whitehall. It is thrilling to be living in London. I knew I should like

17

it and I feel so proud to be living in such a famous and important city.

It is now 2.30 and I must settle down to some work today. I haven't done any <u>serious</u> swotting as such for the exams. I'm trying to get up to date with my notes and am progressing, though my physiology notes are still sadly behind. The trouble is there are so many other things to be done – the washing I did last Sunday hasn't <u>seen</u> an iron, and I have no end of letters to write. Our picnic at Newlands Corner yesterday was super. We set off about 1.45 from here in the hospital bus, and arrived in Guildford about 3pm. There were 15 girls, with 2 sisters, the female receptionist and the driver. Newlands Corner is in the heart of the country and near to a little café where we could get water for our lemonade (1998 – water for lemonade??!!), so what more could you want???! We sat in a lovely grassy spot for our tea, and could see for miles across fields and woodland. The view was perfect. When we weren't eating we went off in 3s and 4s for little walks and had a few minutes of sunbathing from time to time. I felt quite as though I was on holiday! The test was over and we had the prospect of a long night's sleep before us!!

Back: Barnett, Di, Nina, Bish, Wood, Sister Burgess, Ellerby, Gunn
Front: Paddy, Evans, Haworth, Sellicks, Bell, Marles, Sister Slater, Elizabeth Jones, Priest

18

Yesterday's test was pretty awful really – especially the question on the lymphatics, which we don't understand and so haven't bothered to learn! We had a question for nursing on temperature, pulse and respiration and how to take them in a child of 9 months and an unconscious man. There isn't really much you can say in answer to that question, so my 6 sides must have been absolute twaddle! The public health question was on infection and I <u>made up</u> practically everything I said about that! The other one was about hormones and endocrine glands and I missed out half the important points, so altogether I should have done a most <u>impressive</u> paper!

Bish and Paddy have written to your friend Bob, <u>plus photos</u>! They're all three smashing photos especially of Mary, so we expect at least half of St. Aidan's college on the doorstep in the next day or two!

At the moment Bish and Paddy are lying reading love stories – Paddy on her own bed and Bish with next to nothing on, on my bed. Apparently if no one is willing to show them what love is, they just have to learn by reading about it! That was what Bish said a few minutes ago! <u>Mary</u> is now a confirmed spinster she says – but I don't think any of them will be saying that in a year or so!

We had our pay last Thursday – £6.5. This month I've put 30/- on one side for my train fare on the 15th and have spent £2.4.0. on adorning myself with a new blouse and skirt.

3rd July

Our cookery exam this morning was <u>lovely!</u> My guardian angel must have been watching over me. We had to pull out bits of paper from a hat, with the questions on them, and I had to make egg and cheese on toast, trifle and rhubarb and cocoa for a child. Mine was the only child's tray there was, and I'd asked Mummy for a "baby's" tray cloth and 2 little ornamental rabbits in case, so I was as happy as a sandboy! I cut a little man out of toast and put the egg and cheese mixture on top, then decorated him with tomato buttons, feet, hands and mouth, with parsley eyes and nose and a parsley feather in his hat! I decorated the trifle with angelica and chocolate in the shape of a cat and I found a salt pot in the shape of a house, and a green mug to match my tray cloth and rabbit, and a serviette with Mickey Mouse on, so it looked quite sweet. Now there's no more cookery –

ever! (or at least not for the next three years, then I bet I'll be doing little men out of toast again!)

6th July

We have our First Aid exam on Friday 14th, then Anatomy written paper on 15th in the morning. I shall catch the first train home after the exam finishes at 10.30 and forget about exams for a little while. The other exams are 20th, 8.30-10.30 Nutrition and chemistry of foods, 21st 8.30-10.30 Physiology and 22nd 8.30-10.30 Public Health. Mon 24th Physiology viva (9am) Practical nursing 2pm (what a day!) Tues 25th Practical nursing 8.45. Chem of foods and nutrition <u>viva</u> 12pm. We're having all sorts of revision classes, and this morning we had to give talks on subjects which were allotted to us, and which we had 10 mins to prepare. I was 9th on the list alphabetically and had to talk about the large intestine! It was quite a nice thing to talk about and I was quite enjoying standing up on the little platform behind the desk, drawing on the blackboard! The bell went in the middle though, so I shall have to finish next time. Sister said it was jolly good practice for us to stand in front of the class to gain confidence as well as learn the art of teaching, and she seemed disappointed that everyone was so scared! So <u>I</u> plucked up courage and had a smashing time! She said she could see a potential Sister Tutor in me! Ha – ha – there's no Sister Tutoring for <u>me</u>!

Paddy and I are living in the lap of luxury at the moment. On Wednesday morning just after the rising bell had gone, there was a terrific banging on our door and the porter walked in with a jug of tea! He had just enough for 4 people, so there were 2 other lucky ones too! He did the same again this morning! It's a state secret at the moment – especially the fact that we've had a <u>man</u> in our room! I expect we'd be put on a charge!

Last week was my week for cleaning bathrooms and it took me ages! One morning Bish announced that she'd had a bath, so I told her I refused to clean the bath! Before I knew where I was she and another girl had put me bodily into the bath and turned the tap on!! I bet you would have laughed. The photos of the vicar's Garden Party have come out well (<u>1998.</u> Still have it!) so I've ordered one and they'll be good to keep.

What do I want for my birthday? Golly is it a whole year? Well it must be! since we went dashing off to Boots to get my Evelyn Pearce book ready for nursing! In a way it seems only like yesterday. Well all I can think of at the moment is a hairbrush, one that <u>will brush</u>. Mine's a bit worn out or something and it's something I would really like. As for "being broke when we're married" – if I keep on spending now, there'll be no need later on!

11th July
It's 6.30pm and I'm feeling so relieved and happy now that the Anatomy viva is over! I was worried stiff yesterday and nearly went screwy trying to learn all the various muscles and nerves and blood vessels etc. Last night I woke up time and again and each time there were Latin names whizzing through my brain! Paddy was the same – she asked me about 6 o'clock this morning what the muscles of the hip joint were!! We all went up in the hospital bus this afternoon and had to dress up in the gowns as usual. There were three doctors examining us – all very young and as they passed us on their way into the dissecting room I quite fell for the dark-haired one. And then I got him!! Three of us were in at a time, and my luck was in again! You'll never guess what I had to describe – after swotting up all my muscles! I had to give the difference between a newborn babe and an adult! I told him that the first curve in the spine didn't come till the baby lifted up its head, and the 3rd curve wasn't formed until the baby walked etc.

I'm doing <u>no</u> work tonight, washing my hair, having a washday and going to bed early.

By the way we're all in <u>uniform</u> now and look so smashing! It means getting up earlier in the morning though! We had the dresses on yesterday for the first time – so now we feel like "real nurses"!

18th July (<u>1998</u>. We got married on this date 1953!)
Thank you so much for the beautiful pale pink carnations for my birthday and the anniversary of the "pea-patch". Fancy – a year since you popped the question when we were picking peas!!! They are superb carnations and everyone has admired them – the scent is beautiful. We were in bandaging class when they arrived, but practising on our own without a sister, so when two of the girls came

dashing in to say they'd arrived I was able to go and put them in a vase which Sister found for me.

Now it's 7.15pm and Paddy, Mary and Bish and I are having a little party in Bish's room to celebrate. We've had the 19 candles on my cake lighted, and we've been guzzling on your lovely chocolates, and some raspberries and gooseberries which Bish brought for the occasion. Strange to relate we've also been smoking Du Maurier cigarettes! Supper is in 10 mins and I'm sure we shan't be able to eat much! So now I'm also 19 – I've hardly had time to think about that. Physiology written paper tomorrow – never mind. Our results come out on July 28 – the day we go home on holiday! Bish says her parents were making remarks about her looking tired, so <u>yours</u> about <u>me</u> were not the only ones. We shall be nervous wrecks before long!

Paddy received Bob's reply to her letter yesterday and was very thrilled with it. We all read it last night (all three of us). We have to produce a concert before we leave here so are madly thinking up ideas for that now as well as everything else! We're going to Mary Barnett's (? tomorrow) on the 5 o'clock bus.

20th July
I'm sorry I didn't get a letter off to you yesterday but we went to the Sewage Works at Edmonton in the afternoon and didn't get back till 5.30pm. Then I had to have some tea, choose a hymn for Evensong and prepare the lesson before church at 6pm. I nearly died. I'm still so thrilled with the carnations – I never cease to admire them. Sister saw them this morning and said how lovely they are. I don't think I'll bother to be a Sister Tutor somehow! – I'd rather be "somebody's" wife!

I've had quite a heart attack today. We've been given the list of wards we're to work on when we come back in August – if we come back! They've plonked me straight on to a men's Medical ward – I shall be absolutely scared stiff. It's MEYERSTEIN with Sister Hammond in charge and Dr. Hadley is the consultant. I suppose they'll all be a lot of old fogies (1998 – which is what I am now!!) Bish is on a women's Surgical, Paddy on a men's Surgical and Mary on a men's Medical. There are 2 of us from here on each ward, and I'm with a girl called Saunderson who is frightfully clever (1998 –

Saunderson died quite young). They must think I'm as dull as ditchwater and need to be with someone brainy.

Our Physiology exam yesterday wasn't too bad and today the Nutrition and chemistry of foods paper could have been much worse. I only hope that "liking them" means I've passed, otherwise I shall have a big blow! It's the Physiology viva at 9am tomorrow and then Public Health on Saturday; then I'm going to stay with the Goods at Gravesend for the weekend so I shall be broke!

25th July

We had our first afternoon on the wards yesterday. It was great fun but quite hectic. The first hour there was very little to do but discover what was wrong with all the patients, but after 3 o'clock we had plenty to fill our time. The teas are taken round at 3, then I made up an operation bed with the staff nurse. They're all so quick and slap-dash compared with PTS methods. I suppose they just always have to race for time. When the patients had finished their teas we had to wash them. I felt quite scared to be stuck with a male in bed surrounded by screens! He was terribly ill, and could hardly get his breath, so I had to move him under my own steam, and it was no easy job. He couldn't have been more than about 35 but he looked so haggard and drawn. I felt like fleeing for my life! I just took a deep breath, plunged my hands into the water and got on with the job. Then there were beds to make, and just before 4 o'clock one of the nurses asked me to give an intra-muscular injection. I would just have refused outright but luckily I had to go as it was 4pm.

I felt quite tired by then and not a bit like doing my Practical exam in the evening. But it had to be, and I was jolly "FRIT"! Once I was in, it wasn't so bad – I had to do an eye bandage which wasn't too bad, then Bish and I had to change old Flora Chase's bottom sheet, (she being in a chronic heart bed). Then I had to lay up a Back trolley and a trolley for a Rectal Saline. The worst part was the general questions she asked – I got the prone position mixed up with the left lateral and was so annoyed!! We were in the Practical Room for nearly an hour, but I was so thankful to get it over. I could have a good night's sleep! Paddy was <u>very</u> confident about her exam, then she came out this morning saying she'd done everything wrong! Sister heard her saying that and promptly took her into the office and gave her a

23

lecture. She said she'd always had the impression that Paddy refused to be taught, and would come a cropper when she went on the wards if she didn't do something about it. Paddy told us all this herself and didn't seem at all bothered! This afternoon we're going up to the hospital for a lecture by Brigadier Hardy-Roberts, the Secretary Superintendant of the hospital. Tomorrow the vicar and his wife are coming for tea. My last exam is tomorrow morning – Nutrition and Chemistry of foods viva, then <u>packing</u> and clearing up. I'm so looking forward to going home.

There's been a bit of excitement today. The secretary of the Football Association next door to us got stuck in the lift at 10 o'clock last night and was there till nearly 8am today! He shouted and called for ages but couldn't make himself heard so settled down there for the night! The cleaners found him this morning. Reporters and detectives have been round, so we've had a share of the thrill!

So glad your pals Maurice and Walter think such a lot of married life. Never mind it isn't <u>so</u> long for us to wait. Judging by the way these three months have gone I should imagine it won't seem so terribly long. Hey ho! Home now for a holiday before we start nursing in real earnest!

Back to real Nursing! – following holiday after PTS.
(Letters to my parents)

9th August 1950

I'm sorry I haven't sent you any sort of message before, but really! This life is so hectic!! It was a dreadful journey back – I didn't get in till 10 past 9. However it didn't matter. Bish, Paddy and Mary all helped me to take my trunk etc. up in the lift and showed me my room. Then I had to wait till 9.30 to see Sister.

I'm terrifically happy here. It was lovely in the PTS and much more of an easy life (!) but now that I'm actually on the wards I really feel that I'm getting on with something worthwhile. I'm no longer <u>one person in a "family"</u> as in PTS – where everyone knows you and looks after you. Here you are quite independent apart from keeping to rules and are very much just <u>one</u> of an <u>extremely large community</u>. I hardly ever see the rest of the PTS until bedtime because off-duty is so muddled up. We have breakfast in the basement but all the other meals in the big dining room with the other nurses.

I get up at 6.30 – the hooter (like the hooter of one of those old-fashioned cars which makes a terrific row) goes at 6.15am. Breakfast is at 6.45am and we go on duty at 7.30am. We then work until 8pm with the exception of our 3 hours off duty each day either from 9.45 to 12.45, 1.30 to 4.30 or 5-8pm with ¾ hour for lunch and ½ an hour for tea. So it's quite a long hectic day.

Then there's a ½ day once a week – from 1.30pm to 11.15 or in the morning till 1.30pm. One day off per week and one long afternoon (i.e.) 1.30 to 5.30 (instead of 4.30). So when I come home on Monday evening, I have Tuesday at home, returning for 11.15 (doors locked)

I'm on a different ward – we've all been changed around from what we were originally told. It's Howard de Walden which is a women's surgical and very interesting. I liked Meyerstein when I spent a week there but everyone looked so pathetic and ill. De Walden is an enormous and <u>very</u> busy ward and they're mostly people for ops. I was told that yesterday was a slack day on our ward, but I was run

25

off my feet! It was bliss to be off duty and to come to my room after supper and take off my shoes!! My feet ached <u>so much</u>! All I wanted was bed!

I have to do all the less important jobs, but I'd rather get used to it by doing those first. Anyway they're all jobs that <u>must</u> be done and I love every minute of it. Sister is quite nice, though sometimes she goes off the deep end, I'm told! The other nurses on my ward are very nice and helpful. I'm the only PTS person on de Walden but I like it nevertheless.

Our rooms are very nice – just the right size, with wardrobe, cupboards, drawers, dressing table etc. all built in. The bed has an interior spring mattress and is super! I'll let you have a sketch later, but I'm in rather a hurry now. We can make tea in a special urn at the end of each corridor, so I shall bring back some crockery and some tea next time I come home. I'll write again later. I'm having lunch at 12.10 because I'm back on duty at 12.45. Washing the patients again I expect, and teas and making beds etc. It's Admission Day too in our ward, so no doubt there'll be some new faces! It's ghastly watching people coming round after their ops!

15th August
I've got a day off today so I'm writing this while I'm still in bed at 7.45am. Bish and Anne Strugnell between them brought up my breakfast at 7.15 when they'd finished theirs and now I'm just waiting for it to settle before I have a bath. It's lovely to think I have a whole day off – and in any case I'm sure my poor feet couldn't have put up with much longer without a break! It's really chronic the way they ache. I can only hope I shall get used to it in time. I can understand why Monica Dickens called her book "One pair of feet"!! I prefer having tired feet though to having to worry about exams and this life is wonderful. In this work you feel that you never <u>waste</u> a minute of the day. There's always something to be done and it's usually something important and very worthwhile – especially giving bedpans!!! – and taking them away again (that's even worse!).

Now that I've settled down on the ward I have more interesting jobs to do – preparing people for operations, giving inhalations, washing mouths, putting on antiphlogistine poultices etc. etc. The other day we had 4 new patients, and I had to "admit" all of them (i.e.) take

26

down all their particulars and then take their temperatures, pulse and respiration rate and speak to their relatives. Some of the people have had minor operations, and others have had very big ones. But it's wonderful to see them all getting better and going home. The only snag is that just when I've managed to learn their names and what's wrong with them they go home and new ones come in. This week is Emergency week when we are the one ward open to emergencies coming to the hospital. (That is into the men's ward opposite of course.) There weren't any yesterday, though.

The patients are continually giving us presents of stuff which has been given to them and which they can't eat. I've had bananas and tomatoes and sweets, and yesterday one lady gave me a box of Black Magic chocolates! We're not supposed to accept presents from patients but they seem so upset if you refuse.

The days seem to go more slowly now somehow, even though everything is so interesting. One does such a lot in such a short space of time. PTS would be luxury after this! The food is jolly good though, and I always look forward to my meals – even lunch at 11.30am! I must get up now as it's 8.30am.

17th August
This is the first time I haven't been out in my off duty time, the whole time I've been here! I've had such a lovely time with my wonderful "man" staying nearby for a week, so now I need to catch up on correspondence, washing etc. etc!

I've now discovered that I could come home any week for just one night as I'm off duty Monday eve, Tuesday one week and Wednesday eve and Thursday the next. I'll let you know as soon as I decide. It's a blow there are no weekends off. It seemed so strange to be working last Sunday, just like any other day. I couldn't go to church the whole day because my ½ day was changed and I only had an afternoon. Normally I shall be off 1.30 onwards on Sundays, so it won't seem so bad.

The work is getting more interesting now, but there's always <u>such</u> a lot to do. This morning there was only the Head Nurse and myself on duty and I didn't know what to do first! And just when I was busiest one person asked me for a B.P. (i.e. bedpan, commonly known as

Beep!) As soon as I'd given one to <u>her,</u> half the others decided to follow suit! Then it all had to be measured and charted up before I could go back to my first job. Then two females came to x-ray an old lady who was brought in as an emergency yesterday and I had to go and stay with them and lift the old lady. And so it goes on. I much prefer to be busy though – yesterday morning was quite the opposite, with about 5 of us on the ward and I was bored stiff having nothing to do!

Isn't it thrilling to have a baby princess?! Dear Lizzie, so lucky to have one of each now! I wonder what they will call the baby? (Princess Anne!)

I'm enclosing a newspaper cutting which might interest you. There was a terrific "to do" at the hospital about it. This chap had cancer, and when his brother heard he would never recover he went and told Costas, and <u>he</u> threw himself out of a first floor window and fell to the basement. Being on Observation Ward he was in a single room.

Ever since my day off my feet seem to have been a bit better thank goodness. Some days I didn't know what to do with them. The only bother is a sore place on one toe which seems to be developing into a corn, but I'm doing my best to stop it. I must stop now and go shopping before I go on duty at 5.30.

20th August
Sorry I haven't managed to get a letter off to you today especially as it is my ½ day, but somehow I've just frittered it away mainly eating! I bought some salted nuts, biscuits and sweet ration (NB wartime coupons) and have taken great delight in devouring them. I'm always eating these days. I must have Stomachia Megaly or something – incidentally that's a new way of saying enlarged stomach. I've made it up from hearing about one of my patients who has Hepato Megaly (enlarged liver). I wonder if I'm now more than my usual 8½ stone. Probably not, considering all the energy I burn up. This life is just one mad rush – we hurry here, we hurry there and there's never any peace except in bed! And even then that old-fashioned hooter arrangement makes far too much noise too soon, and the daily round starts all over again! It's very interesting and good fun and I love it but honestly sometimes I think I shall go mad. How I can wait another fortnight till I come home I don't know. I should love to get

28

away for just a day. I <u>do</u> envy all those people who live in or near London and can pop home even in their 3 hours off duty each day. That's the only snag as far as I can see – I'm too far from home. I made that remark to one of the nurses on Howard de Walden and she lives in Wales so can't go home very often at all. Her reply was "Well you have to try to devote yourself to your career and leave home in the background!" That's all very well – I expect she'll make a far better nurse than I shall.

By the way. Last night Diane Willis and I <u>walked</u> to Leicester Square. She said she liked the liveliness of Leicester Square on a Saturday evening. So off we went. We had a coffee milkshake in a very crowded Milk Bar, bought some peaches and got back about 9.15pm. Then we made some coffee and ate biscuits and peaches in her room. This afternoon Bish and Paddy and I happened to be off duty together, which is very rare. We collected bread, cakes and milk and jam from the kitchen and had tea in Paddy's room. We made the tea in Bish's teapot and used her crockery – I have bought a Woolworths special cut glass milk jug for 8d and likewise a Woolworths cut-glass <u>glass</u> which was 6d!

Oh yes I'm sure being brought up in a Vicarage has helped me in dealing with new patients, and not least with answering the telephone. That is one of my delightful jobs and it never stops ringing all day, usually when I'm in the middle of carrying a bedpan out to the sluice and Sister gets so mad if it keeps on ringing! It's hard to know what to do isn't it? They do say that 75% of nurses leave before their 3 years are up, and I'm beginning to understand why!

Really I shall be very surprised if I ever become State Registered. The 4th year is out of the question because I want to get married. There's one satisfaction – you can become a Head Nurse in your 2nd year and be in charge of a ward, so that's my only hope at the moment! But from the way Sister tells me off I doubt if I'll even get that far. One minute she's calling me "dear" and being very affectionate, and the next minute you think an Atomic Bomb is descending. I asked her this morning what to do with the empty lemonade bottles. She told me to put them with the other empty bottles outside. I was then in the kitchen and looked everywhere along that corridor for the other empties. She came marching along and said, "You haven't any <u>eyes</u> have you, nurse?" Took me through another door and showed me the correct place. I think I need to be able to see through brick walls and wooden doors now!! My nerves won't stand it! Thank goodness we change wards every 6 weeks. But it happens to everybody just the same and we all laugh about it afterwards. Sister Fletcher is a jolly wonderful person really. She knows all her patients inside out, both in the men's and women's wards and she's very understanding. She gets so worked up though – I expect I'd be like her as far as being flustered and hasty goes if I were a sister!

I had to go and help out on the men's ward yesterday afternoon. It has been our Emergency week and the men's ward have had a terrific lot of casualties brought in – chaps who'd fallen off scaffolding and one who was knocked down on Oxford Street etc. Sister sent me in to one chap who was having fits! Fortunately the Head Nurse asked me to go and stay with another who was coming round from an anaesthetic instead. He was <u>ages</u> coming to, and you should have seen me slapping his face to bring him round because his wife was waiting to see him. We are taught to slap their face but not too hard of course!

You asked about "elevenses" – we have some if we pinch it from the kitchen about 10 a.m. after giving the patients theirs. I usually have a mug or 2 of cold milk with Horlicks floating on the top! and a biscuit if I'm lucky!

I must stop now as I'm going to Evensong in the Hospital chapel tonight at 8.45. It seems so long since I went to church. I completely forget what day it is sometimes. I thought about you going to Communion at 8 this morning and wished that I could be with you.

PS: One of the patients gave me a whole month's sweet coupons the other day!

25th August

Thank you for a wonderful day off – it's given me new energy, although it was awful getting up at 6.30 again after being spoilt yesterday morning! I really did enjoy being home again. It was simply wonderful even though it was only a flying visit. I've been quite busy today – there was another operation yesterday – of the person I had to shave (!) and she's very much down and out today. I feel so sorry for the poor dear – she's getting on for 70 I think, and she was so cheerful and lively before her op. (NB: I'm now 77 myself in 2008!!).

28th August
I'm feeling much happier since being home last week. I seem to have renewed enthusiasm for work. Also I've found a new "trick" for if I get fed up and it's surprising how it works! I read the other day a passage explaining "Let all that ye do be done in love" (Corinthians) and it said "Be sure that there is nothing but love in your thoughts for God, for man and <u>for your work before you begin any special task</u>! This is to put God into it, which means power for the execution and perfection in the result, that is if love is entirely your Master. Love is the motive power behind all Divine activity". After I'd read it I was determined to try and carry it out and I've been so happy ever since. The patients ask you to do such trivial and annoying things sometimes, just when you're in the middle of something much more important and it takes you all your time not to say something hasty to them. But if I say to myself "Do it for love" I find I <u>want</u> to do it for them.

At dinnertime yesterday one of the patients refused everything I took to her – she seemed never to be satisfied and I could almost have screamed. But I made myself see that I could go on till I found the right thing for her, out of love, and she really <u>was</u> grateful when I gave her something she liked.

1st September
I'm settling down much more now and enjoying the work <u>very</u> much. My feet don't get so tired now either and I'm usually in bed with the light off by 9.30pm! And we had our pay day yesterday!! I had a half day yesterday but it was a bit boring because no one else was off around me. But in the evening I went to the flix with 3 girls – we <u>were</u> going to see Bob Hope in "Fancy Pants!" But were too late so went to the Marble Arch News Theatre. Then we walked to York House (one of the Nurses' homes) after we'd taken the tube back to Oxford Circus, and went into the new canteen there, which is open from 8.30-11pm. I've never been in before but it's a super place and

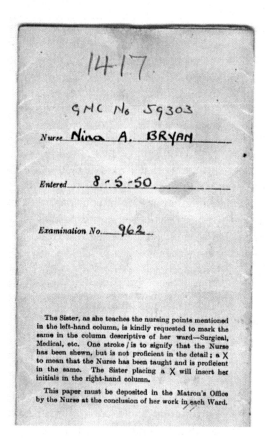

1417.

GMC No 59303

Nurse Nina A. BRYAN

Entered 8-5-50

Examination No. 962

The Sister, as she teaches the nursing points mentioned in the left-hand column, is kindly requested to mark the same in the column descriptive of her ward—Surgical, Medical, etc. One stroke / is to signify that the Nurse has been shewn, but is not proficient in the detail; a X to mean that the Nurse has been taught and is proficient in the same. The Sister placing a X will insert her initials in the right-hand column.

This paper must be deposited in the Matron's Office by the Nurse at the conclusion of her work in each Ward.

Record of training cover

we had ice cream and chocolate biscuits. I was late to bed but it was worth it. Have had lots more presents from patients. We've had about 6 new patients in today.

5th September

We've had a hectic day today and I was so glad not to be on duty this afternoon as the poor dears must have been run off their feet. We had 3 ops. this morning. I'd hardly got the 1st operation bed ready when the dear soul was brought back from theatre. She'd had a haemorrhoidectomy which is a very quick op. But I hadn't even had the chance to have the electric blanket on to warm the bed, then they wondered why she was shivering! I suggested we should warm her up with the electric blanket and it did the trick! Then we had someone with carcinoma of the rectum and then another with an amputation of gangrenous toes. The latter was horrid – I hated making her bed and seeing those black thin toes. But still poor dear she's 67 and very patient because it must be very painful. It's the first amputation I've come across.

I've got 20 crosses now and I was told to aim at getting 20 on my first ward, so I'm very pleased.

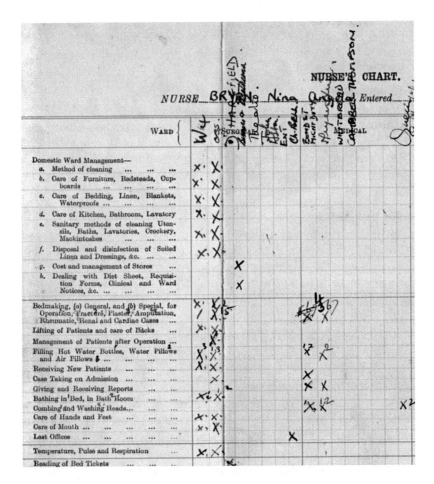

Record of training inside

8th September

I was interested to hear all about Jill training at Guy's Hospital. I bet Guy's "Piggery" isn't as good as York Canteen. Ours is smashing – all done in blue and cream colour, and a waiter to <u>serve</u> us at the tables! It's an enormous room and very clean and tidy.

We're terribly understaffed at present because our Head Nurse has gone off for <u>3 months!</u> holiday after a BCG vaccination (for TB) and two others have gone on night duty. We've got <u>one</u> new girl in place of the 3 we've lost. Thank goodness my next ward won't be a surgical one – maybe there'll be more peace! Bish is on a medical

33

ward and she says she comes off duty ¼ of an hour early often in the evening because there's nothing to do, and I've known it to be 3/4 <u>late</u> when I go to supper.

8th September
I was so thrilled this morning. One of our patients – Mrs. Fell – has been terribly ill and is really the ideal patient. In fact I think she's very nearly a <u>saint.</u> When I went to wash her this morning she said: "Oh I am glad <u>you've</u> come, darling – it's as if my prayers have been answered. I did miss you yesterday!" Don't you think it was a lovely thing to say?

10th September
I'm having my ½ day today. It's been chaotic to say the least on Howard D this morning so I'm glad to get off. There were only 3 of us on all morning and there was so much to do that I went back ¼ of an hour early from lunch to try to help out. It meant I only had 20 minutes for my lunch because I was late off duty in the first place, but I came off at 2pm for my ½ day. We had <u>one</u> empty bed and the porter brought up 3 new patients. I got one into bed safely, then had to ask Mrs. Hibberd (who should have gone home later today) to clear out earlier so that the 2nd patient went into her bed. We had to get another bed brought up for the 3rd person so now we have 21 patients instead of 20. The second two beds weren't made up of course so two of the "fitter" patients made them up with clean linen while I "admitted" the patients. Every time I dashed out to the sluice for something Mrs. Hertz asked me to shoot her because she was in such pain, so altogether I was ready for my off duty!

Yesterday afternoon I was on the ward <u>alone all</u> afternoon! Fortunately it was a comparatively quiet time so it wasn't too bad but my feet had to go quicker than ever!

17th September
I have to go to Matron's office tomorrow morning at 8.40, so think about me! We are all going in alphabetical order to receive instructions about our next ward. I expect we shall change sometime tomorrow, but I don't yet know where or when I shall be going. Sister gave me a most <u>super</u> report. I had to have a ½ hour session with her while she wrote it and then I had to sign it to say I'd seen what she'd written. There were little headings – work; punctuality;

manners to patients, visitors and others; economy; readiness to obey orders; general aptitude for nursing etc. She gave me "very good" for all but about 2 and for those she put "good". She says she thinks I'll make a very good nurse but I mustn't let my spirits get the better of me! She says I dash about too much and she thinks it's because I'm overenthusiastic!! Anyway I think it was jolly decent of her to be so generous after all the tellings-off I've had! Now I can start my next ward with a clean sheet.

19th September
The interview with Matron was OK yesterday. She was very nice indeed. We had to take our cross papers with us and she had our reports in front of her on her desk. She said, "Oh yes! You've obviously worked very hard! Keep it up on your next ward" – i.e. – Observation ward. She said I'd find it quieter and altogether very different from Howard de Walden. There are only 10 patients all in separate rooms, with only about 3 nurses. I went up there and it's terribly different. Just one narrow little corridor with lots of doors along it and a bathroom, sluice etc. at the end. I shall never get used to walking such a short distance to each patient after dashing up and down such an enormous ward! But it should be very interesting. Apparently one of the patients is a tiny baby, so I shall love that!

October
I'm having a super time on <u>Observation Ward</u> (Obs as we call it). It seems so slack after BUSY Howard de Walden. We've been polishing brass door knobs this morning!! and I finished cleaning the cupboards. We've got some nice patients in at the moment – our two male dentals are great fun and we've got one of the Middlesex Medical students in as well. I had great fun waiting for one of the dentals to come round from the anaesthetic yesterday – we had quite a fight! He was completely "blotto", but nearly gave me a black eye!

Our dear patient Mrs. Wells died on Thursday morning only 5 minutes before we went off duty at 7.30pm. I think I told you about her. She had water in her legs and trunk and we drained 19 pints out one day. It was as well she didn't live any longer, but she was so patient. It was terrible doing things to help her, when we knew she could die any minute. But she was always happy and cheerful and we had fun even on the last day. I don't like it when people die however serene they are. I felt peculiar for the rest of the day.

13th October
On the brighter side I'm so thrilled because we have another baby on the ward. He's called Matthew O'Shea. His mother is on a surgical ward having an op, so Matthew is lodging with us. So my latest job is washing nappies! I shall be quite experienced when I eventually have my own babies!

We've got a new case of T.B. – the sort that spreads rapidly to <u>all</u> systems of the body. The chap is an Indian and I can hardly understand a word he says. We have to wear gown and mask every time we go into the room, and I don't like looking after him. It's horrible of me because he's a human being like the rest of us, but I feel I shall never be able to get clean again after being with him. He spilt his sputum mug all over the sheet this afternoon, so I had to change the bedclothes and give him a clean sheet. The carbolic wet the bottom sheet a bit, and he was swearing at me in Indian because he said it would poison him! He took off his pyjama jacket and put it over the patch and refused even to look at it. Then the barber came to shave him, and afterwards he said the barber was "plenty bad man" because his God didn't like him to be shaved. I just don't take any notice of him now – I'm fed up!! He's always ringing his bell for something and I go to see which light is on, every time I hear the bell, in fear and trembling lest it should be him! Then I pretend I haven't heard! He's usually done something utterly stupid and revolting.

We had a chap in the other day who had tried to commit suicide. I had a long talk with him – I did feel so sorry for him. But he's determined to take more steps as soon as possible to finish himself off. It's AWFUL.

Baby Matthew is a joy to have on the ward. I have to bath and feed him and it's <u>super!</u> What's more – now – I'm not allowed to go in to the TB case more than is necessary as I'm looking after the babe a lot.

Somebody has said that it may be nearly the end of November when we go on night duty so that's another 6 weeks here on Obs. I went to

Chapel last night which was lovely. We had a visiting Chaplain who was quite amusing. I've had a morning off today with an hour's lecture.

16th October
Was alone on the ward all afternoon yesterday, and our Staff Nurse told me today that Sister told her I got on very well. Sister brought me some ice-cream yesterday afternoon and said a man had just dashed in and said "Give this to the nurse on duty!" She didn't know who he was, but she brought me the ice-cream!

I'm just waiting to give the Greek lady a bath, having made the tea.

18th October
I was cleaning the Indian's room yesterday morning when he suddenly started chanting "Allah-Allah!" I replied "Yes – what do you want?!!" I thought he was saying "Allo"! He informed me then "I call my God, I call my God". I hope that doesn't sound too blasphemous! I just misinterpreted it! I told the other girls and they went into fits of laughter! Actually – oh dear – it's all very well laughing about the poor old chap but his case is far from amusing. We've all felt rather depressed on Obs today and yesterday. I'm sure he thinks we're trying to kill him instead of help him. I've made all sorts of excuses to go into his room now, so that I could talk to him to try to make him understand, and to try to cheer him up a bit. I'm afraid I was very mean at first, in that I was glad to get out of his way, but when I heard all the others saying how much they hated him it made me realise how unkind I was being. I truly believe now the saying "Love is all". Where there is no love there is unhappiness and that's why Mayna Meah (the Indian) is so miserable. He knows he's going to die, and he has to be stuck there in one room with nobody of his own race to talk to – in fact nobody to talk to at all, usually, so can only ponder on his condition day after day. He said to me yesterday: "I'm finished. I want to see the house where I live and make rice again." He's got one solitary letter from Pakistan, and he has it stuck with a sticky label over his bed. It's so difficult to please him because so many things seem to be against his religion. He's a terrible trial with his food especially and he won't have injections or drugs however much we try to assure him that they are for his own good. The climax came today. He'd had his dinner and suddenly

started to ring his bell frantically. Our staff-nurse, Gibbons, rushed in without a gown or mask, and as she opened the door he threw his dinner plate across the room and it broke in half. Then he leapt up in bed and was just about to jump down onto the floor with arms outstretched but Nurse Gibbons managed to catch him. He was making the most hideous noise and shouting at her, and poor Gibbons was shouting for help. We all dashed in – again without gowns or masks – but she had managed to get him back to bed. For the rest of the afternoon he sat up cross-legged on top of the bedclothes, and we were convinced that he would try to jump out of the window or something. The Resident Medical Officer (R.M.O.) came up with other doctors and eventually they contacted another Indian who could speak English as well as Pakistani, and he gave Mayna Meah a jolly good lecture. After that he simmered down a bit. Apparently he's been in several other hospitals and has either discharged himself or been such a nuisance that they had to discharge him. I felt so fed up. It seemed to me that I'd wasted my time talking to him. I didn't expect him to be "converted" just from listening to me, but I did hope he would realise that we are trying to be helpful and make him as comfortable as possible. He calls to Allah so often, and he's terrified of going against his religion. I wish I could understand his "religion" – if it means so much to him you would think he would be more reasonable. Perhaps he thinks that by doing things for him of which he doesn't approve because they're so contrary to what he believes, we're bringing the wrath of Allah upon him. I wish I could understand. I'm sure it would be so much better if he could be looked after by Indians because it's impossible for us to satisfy him. He shouted at us today because "his religion said that he should shave the hair from under his arms, and we hadn't done so". Well how on earth could we know that, and yet it was pathetic to see the look of fear and anger in his face. All this makes me wonder how missionaries have the patience to carry on their work. They must be wonderful people, and they must have unlimited love in their hearts.

By the way I've had a letter from the Income Tax people with my Code number at last, so perhaps I shall get a bit of rebate with my next pay. Then I can afford to pay to come home!

22nd October

It's our Prize-giving next week and Princess Margaret is coming to give out the prizes. I have a ½ day so I shall be able to go. It's being held in the Medical School Library. Matron had a meeting the other day and there's a rumour that they've decided we are so short-staffed all ½ days are to be cancelled pro-tem. It isn't just a rumour though because some girls have already had them stopped.

How life changes. Observation Ward is no longer the peaceful place it was when I first came here. As well as the TB Indian we now have another precautionary case – erysipelas – which is a contagious skin disease. We have to wear gloves as well as gowns and masks. Life is just as hectic now as it was quiet at first. And the Indian wept when I went into his room yesterday. It was awful.

I just said "how life changes" – now it has changed even more. I've got myself a boil on my wrist and am off sick. I've had a little spot on my wrist for some time and thought it would disappear. But today it suddenly became very inflamed and Sister said she thought I should go to the R.M.O. So I left the ward at 9.30 this morning – had the boil opened and a dressing put on it with a beautiful spica bandage and a sling! I have to have 4 injections of penicillin each day and redress my wrist 4-hourly. So I now suddenly am having a very lazy life! There's hardly anybody left in my set who hasn't been off sick now.

Did I tell you that I went to the Medical School dance the other night? I had lots of partners so I did enjoy it. One chap was a wizard dancer for the last 2 or 3 dances. I expect I shall be on Night Duty for the next one so won't be able to go.

Talking of plights – I had another interview with Matron yesterday morning. She was charming as usual and said that in her opinion I've "done well". When she looked at my cross-paper she said, "Oh, this is splendid." I'm due to go on night duty on Nov. 5th or 6th and going to Marlborough Court (also a hotel) to live. It's on the Bayswater Road.

Oh I forgot to tell you that three of us went to evensong at St. Paul's Portman Square. It was a very nice service but the sermon was too long, and I didn't think much of the vicar!! But I was pleased to see that he went down to the back of the church after the service to say goodnight to his congregation, which was a large one and almost filled the church. We were very warmly welcomed by the churchwarden and his wife.

I now have an antiphlogistine poultice on my wrist and my whole arm aches. Even my hand is swollen. It looks as if I shall not go back to Obs and I wanted to get some more crosses before I left the ward. Also I don't think I shall see Baby Matthew again as he's going home on Thursday.

8 or 9 others of my set are due to be going with me on night duty next Monday, but I don't know till tomorrow where I shall be working. In any case the R.M.O. says I must have a few days at home after sickbay. I had my wrist treated again this morning, (to spare you the gory details!). The boil is slowly getting smaller, but there's a hole in my wrist the size of a pea now! I'm sure I shall have a lovely scar. Now that it has burst it has relieved the tension and I can hardly feel it at all, but it's still bandaged up and in a sling. I'm sure nurses make awful patients. I'm not very partial to having injections! But I shall be able to sympathise with my patients now! We all had to go for a mass x-ray this morning. They can now do them without you getting undressed so it's easier and we had the beginnings of a "pea souper" fog in London the other night.

THE MIDDLESEX HOSPITAL, W.I
SCHOOLS OF NURSING, PHYSIOTHERAPY and RADIOGRAPHY

COL. THE HON. J. J. ASTOR, D.Litt.
(Chairman of The Middlesex Hospital)

requests the pleasure of the company of

Mrs. Bryan.

At the Presentation of Medals and Prizes by

HER ROYAL HIGHNESS THE PRINCESS MARGARET

On WEDNESDAY, 25th OCTOBER, 1950 at 3 p.m.
In the MEDICAL SCHOOL LIBRARY
(By kind permission of The Dean)

TO BE FOLLOWED BY TEA.

R.S.V.P. to The Matron.   Guests are asked to be in the Library by 2.50 p.m.

I have now been told that I can go home for a few days' rest before Night Duty. The boil hasn't anything like gone yet. Apparently it will take ages to heal properly but at least it is on the mend. I'm having my last injection this evening thank goodness! I have to pack my trunk and take it to Marlborough Court for Night Duty, then I can come home!

Night Duty – November 1950
Bond St., Women's Orthopaedic

8th November
Thank you so much for my 3 days at home. They "flew by"! It seemed very strange to be back at the Nurses' Home – especially as I couldn't have my own little room, 403, on the 4th floor as I'm moving to Marlborough Court for Night Duty. I felt quite upset not to be in 403, it seemed quite odd. However I was asleep by 10pm in my temporary room and slept till 7.30 this morning. I went to surgery at 8.30 and Dr. Bremner (after much pondering!) decided that I could go on duty tonight. I have to report to Matron at 5 to 8 – so now I'm having a bit of peace in the library before I go to Marlborough Court to unpack. I'm planning to have my lunch here at Foley St. at 1pm and then go to bed this afternoon till 6.30, after unpacking.

I've collected my rations this morning, and found my clean laundry so everything is fine so far. My address will be: Nurse N. Bryan, 107-109 Marlborough Court, Lancaster Gate, London W2.

Later
I've been to M. Court and seen my room which is 403 – the same as my old one! I'm sharing a room with a girl I don't even know. But she's on nights off at the moment and is going altogether on Monday. It's quite a nice room but I'd rather be at Foley St. Everything seems very strange with the new routine. I've just had my lunch and I'm going back to M. Court to bed!

9th November
Just a few lines from a weary night nurse! This time after a night on duty and not before! It's about 11.30am and I shall soon have to go to bed, but I don't really want to – it seems so strange.

Yesterday afternoon I was in bed, undressed by 3.45pm but couldn't sleep a wink. I suppose it was hardly surprising really. At 6.30pm the telephone rang to wake me, and I got up all bright and breezy! At 7 o'clock we had cups of tea brought into the lounge downstairs and at

7.15 the bus came to take us to York House. Breakfast there at 7.30 and I thoroughly enjoyed it. I wasn't quite as ready for <u>lunch</u> at 11pm! Then we make our own tea on the ward about 4am and have supper as soon as we come off duty in the morning, which is normally about 8am. The bus comes to York House to collect us at 8.45. Breakfast and supper are at York House and lunch at Foley St.

I am on "Bond Street" ward which is a Women's Orthopaedic ward. Of all the kinds of nursing I'm quite convinced that this is the worst! There are only 16 patients but 12 of them have to have their backs done 4-hourly (<u>my</u> job) and being bed-ridden there are the everlasting Beeps! (<u>my</u> job of course!) Fortunately they all sleep fairly well, so once they're off to sleep the ward is fairly quiet.

On alternate nights I have an hour off from 3-4am or 4-5am (i.e.) 3 one night and 4 the next. In that time I am allowed to go into the "Bunk" (sister's room) and sleep or do what we like. We also have an hour for lunch at 11pm. The Head Nurse goes later. There are just a Head Nurse and her pro (me!) on each ward and I'm sure the pro works harder than the Head Nurse!!

By 4.30 I was beginning to be a bit lifeless! – but as soon as daylight came it was surprising how much I revived. I felt quite wide awake by 7am. At the moment I feel rather drowsy – my brain won't function properly! But it's horrible just when day comes at last to think you've got to go to bed!

Wood and I have been out for a coffee in Marble Arch Lyons – about 10.15am. Several of the girls are still out because they can't sleep. My nights off are Nov. 18.19.20 and 21st (Mon-Tues-Wed-Thurs) returning Friday night. I shall always have those days off, so every alternate week I can be home from Monday to Friday. That rules out Christmas but means I come home on New Year's Day.

Oh to be back to normal civilised living! Maybe things will improve after a day or two, when I'm more accustomed to all this, but at the moment I long to go back to Day Duty! As far as I can see one is just as busy on nights as during the day – lots of sitting down jobs but always <u>something</u> to do, and an unearthly rush from 5am onwards. I'm writing this in an armchair by a fire in the entrance hall/lounge and it's quite cosy. I'm liking my bedroom more now too.

Sat. 10th Nov./Sun. am. 11th November

It's almost 2am now and I don't seem to have very much to do for once. Sorry to be writing on mi/mu charts and in red ink. We always write everything in red ink on night duty. I'm alone on the ward at the moment. I'm now liking night duty very much indeed. In fact I think I prefer the actual atmosphere and work to day duty – it's so much more peaceful and quiet. But I shall never like going to bed in the daytime! I come off duty at 8.15am, have supper and get back to Marlborough Court on the hospital bus about 9.15am. To have 8 hours' sleep one really needs to be in bed by 10.30, but what a life that would be! It's so lovely to see daylight after 12 hours of darkness that the thought of going to bed is horrible. It would be chronic to merely work and sleep for 3 months. So I normally go out for a walk round the park, or for a coffee with one of the others and get to bed about 12. Then when 6.30 comes I feel that I could go on sleeping forever!

The first afternoon I didn't sleep a wink – next day I slept soundly for 5 hours. On Friday I could <u>not</u> go to sleep and had only about 4 hours at the most. I wondered how I should ever get through the night – but it's surprising how different one feels when one is actually up on the ward. Yesterday however I slept well all afternoon.

4.30am

At that point I had to do some job or other and now here I am after my rest hour. I kept falling asleep all the time, and felt quite lifeless when I got up, but now I have revived, and am alone again for an hour, while the Head Nurse has <u>her </u>rest. I usually begin to feel tired about 4am and then wake up again at daylight!

12th November 1.45am. Monday

Here I am again with another new Head Nurse this time. I've had three different Head Nurses so far, and they've all been quite nice. It's nearly 2am again and tonight is my "Cross night". I expect one of the Sisters will be coming fairly soon to do my Medical fomentation with me. So hopefully I shall get a "cross".

I didn't get to bed till 12.45 (11th Nov.) yesterday as Wood and I went to the Cenotaph for the ceremony. We saw the King and Queen and Princess Margaret in the distance, but there were so many people that half the time we could hardly breathe! But it's grand to think we have actually been there on Remembrance Sunday even if it was a squash!

The girl whose room I've been sharing is leaving tomorrow and I'm moving down to the first floor to share a room with someone I do know – Anne Key. Apparently it is big and beautiful but I haven't seen it yet. Bish is at York House after all, but Paddy and Mary are coming to Marlborough Court tomorrow to begin their nights.

I thought you might be interested in my "programme" for night duty – the things one does (apart from bedpans! – those eternal darlings – throughout the night!) are the same every night.

8pm	Round of patients and make drink list and take round drinks.
8.10pm	Move desk to under lamp. Put blanket on floor and on desk (to muffle noise). Shade lamp. Fill sterilizer and turn on.
8.20	Beep round (!!!! Great joke). 4-hourly backs (another joke!). Collect up cups.

9.30(approx.) Sluice
- (i) Make brown wool swabs.
- (ii) Tie up laundry.
- (iii) Clean back trolley and refill with talc spirit etc.
- (iv) Lay mouthwashes on back trolley.
- (v) Wash any bedsocks (from operations).
- (vi) Do flowers ready for morning (i.e.) patients flowers.

Kitchen:
- (i) Wash up cups etc.
- (ii) Tidy kitchen.
- (iii) Make coffee for Head Nurses.
- (iv) Lay trolleys for breakfasts and leave outside kitchen covered with clean t-towel.
- (v) Scour out milk pan.

10.30pm	Go back to ward and have report from Head Nurse, who then goes for her coffee.
11pm	Lunch in Foley Street (reached by underground corridor).
12am	Return. Sit in ward.
	Start to make stock (cotton wool pads and gauze and woolly balls for dressings).
	Make dabs for theatre – these are big squares of cotton wool covered with gauze and oversewn round edges.
2am	Cut bread and butter when Head Nurse returns to ward from lunch
3 or 4am	An hour's rest, alternately with Head Nurse (during which time we sleep or read).
	If you go to 1st rest you do kitchen.
	If you go to 2nd rest you do tea at 4am for the nurses on duty (men's and women's wards)
	(i.e.) tea and toast usually.
	2nd rest pro takes dabs up to theatre between 4 and 5am.

Kitchen (1st rest pro)

5.15am	Put on 2 kettles and 2 large jugs of water and jug of milk if there is porridge.
	Put porridge in oven to heat.
	Put bowls out to heat.
	Wash up and tidy up.
5.30am (approx)	Take round mouthwashes QUIETLY and collect up water jugs.
	Take blanket off table and floor.
6am	Unshade lamp. Put desk back.
	B.P. rounds. 4-hourly backs.
	Collect up mouthwashes.
6.40am	Make tea.
	Take round breakfast trolley.
7.10am	Second cups of tea.
	Clear everything away by 7.30am.
	Add up mi and mu charts.
	Wash and put away mouthwashes. OFF DUTY!!

3.45 (12th Nov.)

It's my night for making tea, so must slip off and hope the patients won't fall out of bed!

I've done and got my cross and have just been with Sister on round of ward and given her a report.

Am going to sleep in my new bedroom today. It's absolutely glorious – so big and lovely.

Thanks for the cutting about "nurses as wives"! So we're not domesticated?! That matron obviously isn't acquainted with training in a good hospital!

Oh by the way – I must tell you that one woman called me a little while ago to tell me that she was terribly worried because she'd just been dreaming that somebody had painted her legs green! A few nights ago she dreamt that all the patients took their false teeth to her in their tooth mugs and she had to clean them!! There's never a dull moment.

My 4th night since I came back – time does fly. The nights go more quickly than ever the days do. It will soon be next Monday and I shall be coming home again.

I've got a new Head Nurse tonight. Nurse Bleasdell has gone back to day duty and now I have Nurse Powell. Poor girl finds it rather awkward being up here because the chap to whom she is to be engaged next June is a patient on Dresssmakers – the Men's Ward here. The poor girl is Head Nurse here for 6 nights and then 2 nights on Dressmakers as Pro. Fancy having to nurse the man you're going to marry! He's rather a nice chap but has had some bad illnesses. He often stays awake at night worrying that Anne will decide she can't be bothered with an invalid like him, but there's no fear of that.

Yesterday morning I went to the hospital accounts office about my sickness benefit. They say that 30/- has been deducted from this month's salary and it's too late for me to have it this month now. However – we're being paid on Dec. 21st instead of a week later, so my 30 shillings will be added on to that. I'm so glad I haven't lost it.

On Sunday morning after I posted your letter I went to Christ Church, Lancaster Gate for Sung Eucharist at 10 a.m. It was a lovely service, though there was a visiting parson and nobody sang the hymns. Before I went I had Anne Key's wireless on and listened to the Silver Chords choir and to the morning service.

Both Sunday and yesterday I was in bed by 11.45am. Tomorrow I shall be even earlier I hope – I'm still taking Halibut Oil capsules according to your orders!

Priest and I had a row with Sister on Sunday night. She told us we'd left the kitchen disgustingly untidy on Sunday morning. That was after we'd made an extra special effort to clear it up. So I told her I couldn't understand why it was untidy because we'd spent an extra 10 minutes or more on it after hearing that the maids had been complaining. Then she said, "Well it wasn't so much the kitchen as the way the trolleys were stacked" – the maids weren't expected to put away the salts and peppers. How the dickens could we be expected to know that?! Anyway yesterday morning she said she was better pleased. After we had gone she told the Head Nurse that she didn't really approve of the way I'd spoken to her, but she admired my guts!! She said it took a lot to keep a straight face!! The Head Nurse told me all this afterwards.

I hardly dare <u>breathe</u> when some sisters are talking to me, but this one made me so mad, because there's so little time for <u>anything</u> in the mornings. She's very nice and I like her very much all the same. Don't forget to listen to the dear lady on the radio on Thursday afternoon – she's young and has fair hair and is rather short and dumpy. She's going to marry a doctor next June.

It's now about 3.15am and my Head Nurse has gone to rest for 2 hours. Lucky "so and so"! The Head Nurse from Dressmakers has let Powell have her rest hour now as well, as she's going on Nights off tomorrow.

One of the nice things about Night Duty is that you are left alone in charge of the ward a lot. I used to think I would be scared stiff to be alone on any ward on night duty, but now I don't think I'd mind at all.

16th November

8 nights gone already and only 4 more before I come home. 12 nights seems an age to wait for a bit of off duty. Anne Key came back yesterday and she says she felt she'd been away for ages. The first night at home she went to bed at 6.30pm and slept for 14 hours till 8.30 next morning! I'm sure I shall too, because here I never get more than 6 hours' sleep in one day. Last night I was tired out at 4am and I was glad to get back onto the ward because I could do jobs to keep me awake. I don't like sleeping during rest hour because one feels so awful afterwards.

I hope to goodness I go on a men's ward after this – women are such a trial to nurse – men make much more cheerful patients on the whole and don't "grouse" so much. Of course there are exceptions in both cases. We have some real saints on our women's ward, and there are one or two terrors on the men's ward, but really I do prefer men. Last night was hectic. I had to take 4-hourly pulse and blood pressure on one woman (a tricky job) and there seemed to be endless Beeps and cups of tea needed. I took my cup of tea onto the ward the other night and I thought to myself "I bet Mrs. Heather smells my tea in her dreams"! And blow me she did! In a few minutes she was sitting up in bed calling "Nurse" for all she was worth! I went straight to the kitchen to get another cup without asking her.

Yesterday morning Mary, Paddy and I missed the hospital bus at 7.15. We were down in time but they said we were late and didn't wait. That ridiculous sister has no sense of decency! We had to get a taxi because we're not allowed to go on ordinary buses in our uniforms.

Night duty is simply super but I can't wait till next Monday morning. Sunday is the last night so I'm looking forward to Sunday to make it seem sooner!

I must fly out and post this, then have a bath in our "posh" bathroom. Anne and I are going to knit before we go to sleep as it's only 10.30. The bathroom to my new room is a private one, and once I'm in there nobody can get me out! And it's so much nicer than anyone else's. Anne and I are very lucky. I adore this new big bedroom. I do wish you could see it. The carpet is pink and the bedspreads (on soft divan beds), armchair covers and curtains are all of a dark-brown

49

heavy material with pink, green and gold flowers and leaves on them. There are two wardrobes and a dressing table and washbowl, and it's super. It looks over Kensington Gardens and has a lovely big balcony. I'm sure it's the nicest in the hotel and Anne and I are such good friends.

2nd December

Dear Mrs. Bryan

I am sorry to tell you that your daughter has been taken off duty as she has a stye on her eye. She is resting in the Nurses' Home where she is receiving every care and attention. I hope the stye will soon resolve and she will be quite fit again.

Yours sincerely
M.J. Mariott
Matron

3rd December

I'm terribly sorry but I can't come home tomorrow after all! The awful thing is that I have another stupid stye. I went to the office on Friday/Sat. morning to get a slip for my ration book to bring home, and Sister Smith noticed that I had a stye. She asked if I'd had one before so I said "yes" and I told her about the boil. She said I ought to go and see the R.M.O. about it because obviously it was an outbreak of sepsis and the infection was still there. So I went yesterday morning to the R.M.O. when I came off duty, and, as he always does, he took me off duty. Sister was very emphatic that I shouldn't be on an Orthopaedic ward with sepsis. I'm having penicillin injections twice a day, and hot bathes and one drop of Albucid twice a day. It would have been terribly awkward to stay at Marlborough Court, so I've got a room in Sick Bay at Foley St. Though this morning I've come back to Marlborough Court to see Paddy and Anne Key and to fetch some more things. I've just had lunch here and I'm going back to Foley St. when I've written this letter. I prefer to be at Foley St. because there's nobody I know here – they're all asleep!

Yesterday I couldn't go to bed till I'd had my treatment in Sick Bay at 5.30pm. Priest and I had lunch together here at Marlborough Court. I had tea here and then went back to Sick Bay. I was <u>so</u> tired I didn't know how to keep awake. However I had my treatment and was in bed and asleep by 6.30pm and slept soundly till nearly 6 this morning.

It was such a scream – at 6 o'clock this morning the Sick Bay Night Nurse came marching into my room, turned on the light, took my pulse, took out the thermometer, turned off the light and departed! I didn't have time to protest! I thought "Ha! Ha! A bit of my own medicine!" Now I know what the patients think when I wake them up in the morning and give them a bedpan! It can't be exactly pleasant to be wakened up and have a beep thrust at you!

However I'd had a long sleep and was awake in any case. I had my breakfast brought to me in bed about 7am, then a cup of coffee at 9.15, and also an electric fire in my room! I got up in time for surgery at 9.30am. It's nice to be waited on hand and foot for a change, though I felt a bit stupid when there's really nothing much wrong with me. The R.M.O. said I was still to be off duty when I saw him this morning and announced that he thought he would take out a few eyelashes round the stye. It's on the top lid this time, but the same eye. Sister Chalmers told Nurse Mann to prepare a sterile tray because I was "for epelation" or something – I think that's how you spell it! It was a horrible process, but dear old Dr. Bremner congratulated me on keeping so still! I just had to hang on tight! What I hate is having that drop in my eye. Nurse Mann says she doesn't know how she ever gets it in, because I flinch before she's even dropped it! I sit with my head back waiting for it to drop, and it's such a horrid sensation when it does drop! And I make all this fuss just for a little stye! Heaven help me!

Anyway I'm so upset that I can't come home tomorrow, but maybe from your point of view fate has stepped in because you already have visitors staying. From my point of view perhaps it's a good thing because I want to get rid of the cause of all these things and I'm enjoying being a lady of leisure. There's plenty of time for knitting and Christmas shopping and it's glorious to have a nice long sleep and no telephone to wake me up to go on duty! And when I come home I shall feel refreshed. I expect I shall be given sick leave in place of nights off but I shall see I don't miss my nights off! I expect it will be towards the end of this week. I will let you know.

51

I've just heard that in Picture Post next week there is to be a series of pictures of life in hospitals at Christmas – the Middlesex Hospital! And the photos are of Bond St. – <u>my ward!</u>

R.M.O. allowed sick leave.

5th December

Telegram to parents:

COMING TODAY. MARYLEBONE 12.15. LOUGHBOROUGH 2.58PM. WILL BUS IF NO CAR

12th December

Back on duty – and how I <u>hated</u> coming back. I always feel utterly miserable when I just arrive back here. But <u>now</u> I'm enjoying being back having re-settled myself. I have a very nice new Head Nurse, but she doesn't help me very much so there's masses to do and I get all behind. Last night the patients were very restless and we were running about all the time. Miss Heather hasn't departed yet – somehow I thought my eyes would behold her shining face as I walked into the ward! My poor women were quite worried about me apparently – they didn't know where I was. They guessed I'd gone off sick though, because they thought I looked very tired when they last saw me. Thank you <u>very</u> much for my 3 days with you. I enjoyed every minute.

I'm feeling quite pleased with life now though, because I came off duty at 7.45am instead of 8 o'clock and <u>actually</u> had the breakfast trolleys out of the ward when the day staff came on. But my women are quite a handful sometimes. They seem to have a craze for cups of tea in the middle of the night. It's so funny – I take a cup of tea to one person and then the others begin to cough and move about in bed. That's just a hint that they're awake and want a cup of tea themselves! I think I shall stand up on a chair in the middle of the ward one of these nights, and say that I wasn't aware that there was to be a Bond Street tea party in the middle of the night!

A horrible thing happened yesterday morning on the men's ward. One of the new men had 7 epileptic fits one after the other in the space of 3 hours (5-8am). No one seemed to realise that he <u>was</u> an epileptic till he had these fits. In the end he was so exhausted that he couldn't breathe, and had to be given carbon-dioxide to stimulate his breathing. But he just collapsed from heart failure. He was so sweet – quite old and had lovely silver grey hair.

Mary Barnett has asked Paddy and me and Bish to go to her house in Upper Norwood on Christmas Day. It will be rather nice, but it will mean that we will have next to no sleep and that we shan't be able to go to church which will be rather a pity. Must stop and get ready for bed now as I had a late night last night.

13th December
I've only a moment or two to write but I want to ask if Papa doesn't mind (I suppose it's not much use minding and he doesn't have much choice) I <u>would</u> like to borrow the 30/- for my ticket – don't bother about the sixpence. I would love to come home next Monday, but I do need my money for Christmas presents now as it will be too late when I get my next pay. I should feel rather lost if I stayed here and it would be a pity to miss a chance of coming home.

15th December
I was so busy last night that I didn't have time even to <u>begin</u> a letter to you and now I have only a few minutes as I've come back from church and must go to bed. I've been to Sung Eucharist at Lancaster Gate Church again. It's a lovely service, but would be even more lovely if only the congregation would do their share. Nobody sings or joins in the prayers, and in such a big church it's even more noticeable. I do my best, but one little voice doesn't go very far! Dr. Hardman is still away and we had a visiting preacher again.

Anne Key is on nights off, so last night I was alone in our big bedroom. Tonight Diane Willis is coming to sleep in Anne's bed to keep me company while Elizabeth Jones (who shares a room with Di) is also away.

Mary Barnett is completely crackers over a veterinary student who is a patient on their ward, and has some strange disease of the intestine. His name is Roy, and he's 24. I've never seen her in such a state. Last night during my rest hour, I had to make an excuse to go down to her ward so that I could see him!! She can't make out how he feels about her!

17th December

Here I am coming up to the 5th night back on duty after being home. Thank you very much for the money. I hate asking for it because I owe you pounds and pounds. However I was glad to be able to get my ticket and think about seeing you. It's just after 3.30am and I'm having my rest hour at the moment, sitting in Sister's office. Nurse Margetson is here too – she's the Head Nurse on the Men's Ward. She's doing a crossword one minute and trying to go to sleep the next! She's resting her feet on a biscuit tin – Huntley and Palmers: "Petit Beurres"!

We've had quite a lot of snow in London during the past few days and it's bitterly cold. The wards are very warm though thank goodness. Time to go back to the ward soon so will stop. The women are a pest tonight, but only one more night then HOME GEORGE! on the 10.15am from St. Pancras. I'm bringing my ration book so that you can have my rations for a week.

A MIDDLESEX HOSPITAL CHRISTMAS – 1950

24th December

After a wonderful little break at home I arrived back for another spell of night duty, to find several Christmas cards in my pigeon-hole. I sat and knitted from 4pm-6.30 but still couldn't quite finish the pullover for Ernest. It took me so long to pick up 200 stitches for the neckband and 152 for each armhole. So my lovely man will have to receive it as a New Year present!

It seemed so strange to go back onto the ward on Friday evening – the atmosphere was so entirely different. The whole ward was decorated with streamers, and holly with lovely red berries and it was more as though I was walking into a party of old friends than a bare ward of sick patients. Bond Street had had a party that afternoon with the most delicious food imaginable, and Henry Hall had been to give out presents! Our women had some really lovely things – one had a pair of pink slippers with a fluffy lining and Granny Caswell had a shawl. What's more, there were presents for all the nurses on Bond St. and Dressmakers too – a pleasure which the nurses on the other wards do not enjoy. I had a pair of pure silk fully-fashioned stockings, a tin of Elizabeth Arden talcum powder, a box of Yardley face powder, a pot of Yardley make-up base, a super gold tube of Yardley lipstick (which I exchanged with another girl for a rather nice diary because it wasn't my colour!) and a Christmas card with a 10/-note in it. Also I had a ten shilling note from a lady patient who went out earlier in the day.

The Christmas tree had been decorated and the lights put on earlier in the day – a big tree reaching nearly to the ceiling and surrounded by big model candles standing on the floor and about three feet tall. The ward and the patients with their Christmas cards stuck on the wall behind their beds, paper angels at the head of their beds, and coloured paper shades on their lights, looked really festive. Just outside the window at one end of the ward was flickering the big star on the top of the Christmas tree outside the hospital, standing on the balcony over the front entrance.

I seemed to forget that I had work to do, with all the hilarity and happy faces – and one of the patients remarked to me, "Well, Christmas in hospital isn't so bad after all." She was one whom Henry Hall had kissed under a sprig of mistletoe hanging over her bed!

All the nurses are working really hard to make Christmas really cheerful and merry. I've been decorating the Back Trolley with Christmas paper and holly etc. tonight, and I've hung a stocking filled with red paper from one corner of it. I've stuck a label on the top shelf saying HAPPY CHRISTMAS! When I came on duty tonight I saw nurses on top of ladders fixing decorations – as if they had no other work to do! The kitchen and plaster room are littered with stale sandwiches and broken bits of icing and bits of silver frost, after this afternoon's party.

But it's not only the nurses who have been preparing surprises for the patients! The patients have been hard at work too! Last night the Head Nurse on Dressmakers (the male ward) was presented with a laundrybag filled with bedpans, tooth mugs and soap dishes etc! After she'd opened it the men proceeded to play football with a child's potty – which came out of the bag!

Tonight I noticed two of the chaps wheel a trolley into the ward with something on the top shelf. Later I discovered that the parcel was for me! It was wrapped in a green plastic pillowcase, and tied up with bandage, with a ticket addressed to Nurse Bryan on it! Inside was a tray laid up with knife, fork, spoon, plate, cup and saucer etc., and all these were stuck to the tray with sticking plaster! This was my Christmas present from John Turnbull and Leo! The idea came from one of the women and the lads carried it out!

Christmas morning 1.30am
So yesterday morning before I went off duty I presented them with the plate of stale sandwiches from the plaster room, mixed up with chrysanthemum leaves and carnation stalks! – all wrapped in newspaper! The only answer I got was that it would cost me a kiss on Christmas Day!

Well now it is Christmas Day so A VERY HAPPY CHRISTMAS even though the greetings won't reach you for a day or two. I posted a little parcel to you on Saturday and I managed to finish knitting the pullover for my gorgeous man!

I didn't get much sleep on Saturday so yesterday I was asleep by 11.30am and feel quite bright tonight. In any case one wouldn't need much brightening up today – there's been a hullaballoo ever since I came on duty. I'm <u>mad</u> at the moment because one of the medical students has just been in here and wakened all my women up – so now they're all wanting beeps and cups of tea! There are two students drinking coffee in the kitchen. They're contemplating spending the night in the two empty beds on Dressmakers!!!

Earlier during the evening before the patients went to sleep, but after the lights were turned off, I happened to go into the Men's ward, when Priest called me. She was in a clinch with one of the men (Leo) and was yelling for help! Foolishly I went to her rescue – after that it was <u>I</u> who needed <u>her</u> aid! From there I had to visit Mr. English, also demanding a Christmas kiss or two and then to Peter Phelps (married with two children) demanding even more wacking kisses! My special man would have had a fit, but Christmas comes but once a year and the patients need a bit of fun from time to time!

We've been ordered to wake them at 5.15am. (the same way as we sent them to sleep!) so that they can get up and make tea for the patients on <u>both wards</u>!

The carol singers – about 30 of them – (both nurses – about 20 – and doctors) started outside the front entrance of the hospital at 8 o'clock, sang three carols on each floor, and ended at 10 o'clock with four carols round the Christmas tree in the courtyard. All the wards were in darkness except for the lights from the Christmas trees and the candles which the nurses were holding, and Matron was with them singing as well! The conductor was one of the doctors who stood on a chair in the middle of the circle of singers. Outside, the tree in the courtyard was lighted, and again the nurses had their lighted candles. They ended with "Sleep, Holy Babe" with a solo from one of the nurses. It was really moving to listen to.

Boxing Day 12.15am
It will definitely be January 1st when I come home. I had to go to Sister Smith the other night, and I'm moving to De Morgan Thoracic

Ward next week – presumably after nights off. I'll be home on Monday to return on Friday afternoon.

Well that's Christmas on the ward, but our "gang" were invited to Mary's home in Upper Norwood for Christmas Day. It was so kind of her parents to ask us, but I'm feeling a bit "rough" now! The others stuck the day through, apart from ½ an hour rest before lunch. But I went to bed in Elizabeth's bed for an hour and went fast asleep. I'm sitting alone in the ward now, and honestly I'm afraid to even rest my chin in my hands and close my eyes! I've never been so tired before in my life! Paddy must be quite in a state because she never appeared for lunch at all. She's just returned from nights off so had no sleep on Christmas Eve, worked all night then no sleep yesterday. And now she's found she can't go to the hospital dance because she can't get anybody to relieve her. She was making such wonderful preparations and plans about her dress and now it's all off. She's utterly miserable.

We had great fun last night – "Christmas Eve-cum-Day". I decorated the breakfast trolley and put on a big notice on it saying "Happy Christmas". The women seemed very thrilled. We woke them at 5.30am yesterday morning. Most wards seemed to do just washing and beds, but we simply TORE around and did Beeps, washings, beds and breakfasts! The day staff didn't have anything to do when they came on.

When we got back to Marlborough Court we changed straight away and were at Mary's home before 11am. We all sat round the Christmas tree first, and were given presents. I had a beautiful blue jar of talcum powder from Mary's family, and a big box of talc from Paddy and Mary, and two hankies from Bish.

Mary's father especially is charming – he is a perfect host. We had a WIZARD Christmas Dinner – started at 1.30 and finished at 3.30pm! with a short interval after the Christmas pudding before we had fruit and nuts etc. We had a goose but I must say that I prefer chicken. Goose seems more like lamb to me.

27th December 2am
I had 8 hours' sleep yesterday thank goodness, so am feeling slightly more refreshed tonight. I've never had such an awful night as last

night for feeling tired. I slept during my rest hour and consequently felt even worse when I got up! It was wonderful to get off duty and go back to Marlborough Court. I had a bath straight away and was in bed by 10.15am.

Part of my tiredness was probably the amount I had to drink on Christmas Day at Mary's. I started off with a glass of Burgundy with my dinner, followed by a glass of something they called "cup" – a mixture of cider and gin and something else with apple and cherries floating in it. Then when I got back to the ward, Mrs. Stannard gave me a glass of port. Mrs. Darlington wanted to give me some sherry and someone else some whisky but I thought it would be better to refuse it!! The patients were teasing me for being in such high spirits. It felt <u>wonderful</u> then!

One of the patients gave me a box of talcum powder, and two others a box of chocolates each, and another 2 hankies and some soap. Sister gave me a mug and the same to all the other nurses. We're on very good terms now – she talked to me for ages the other night about the festivities etc.

As Paddy can't go to the dance after all, the others have asked me to go. It's evening dress and should be fun. I shall go to bed on Monday am and still have time to get ready later. Then I can have the night at Marlborough Court and catch the 8.15am train on Tuesday to Loughborough for my nights off with you at home.

Well I must stop – after umpteen attempts to finish this letter and I've been resting for 1½ hours – I cleared the bed in the side ward and went to sleep on it! Now I feel quite refreshed and full of beans at 5am. So I look forward to my nights off at home and then De Morgan Thoracic.

PS: I'm coming home Monday after all as Paddy <u>CAN</u> go to the dance!

Sorry to hear you've all had colds and flu. I'll think about you on New Years' Eve. By the way Mrs. Caswell (82) has just complained of having palpitations, but it's quite clear from her pulse that she has no palpitations. Well I suppose that's what she meant – she kept saying "Palpi, palpi, palpi" – There's never a dull moment. Then Granny Caswell wanted a cup of tea. I've done oddments of cleaning up in the kitchen but you see even when the patients are supposed to be asleep there's plenty to do and I write a bit more letter in between.

Well now I look forward to the New Year and being with you, and then a new adventure on De Morgan.

1951 (De Morgan Thoracic onwards)

December 31st 1950

SHALL BE THINKING OF YOU, ESPECIALLY AT 12AM (MIDNIGHT)

Thank you very much for yesterday's letter – but how awful that you have all had a dose of flu and been in bed. I can see you need a bit of nursing – it's just as well I'm coming home tomorrow! Actually I've been rising in sympathy with you – I had a streaming cold all through Christmas night after I'd been at Barnett's all day and then it turned into a cough and laryngitis. For two or three days now I've hardly been able to talk and have been doping myself with Linctus and gargling with T.C.P. This morning I think it has improved slightly but I'm still horribly hoarse.

Tonight is my last night on Bond Street Ward and I move to De Morgan Thoracic on Friday. One of my women cried her socks off when I told her this morning that I am leaving. Must stop now as I'm going to bed early today. I'm listening to the Communion service on the wireless as I'm too hoarse to go to church. SEE YOU NEXT YEAR! A VERY HAPPY NEW YEAR 1951 TO YOU ALL. I think I shall take all my women cups of tea at midnight tonight!

6th January 1951

Back on duty again! And how I hate changing wards. I simply long to be back on Bond Street. I just don't know how I ever finished all I had to do last night – the whole night was so hectic. In the first place the routine wasn't the same altogether and in the second place I was the only probationer for both plastic and thoracic wards and had to do the work of two people. Fortunately the Head Nurses helped me quite a lot but even so I nearly went scranny. Sister had the bright idea that the pro should wash AND IRON (an unheard of thing) the masks when usually the Head Nurse does them, and I also had to test urine and clean blood transfusion sets and Heaven knows what. Perhaps tonight I shall be a little more organised and not be in such a rush, but oh! How I wish they would send a pro for the plastic ward. I had no rest hour at all, I just had to go on in the hope of getting it all done. The trouble is that the girl who <u>was</u> up here flew to Guernsey for her 4 nights off and hasn't <u>come back.</u> NOBODY KNOWS <u>WHY</u> SHE HASN'T! I think when there are two of us and it isn't so hectic I shall enjoy it, but at the moment it's pretty terrible. And believe it or not I had such a pleasure awaiting me when I came off duty. You may know that there is an epidemic of smallpox in a hospital in Brighton. Well a female from Brighton has just come to the Middlesex with suspected smallpox and everybody on the staff of the hospital has been advised to be vaccinated however recently they were done before. So I had to go and "be done" too. This female, by the way, is on the floor from which I've just come. It was so funny queuing up this morning with all the plumbers and porters and goodness knows who else! It was like going through a factory – one person took the names, another dabbed the spirit on, the R.M.O. did the vaccinating and somebody else put the dressing on. And that was that!

I had a good journey back yesterday and got back here about 10 to 4. I went to bed almost straight away, and though I stayed awake for ages, I <u>think</u> I dozed off. Thank you so much for my time at home. I did enjoy it. I'm now looking forward to January 23rd! Must go to bed now as it's 10.30am and I want to have a bath.

Monday 8th January 2am
I nearly tore this letter up as I hadn't posted it and I would have written quite differently tonight. But I thought I would leave it as it would have been a waste of all the time and energy I'd spent on it! Last night I enjoyed being up here much more, even though I was still alone. I felt I knew the patients better and I knew what work I had to get through too. I forgot to tell you, by the way, that all the patients here have a cup of tea at 6am to wake them up. That's another of Sister's crazy ideas. All right from the patients' point of view no doubt!

Later
Couldn't finish this during the night and am tired out now and <u>must</u> go to bed. I was carrying a cup of boiling hot coffee (straight from the urn) to my place at the table this morning at supper time, when Haworth bumped my arm accidentally and spilt the coffee all over my right arm. A lot of the skin peeled off and it blistered rather badly

and I was sent to the R.M.O. I've now got wads of tulle gras and gauze dressings and bandage on it and am off sick for 3 nights. No doubt you will be hearing from Matron. It's now 4pm and I haven't been to bed yet as I had to wait to see the R.M.O. But now I can sleep and sleep! I'm good at going off sick aren't I?!

I love De Morgan now. The men are such fun and love to help me. We're no longer strangers and it does make a difference. One of them, when I took his morning cup of tea today, threw his arms round me and kissed me!!! Nurse Sebire is back now, so there are two of us to do the work, and it's lovely. I think I might like it even better than Bond Street. I went to see all the women on Bond St. this morning. There are lots of new ones, but the old ones seemed quite pleased that I went.

Matron's office, 8th January

Dear Mrs. Bryan

I am very sorry to tell you that your daughter, Nina, has been taken off duty as she spilt some boiling coffee over her arm, and scalded it. At present she is resting in the Nurses' Home, where she is receiving treatment for this scald, and I hope your daughter will soon be better and able to return to duty.

Yours sincerely

M. Marriott (Matron)

Telegram 11th January 11.40am

COMING HOME TODAY. ST. PANCRAS 2.15 LOUGHBOROUGH 5.30PM. WILL BUS HOME.

17th January

Thank you again for my days at home. I had quite a good journey back, though the compartment I was in was terribly hot and stuffy and smokey, so I was glad to get out into the "fresh air" again. I got into Marylebone at 7.20pm and felt too lazy to drag my luggage and myself to the bus with the prospect of waiting in the cold and drizzle so I got a taxi and was back here soon after 7.30. I had my supper, and then unpacked my things. After that I felt so tired that I had a hot bath and was in bed just after 9pm. I had a very strange night though, I woke up almost every hour feeling like a boiled beetroot and dreaming the most weird and nonsensical dreams. In the morning I was still hot and had an awful ache over my eyes and in the back of my head and I really thought I was going to have flu. However I stayed inside for most of the day and didn't eat much, and then was in bed by 8.30pm. I must have slept from 9pm to 7 this morning and today I feel completely recovered!

Yesterday I got up at 7 and went to Foley St. for surgery at 8.30. Dr. Bremner said my scalded arm was healing most irregularly!! I exclaimed "irregularly?" Poor man was quite surprised! He seems very amazed that the scald was all done by coffee. So now I'm off till Sunday, lazing about with nothing in particular to do. I think I'm going to the cinema with a friend tonight. Sebire is on 4 nights off and can't go home as she lives in Jersey. Altogether it's rather boring but I can go to bed early. Now I'm going out for a little walk as it's quite nice and sunny after this morning's rain. So there's really nothing more to tell you as I'm not on duty. Sebire has been pro-ing on De Morgan Thoracic while I've been off sick, and one of the men nearly died the other night. He's got carcinoma of the lungs and is likely to have a haemoptysis (big bleed) any time, but it flowed into his lungs until there were 2 pints there very quickly. He was on continuous oxygen through the night and his relatives were called in the middle of the night, but he's completely recovered now. What a pity I can't still be at home now, with these extra days off sick.

19th January
I'm still messing about here at Marlborough Court and am so lazy. I sleep for 9 hours nearly every night yet don't do any rushing about during the day. It will be a shock to go back on duty.

On Wednesday night I went to the Odeon, Marble Arch, to see "Born to be bad" and "Where Danger lives" and wished I hadn't gone – both the films were so miserable and the stories so silly! But it made an evening out and Sebire wanted to go.

Yesterday evening I went with the nurses on the hospital bus to York House and had a "sort" of supper at 7.30 with them and then went to Foley St. to wash my hair. But all the dryers were broken so I had to come all the way back again and had achieved nothing! When I got back Paddy told me she'd had the offer of a free perm and would I like it as she didn't want it. I thought it was a super idea and rang up to the Polytechnic place this morning. But they said that the next offer wasn't till 31st January and I shall be back on duty then. Pity! This morning I've been up to York House to collect my laundry and spent about 2 hours looking round shops on Oxford St. – a safe enough occupation when I have no money!!

21st January

I went to the R.M.O. this morning and it was Dr. Jelliff, not Dr. Bremner. He said he thought the burn was healing well and that I can go back on duty tonight. I'm glad because I was getting a bit fed up and I don't want to have to make up for all this when the others have gone off night duty. I heard today that one of the females on my ward, a girl of 27 who was a Blue Baby, died in theatre the other day. I wonder what is in store for me when I get back.

23rd January

Well I went back on duty Sunday night and now I'm off again for 2 nights! These are my ordinary nights off but I didn't ever expect to have them. However Sister Smith says it's more convenient to them if I do have them!

On Sunday night I went as usual to my De Morgan Thoracic and I'd just been round saying "Hello" to the patients and made their drinks when the phone rang and Sister Smith said I was to go to Charles Bell (a men's surgical) and pro there instead. I hadn't been <u>there</u> more than 20 minutes when <u>their</u> phone went and dear Sister Smith said I was to leave Charles Bell and go to Webb Johnson, a men's Genito-Urinary Surgical Ward! I did eventually stay there and was there last night too. It's a big busy ward, but I enjoyed it very much indeed and would actually rather be there than De Morgan. I was moved around to replace nurses off sick. One little man of 81 started to get out of bed just as we were settling them down for the night. When we went to him and asked what he was doing he said, "I'm getting up" – he's never allowed out of bed. When we said he should stay in bed he said, "But when <u>can</u> I get up? I <u>must</u> get up. I've got to go on duty." My Head Nurse told him to do his duty and go to sleep! Apparently sometimes he says he's got to go to a Rugger Match and so on! He's losing his memory and reason and is going to be like a child, but he's so sweet and adorable.

Sister Smith told me on Sunday that I'm due off night duty on 19th February, but having been off sick for a fortnight I've got to stay on until 5th March. That will give me just 2 weeks on Day Duty before my holiday. It's just what I expected to happen. But there will still be some of my set left on with me, of the ones who went on later than I did.

Tomorrow I have to go and be vaccinated again. Mine hasn't taken, and all those people who haven't had any real result have to be done again.

Anne Key is still on nights off, so I've got the room to myself. The weather seems to be improving and it's quite warm now. Yesterday morning I went for a walk in the Park. I couldn't resist the lovely sunshine.

30th January
Sorry I've neglected you so badly but somehow I haven't arranged my time very well. Thank you for all your letters though – I've now bought some turquoise blue baby wool, and I'm knitting a bed jacket for myself. It's something I haven't got and I simply hate not having anything to do in my odd free moments on night duty. The pattern is very pretty. I'm so glad you like your birthday pullover, Daddy – I was pleased I'd finished it just in time. Sister now says I shall come off night duty on 2nd March. My next nights off are 4th – 8th February, and I will come home then. The Sunday train time is 10am from St. Pancras arriving in Loughborough 12.35. I'll get the bus home.

Actually De Morgan is extremely slack at the moment and most of the patients are up and about. The three women are quite pleasant but never stop talking, the four children are rather sweet and the men are simply grand. They get up at 6am and come to the kitchen to fetch their tea. Then they come and take round the breakfast trolley for me (with a little guidance from me) and are a tremendous help. It's a bit confusing to have about 4 of them in the kitchen, when 4 nurses are trying to cook though! They slop the porridge into the bowls, and fry eggs and goodness knows what! They're such fun – I can't tell you how happy I am on this ward now. When you know the patients and exactly how to treat them it makes such a difference. We've got 2 young ones in at the moment. Bobby, aged 19, is going to be an actor and is rather conceited but very amusing and helpful. He calls me Nina and Honey all the time despite my continual corrections of

"Nurse Bryan to you!" The other one, Arthur, is 23 and one of a family of 10. He's quieter and very charming. He told me last night that he looks forward to night time and the little green light over the desk, and the whispers! Really quite bewitching. Even when there's only me, as the pro, there isn't much work to do and I never really need to rush about. With 2 of us on it's just as lazy as could be! We drink coffee in the kitchen most of the night.

This morning Sister Smith rang up at 4am and said I was to go to Bernhard Baron (the children's ward) from 5-6am. I had to feed one of the babies and take a few temperatures. The baby was sick all over me but it was quite a change!

The houseman on De Morgan is a Monk. He's going to be a doctor in the Monastery when he's finished training. He makes all his own shoes! He's really a delightful person – very quiet but so different from some of the other conceited doctors and students. It's a pleasure to talk to him.

We've had several glorious days here, but yesterday was foggy. It's terribly cold now.

Did I tell you that I'd been re-vaccinated? It's come up really smashingly now! Dr. Bremner saw me this morning and saw my scald at the same time. It seems as if it will never go. Sister Clarke said, "Do you think she'll live, Doctor?!" So old Brem said he thought I might survive, and if the scar didn't go he'd find me a husband even if he had to do it in the dark! I laughed and didn't inform him that I already had a future husband waiting for me!

I was a "Guinea Pig" the other night. They were still inoculating this flu vaccine into the nurses when I got there. There have been 1000 vaccines prepared in England and issued to London hospitals. We had 200. It was dreadfully painful for some hours after it was done, but some people's were much worse than mine.

My poor husband to be (eventually!) is in bed with flu and sounds very miserable. The Doctor won't allow him to get up yet. I must write to him before I go to bed.

Thank you for sending me your first aconite. I've put it in my Bible. Anne and I went to Communion on Sunday. It was lovely.

2nd February

When I come home on Sunday I'll wait 20 minutes at the station and if I don't see the car I'll start walking to the Bus Station and look out for you on the way. I'm a bit worried that you want me to give a talk on Nursing at your meeting. I'm sure I will do it badly!

I had such an upsetting night on De Morgan last night. I think I told you about Mr. Blay, who always had to have his right leg in one position, the left in another, his head this way and his arms just so before he could go to sleep. I always used to feel very impatient with him when I had so much else to do, though I didn't show it of course. He was supposed to go out yesterday but when I came on duty he was still there. So I said, "Are you still here?" in a joking way, and he said he couldn't go home because his wife was ill. He was <u>so</u> <u>distressed</u> and kept crying while he was telling me how everything seemed to go wrong for him. It would take ages to tell you all he told me, but it did upset me and I stayed with him for ages trying to comfort him. He's lost the use of legs and arms, can't move his head very easily, is going deaf, has lost one eye completely, and the sight of the other is going too. There's only one job he can do now, and if he doesn't get back to it by 1st April he will be sacked. He says, "How can <u>anybody</u> give me a job? I'm just a crock – a burden to everybody and it would be better if I died." He said he only lives for his wife and daughter, but he started being ill when she was 7, and he's never been able to play games and have fun with her. He is <u>devoted</u> to his wife quite obviously and says that she's the only one who understands him. She dresses him, baths him, and does everything to try to make him happy, and the day anything happens to her, he's finished. But he feels he's just a burden to everybody. If he loses his job his wife will have to go out to work instead. And so he went on. I understand him so much better now, and I feel I could do anything, however small, to help him, even if it does seem a bit of a nuisance. When I left him he got hold of my hand and said, "Thank you, nurse, for spending your time with me. It's such a change to find somebody who bothered to try and understand." You know that's what is so wonderful about nursing. Money doesn't matter, even "tellings off" don't matter if somebody says something like that to you. It's worth all the riches in the world to hear somebody, who's so miserable indicate that you've helped to make them a bit happier.

Afterwards my Head Nurse told me that I shouldn't spend so much time with Mr. Blay when there was so much work to be done, and that in any case he was only playing up to me. But I didn't care because I knew I was doing right to talk to him. I asked him if he ever went to church, and he said he used to but can't now. In any case he can't be "religious" any more. He says he's prayed for 14 years that he could get better and work for his living but this is all he gets. He told his wife last week that he <u>felt</u> something would stop him going home yesterday. She said "Well pray that everything goes right!" He prayed every day about it. Yesterday morning they got him up, dressed him, and he was waiting for his wife to fetch him when he was told she was ill. He said, "How <u>can</u> a man believe in God and prayer when that always happens?" He's always tried to live a good life etc. etc. trying to do for others what he would wish to have done for himself, always trying to smile through his suffering, and still his suffering is increased, and nothing goes right for him. Honestly I didn't know what to say and I felt dreadful. He was crying when I said goodbye to him this morning. However! What a lot one learns from meeting and getting to know people. And how thankful one feels for health and strength and love. I hope you're not bored and I know you'll probably say that at last I'm beginning to find out what you've been trying to teach me for so long, but I think you will understand how I felt, and <u>do</u> think about it.

By the way, the little boy on our ward has developed measles and is on full precautions. Yesterday I was hugging him a lot, so heaven help me! My Head Nurse had a headache and sore throat last night so I hope she isn't getting measles. I must go to bed now. I need some sleep!

9th February
I want to thank you for my nights off. I thoroughly enjoyed them and seemed to do quite a lot during the time. I had a good journey back and the train arrived on time in Marylebone. I was at Marlborough Court before 4pm and in bed by 4.15. I actually went to sleep too, from soon after 5 till 6.30, and then both Anne and I went to sleep again after the telephone rang, and didn't wake till ten past 7! We nearly missed the coach to the hospital! As a result all my clothes were left strewn all over the bedroom till this morning!

It was lovely to have such a welcome when I got back to the ward last night. It was quite a decent night, though I was terrified that one man was going to fall out of bed, and we were expecting two of the men to die anytime. They've both got cancer of the lungs and they're so nice.

Barbara Sebire has recovered from her flu and is back on Plastics, so there were two pros last night, and I actually had my rest hour. I was finished earlier this morning than ever before. Breakfasts were all cleared away by 7.15am so I made three beds to help the day staff.

Bobby is still there and as idiotic as ever. I like the women more now – their ops are over and they're not fretting and fussing as much and are quite good fun. Must go to bed now.

12th February
There's about ¼ hour before I have to continue with my work, so I'll have time to write (—interruption number one!) a few lines! I don't know what's the matter with my men this morning – they must be feeling full of the joys of spring or something as several of them are awake already.

I've been pro-ing alone for the past three nights, but we're a bit busy now so Sister is letting Sebire come and help at 5.30am. They've had an emergency on Plastics, and he has to be fed at breakfast time, so I've had to do all the breakfasts for both wards. My feet ached so much yesterday morning, when I'd finished dashing around.

I went to the office a few days ago to confirm my holiday. When I told Sister that I was due to finish night duty on 2nd March she said she'd have to take me off sooner (2nd interruption – my latest conquest! A Cypriot who has proposed to me already!) – So I'm finishing on 26th February and now have only 7 more working nights!

That's how much I got written in that short time!

If I don't get pneumonia I shall be surprised. Four of us spent about an hour out on the freezing cold balcony from 7.30 to 8.15 this morning <u>without</u> cardigans on, helping with the great linen count. We had to put all the dirty laundry in piles and then count it and label it. It was a dreadful job!

Yesterday it poured with rain so I didn't go to church. Anne and I listened on the wireless instead.

On Saturday night I did three more crosses but I've still got about 29 more to get. I have to do reports now for 3 days to get another cross, so my Head Nurse will have a rest in the mornings. See you a week tomorrow! How the time flies!

14th February
Nights off again and I'm sitting in the hall at Marlborough Court with half an hour till lunch at 1pm. I went to see Sister Smith last night and she said definitely that I go on Day Duty at 4.30pm on Monday 26th February. So now I have six more working nights on De Morgan and my 4 nights with you next week from Tuesday to Saturday. Life is simply wonderful, and I'm sure I shall not want to leave De Morgan. Last night I had to go to Bond Street for about an hour to help the other pro. I was quite ashamed at the dirt and untidiness in the sluice and kitchen − especially after De Morgan which has such an efficient Sister. However by the time I went back to De Morgan, Saunderson and I had set it back to rights so I was happy once again! I was sorry all the patients were settled down when I was told to go down to Bond St. so I couldn't speak to any I might have known from Day Duty there. I did hear old Granny Caswell yelling "Nurse, Pi-pi" about 3 times during the hour though and was jolly thankful I wasn't permanently there! It was actually a delight to go back to De Morgan.

My men are simply grand, though Ali, the Cypriot, is getting to be a nuisance. They call me Nurse Angela, and Susie now! Robert says I'm "the dearest, sweetest and most wonderful girl in the world"!!!! And Ali calls me the "Queen of Beauty in the Middlesex Hospital"! They make me die with laughter. I shall miss my two women. They're going out before I return from nights off. I call Mrs. Scovell "Flotsy" and she thinks it's a great joke. She tells everyone that she's had 14 children, 7 miscarriages, and eleven illegal operations − she weighs 13 stone.

We had a dreadful time this morning giving one of the children her pre-medication and changing her into op-clothes. She yelled the roof down − nearly − and kicked. I had to nearly lie on her to keep her still, poor girl. She's a Blue Baby.

Sister Stone told me this morning she didn't think I was behaving professionally! I think she thought it was quite a joke. I asked my Head Nurse if I could go off duty and she said, "Yes – HURRY!" and shooed me away. So I threw my arms in the air and said something crazy. Sister Stone saw me and said: "I don't want you to be solemn and uninteresting but remember you are a nurse!" I was squashed!

I don't think I told you that all the nurses on De Morgan have had 5/- gift vouchers from Arthur Harden – I told you about him before. He wrote a lovely letter to us all, and I was particularly impressed by his super writing.

I've been meaning to tell you for ages that your special Honeymoon hotel "Florence" has been re-done and is finished now, but it's no longer called Florence. She's now the Merchant Navy's Welfare Hostel. She's painted a blue/grey colour and looks lovely.

16th February
What a miserable day it is – rain, rain, rain! Yesterday was glorious sunshine. So I'm sitting in the lounge at Marlborough Court without much enthusiasm for going out. Thank you for yesterday's letter. I received it in style! Being my day off I sat in bed like a grand lady and Anne brought my breakfast to me and your letter at the same time! I go back on duty tonight and only have to work four nights before I come home. But I've got to write the report for three nights for a cross, do 2 big crosses on Saturday night, and my lotions cross (the worst of all) on Monday. Then after my nights off I shall have to move all my things back to Foley St. for DAY DUTY! My room will be on the 5th floor and has pale blue walls – nicer and bigger than my previous Foley St. one.

28th February
Well here I am back to Day Duty after a lovely time at home. I had to go to see Matron to see which ward to go on and life is wonderful! However nice Night Duty can be there's nothing to beat Day Duty! I can really see where I'm going in the daylight! On nights with shaded lights etc. you have to "grope" your way around!

On Saturday and Sunday I was on Dressmakers Ward – the men's side of Bond St. (Orthopaedic). It was quite nice but I missed my patients from De Morgan. I went up to see them on Monday, and the men said they were heartbroken!!! Sister Stone gave me my cross for writing the reports. I gave in my case history report on the child with Broncho-pneumonia and Sister Ransom gave me my cross. I also did my lotions cross with her. I was dreading it but it wasn't too bad after all.

On Monday morning I spent my time packing and then unpacking. It all took a long time. We managed to get all our stuff (Paddy, Mary and I) to York House and then found a big trolley (like those they have on railway stations for luggage) down in the basement of the hospital, and having carried all our baggages as far as that we put them on the trolley and pushed them along the underground passage to the Nurses' Home. Then we took it in turns to ride back on it when we'd unloaded our things! You might imagine what tucks of laughter we were in! Not "professional behaviour" at all!

We had heard rumours that there had been rather a muddle over this change-over of Night Nurses and that there hadn't been time for the maids to clean out the rooms for us. We understood that 20 beds had been put up in the nurses' home lounge and that we were all to sleep there for a night or two. But the women were absolutely wonderful and our rooms were all ready for us by 10am. As I said, mine is on the 5th floor, overlooking Foley St. It's number 569. Being on that side it is larger than the other I had. I've changed the bed round, so that it is <u>across</u> the room. I get all the morning sunshine – I say "all"! But it looks good the way I've done it. The pity is I shall only have it for 3 weeks. We couldn't arrange to be near our friends unfortunately. Bish is on the 1st floor and Paddy and Mary on the 4th. There is a school opposite, with the children's playground on the roof, so they make a terrible row in their playtime!

Having got settled we all had to go to Matron's office and Sister Johnson told us which wards to go to. I went to Meyerstein – the Men's Medical to which I went for my afternoon from PTS. I told you I was expecting a Men's Medical didn't I? It's not very busy so I've plenty of time for crosses. What's more, Nurse Withie, who was my Head Nurse for a long time on Night Duty, is the Staff Nurse there. She's so sweet, and more of a friend than a Staff Nurse. The men are quite decent too, and the nurses working with me are very nice. I keep popping round to De Morgan to see my men there too. I can't bear to leave them. Bobby is now in a side ward and tells me he's a suspected epileptic.

I had a surprise parcel today from Mrs. Budd. You remember she was on Bond St. and on the Women's Hour programme on the wireless. She used to be always making Bambis out of felt and she's made an adorable little white one for me with a green tummy! I've had a nice letter from her too.

I had a 4.30 evening off yesterday (i.e.) finishing duty at 4.30 instead of 5.30, the latest idea. And today is my day off. I was asleep by 9 o'clock last night after a lovely hot bath and got up about 9.45 this morning. The bother is that the hooter wakes me up at 6.30am and after that I can only doze because of the racket with doors banging, and lifts going up and down. I put the hot plate on in the bedroom when I got up, boiled some water in the boiler at the end of the corridor, and then put it in a saucepan on the hot plate to boil an egg! An hour later the water boiled on the hot plate! By then I'd eaten a fruit salad made with an apple and orange, and a piece of bread and butter – threaded my white beads which had broken, made my bed and got washed and dressed! Then I proceeded to eat the egg and some bread and marmalade! But it was "Jolly D". I went shopping this morning and bought myself a woolly dress! NO RUDE REMARKS PLEASE – I told Mummy I was going to buy one. It's wine red, with a fairly full skirt, ¾ length sleeves with little turned-back cuffs, a narrow belt with a little buckle in front, and a high neck with a little white collar. It fastens with a zip down the back. It was 4 pounds 9 shillings from Bourne and Hollingworths and I'm very pleased with it. I'm sure you will like it.

Now I'll stop and write to my beloved man before the post goes, and I'll ring you up a 6.30pm. I hope you'll be in.

MEYERSTEIN MEN'S MEDICAL WARD

21st February
I was thinking the other day what a lot of people I've already met in my life, and I'm only 19! Growing up in a Vicarage I had lots of opportunities to meet people in all walks of life, and <u>now</u>, already, in 10 month's of nursing I've met so many people I wouldn't have met otherwise. Apart from the nurses and doctors there are 20 people – 20 new faces – every time I change wards, and even those faces change during 6 weeks. I feel very lucky to have such an interesting life compared with some people who lead a much more secluded life.

2nd March
Thank you for today's letter. I've just come off duty for an afternoon's REST! We've had a hectic morning so it's nice to sit down! I think I've just about made up for sleep I missed on Night duty. Monday I was in bed by 10, Tuesday 9 o'clock, Wednesday 11.30pm because I went to see "The 13th letter" at the Odeon, Marble Arch – Priest was off too, so we went together and it was quite good. Of course it cost us 4/7 (4 shillings and seven pence) <u>for each seat</u>, but it was worth it. Last night I was in bed before 10pm.

Meyerstein is still going strong, though we've been rather busy of late. Yesterday we had 3 of us on in the evening, but one was a new pro who's been on the wards nearly 2 weeks and so is rather slow. I know she's new and therefore a bit clue-less, and I hate telling her off because after all I'm only 6 months her senior, but really she's a bit awkward. This morning I asked her to give one of the men a B.P. because I was in the middle of doing something else, and literally she took 5 minutes to do it – getting it off the shelf, warming it and drying it! I could just as well have done it myself. I try to be patient because I know how I felt myself when I was new, but she just doesn't seem co-operative or willing to co-operate at <u>all</u>. My head nurse says she's fed up with nagging! So last night we didn't get off duty till 8.30, and I had to do this pro's work and my own too.

5th March

I've just been away to stay one night with Godmother Joy and family in Ruislip and had a wonderful time... I went to the first hospital social since the end of October last Friday. It was quite good fun – especially when a gang of students burst in with a notice "WOMEN ONLY" on the end of a long stick! It was so funny! I had some interesting partners, though the more I see of our medical students the worse I think they are!! I'm biased because I have such a wonderful young man in my life!!

My latest name on Meyerstein is "SMILER". The men say I have a very happy disposition. I told them that's because I <u>AM</u> HAPPY!!

8th March

Darlings – don't despair! I haven't forgotten you! Yesterday was so glorious that I went for a walk with another nurse friend on my off duty – it seemed silly to miss such lovely weather in the fresh London air!! This morning I stayed on to do a skin preparation for a cross, so bang went my off duty again. Again, silly to miss the opportunity though. I will write again tomorrow. Am going to Tomlinson's dancing class in the evening.

9th March

So sorry about the little scribbled effort yesterday but I just hadn't time for any more, and thought you'd like to know at least that I am still alive! I'm thinking you're just about leaving the dentist, Mum, as it's 5.30 – Hope you haven't had any fillings to spoil your supper at the Martyr's tonight. I'm going to Tomlinson's tonight for 8 o'clock. Mrs Tomlinson rang up and asked if I could make up an "8" for their little dancing class. I've got an evening off so I said "Yes". I'll let you know all about it afterwards – I expect it will be good fun.

My crosses are still progressing. I've got 15 left to do now apart from about 5 which I do automatically in Block. I shall still have 5 or 6 to do <u>after</u> Block, on my next ward I'm sure, but I do feel that I'm getting somewhere at last. It will mean that I shall be only a week overdue for my epaulettes, and people <u>rarely</u> get them on time. Two or three in my set still have 50 to do. Bish has 30. Anne Key has only about 3 – she's been jolly fortunate, having nice "crossy" wards and "crossy" sisters!

I'm sitting in my room at the moment and it's a bit cold so I won't write much more. Anyway the post goes very soon and I haven't really anything else to tell you. I'm on a level with the hospital theatres here – or almost – and I often stand at the window and watch the operations! All I can see is lots of <u>white</u> <u>people</u> bobbing to and fro, but it's quite exciting even so. The men on De Morgan told me a week or so ago that they'd seen me doing exercises before I went to bed!! Their ward also faces my bedroom window! We've got a new patient today – a black man with T.B. Poor chap isn't used to cold weather and has to be nursed out on the balcony, so he's nearly freezing to bits. I'll write again at the weekend all being well, and see you in just <u>over a week!</u>

10th March

I'm really busy these days – I thought I would have much more time to myself on Day duty but I seem to have less! But it's wonderful not to feel tired when I <u>am</u> free, and to be able to go out. I really prefer it to Night duty.

I went to Tomlinson's last night and so glad I could go. I found my way on a number 14 bus to Chelsea. One of the males didn't turn up this time so there were 7 of us – Mr. and Mrs. Tomlinson, Fred Jones and Jo, a male called Tony Carter, Anne Somebody and myself. I was surprised that Mr. Tomlinson looked so young compared with his wife. He isn't grey at all. Perhaps Mrs. T. looks older because she <u>is</u> grey-haired. Their daughter Jo is very nice indeed, has her hair done in a sort of plait at the back, doubled up, and wears a bit of make-up. The only thing I didn't like about her was her shoes. They had ridiculously high heels, and were made of nothing but straps! Perhaps she'd borrowed her mama's! Fred Jones was a scream. He says I'm to tell you specially that I danced the Lancers with him! He said you'd be sure to laugh, as you have memories of him in your young days! He told me that he used to dance with Mummy quite a lot. He's fat and has a tremendous moustache, but doesn't really look old, though he's rather bald!

Tony Carter was <u>extremely</u> nice – I suppose he's about 20 or a bit more, and very tall dark and handsome! The funny thing is that he's a Medical Student at the Middlesex so we had lots to talk about. He's on King George V ward, a men's medical two floors below me in the same wing, and started sometime before Christmas. This morning by some strange coincidence I was late going off duty and I met him on the stairs as I was walking down about 10 o'clock. I suppose he was just <u>starting</u> work! We had a little chat and then departed. I couldn't quite make out whether or not he's a boyfriend of Jo Tomlinson. I rather think he is. He lives just round the corner from the Tomlinsons and buses to work every morning. I suppose I shall see quite a lot of him now.

Oh! I've forgotten to tell you the most important thing – telling you what we did last night! I arrived about 8 o'clock and was presented with a glass of sherry as soon as I got into the room. We all sat and talked for a little while and then put on the gramophone and started dancing in their big room, which is actually smaller, I think, than our big drawing room. We all did the Lancers and then Mrs. Tomlinson dropped out and 6 of us kept changing partners as we did the dances – waltz, slow foxtrot and quickstep. I learnt some new steps. Mr. Tomlinson knows quite a lot about dancing but I don't like dancing with him because he's so stiff and jerky! Fred Jones dances very nicely. I got on well with him, and Tony dances quite well too.

Then we had an interval for refreshments. We had savouries (home-made) and cake and cups of tea. Then all the others, except Tony, sang madrigals with Mrs. Tomlinson playing the piano, followed by a general sing-song in which we all joined. Then we returned to the big room for 2 or 3 dances. They all dance and sing well and it was <u>great fun</u>. Fred Jones is Bass and Mr. Tomlinson tenor. Apparently Tony has a super tenor voice but he wouldn't let us hear it! I left about 10.45pm with the others. Mr. Tomlinson took Anne in one direction and I went with Fred and Tony in the other. Tony left us half way and Fred took me to the bus. I got back about 11.15. It was quite a change to have a late night – I've been going to bed so early recently. I'm going to ring them up again when I return from my holiday. I haven't yet discovered about trains, but I will do so at the first opportunity – next week, and then let you know.

We've just had orders to collect our entry forms for the Preliminary State examination – exams again – isn't it awful?! It's a <u>State</u> exam, not a Hospital one. But why worry?!

16th March

I have another bit of a drama story for you, but not about nursing! In my off duty last Saturday I went to see the old lady you asked me to visit and was there from 3.45 till about 6.30pm. I really quite enjoyed it, though it was a bit trying making conversation with such an old lady. She's 90 this week, but she certainly knows what she's talking about and doesn't miss much! I could hardly believe she's as old as that. I got in a bit of a muddle trying to find my way there, to Denmark Hill. She told me to get a 68 bus from Tottenham Court Rd and that it passed her house. Well of course there were <u>No</u> 68s running along Tottenham Court Rd and nobody – even conductors – seemed to be able to direct either to the 68 or to Denmark Hill. So I went across to Goodge St. Tube Station and asked the man in the Booking Office how I should go. He told me to get on a bus to Elephant and Castle and change. By then it was fully 3.30 and I'd promised to be there between 3 and 3.30 so I was desperate! I decided I'd have to get a taxi since it was a sure way of getting there and getting there reasonably quickly. When we arrived at Denmark Hill it had taken about ¼ hour. The driver told me it would cost 9 shillings – I was <u>furious</u> I might say because the Indicator said <u>4</u> shillings. So I said, "<u>It will not</u> you know!" and opened the taxi door and pointed at the Indicator. He said, "Well I've got to go back you see," so I said that was utter nonsense as there was a perfectly good taxi rank at the bottom of Denmark Hill – I'd seen it as we passed. Also I'd never heard of paying for a return journey! He babbled on so I put the tip up from 6d to a shilling and said: "I'm sorry – here's a shilling tip and that's quite enough! Will you please go now!" Anyway he did go and I just walked off and up to the house and that was that! I was a bit afraid he'd come after me!

Mrs. Cunnington (Mrs. Green's daughter) came to the door and took me to Mrs. Green's flat on the first floor. Mrs. Cunnington lives next door. She made the tea and burnt the bottom out of Mrs. Green's silver teapot! She stood it on the electric hot plate to heat it! Anyway they were all very nice and I enjoyed it.

After tea a Mrs. Woodruff (a neighbour) came in and said she was an acting Staff Nurse at the Middlesex hospital some time ago. It was very interesting to talk to her and discover which wards she'd been on. She told me which bus to get back on, so when I went at 6.15pm and it was "plain sailing" – I shall know to get a no. 12 bus from Oxford Circus next time!

On Wednesday Bish was off duty at the same time as me so we went to Olympia to see the Ideal Home Expedition. We went by bus, spent about 2 hours there, and returned for 5.30. It was very good, especially the gardens, but how I hate being in crowds of people all the time, and not being able to see where you're going! As Bish said: "It's worth seeing once, but not repeating it." I'm sending off my forms for Preliminary State exam today. It is costing me £2-12-6. See you on Monday – hurray!

19th April
The time since I had my lovely time with you at home seems to have flown, and now this will only be short because it's getting late and I won't have a chance to write tomorrow. But I'm sending my love and greetings for your 21st Wedding Anniversary. I hope the next 21 years will be as happy as the first 21 have been. For I know that you've set an example of loving partnership to be envied by many. I shall post a parcel to you tomorrow.

There's really not much news – except that BLOCK is going OK – we are having a Public Health test tomorrow (2 half-hour questions) and a Surgery paper on Saturday.

Our State Prelim as you know is in June, then on July 2nd we have an Elementary Nursing Exam (a hospital one) and on July 30th our Surgery exam. The lovely thing is that once the Surgery exam is over we don't do any more surgery exams for the hospital – it's treated as "Hospital Final"!! The Materia Medica is continued in 2nd year Block and we do the exam next year.

We're going to a Museum on Saturday morning before our test. In a week or two we give our speeches. We're writing them in groups of 2 or 3 and one gives the talk. Barnett and Bish and I are doing "Recreation for Nurses" and I've got to do the talking for 4 minutes.

26th April
We had another film (2 films) the other day – one on Orthopaedics and the other on the operations on Varicose veins. It was horrible! It was in technicolour and the blood looked even bloodier than it must in real life. Mary and I gave up watching after a while, it was so

awful, and we played noughts and crosses and Matchboxes to take our minds off it! (Please note, readers! I worked for 25 years on the operating theatre till I was 60!!! AND LOVED IT!) It was just butchery! One girl fainted in fact.

The night before last we had an hour in the swimming pool and played with life belts (against the rules!) What's more, Sister came down, but she didn't say anything about it!

We've had wizard weather here recently but today it looks like rain and it's much colder. Last night we went for at walk in Regents Park for about an hour. We've been several times just lately. It doesn't take long to get there and it's wonderful to see a bit of nature after all these houses and dirty streets. Even the tulips are coming out and the trees are quite green. Everything seems to be coming to life with the warm sunshine,

Now I <u>must</u> do some work – it's really study time!

30th April
Thank you for the 1st of the 5 weekends at home during BLOCK. I so enjoyed it as always. I had a good journey back. It didn't get dark till St. Albans. I had to stand till Leicester and an army guy started talking to me. We had an interesting conversation about our work. His name was Norman and he's got two sisters called Sheila and Barbara. In fact I gathered quite a lot about him. He dived into the compartment at Leicester, put my case on the rack and sat next to me, and continued to talk so I kept making mistakes in my knitting! He's in the regular army. I was back at the Nurses home by 9.30pm. Paddy and Anne Key were in bed. Mary was just going to bed with a hot water bottle because she had a pain. I unpacked and ate, and put the lovely daffodils in water and they really look super. So my light was on when Bish came back, so she came and told me she wished she'd not gone home because everything went wrong. Her father's printing works got on fire and Mrs. Bishop had an abscess on her gum, and her sister had to go back to college a day earlier, so <u>she</u> was upset!

This morning was stocktaking, and we all had to have our beds stripped by 8am. I was just going back to my room after breakfast when I saw Sister Clarke's hind quarters disappearing into the room next to mine, and my bed wasn't ready! So I called Paddy and Mary and we started furiously to rip off the bedspread and blankets before she came in! So when she did come – sooner than I expected – the room was just an unholy mess! Sister stood there and said, "What the hell is this, girl?" and let out a tremendous cackle! She's so funny and human, not a bit like a Sister. She's elderly and fat and waddly and rosy-cheeked and cackly and jolly good fun! She asked if I had a quilt and I said no! She nearly knocked me flat when she saw the bedspread was there all the time! Then I told her I had one grey blanket and two dirty white ones, and she wouldn't believe me when I said I'd only got one pillowcase! She said to the others, "I don't trust this girl – there's something funny about her!" And so the hilarity went on! When she'd gone I noticed the cackling hen thing that I brought back and went and cackled it outside Paddy's and Mary's doors. They insisted that I went after Sister with it so I did! She exclaimed, "Merciful Heavens, don't say we've got chickens on the ground floor too!" As a result of all this we were nearly late for chapel. Ever since then we've been playing with the silly thing a lot and we dared Bish to wind it up in Professor Selby's bug talk, and she took the dare! She was just going to pick it up, about half way through, when she accidentally bumped the handle with her hand and it made the most awful row! So of course we were in hysterics the whole time! I'm sending you today's efforts in the "bug line".

The bug practical this morning was different from what I'd expected. Most of us had <u>one</u> thing to do. I had to take a swab from the handle on the inside of the W.C. door. Mary had to cough violently onto a special glass thing, and Di and Paddy had to sweep their rooms with the glass culture plate on the floor! Bish had to take a throat swab.

Our life here is grand – and it's so much nicer to be all together in Block, instead of split up as we are on duty on the wards. Most of the Sister Tutors are <u>extremely</u> nice, and we're all so happy.

Now I must stop and go to the post, and have supper and go to bed early if possible. But the "gang" want to play Canasta so we'll probably not get to bed at all!

2nd May
We're all in the lecture room at the moment making a hideous row – Mr. Newman (the Orthopaedic Surgeon) is due any minute to give us

a lecture. I'm not off till 6pm so I thought I'd try and get a few lines written now, while we're waiting for him to arrive.

I rang up to the Tomlinsons last night to say I couldn't go tonight to the Dancing Class. I've got so many notes to copy up, and so much to learn for our First Aid test on Friday, and Surgery one on Saturday. Jo Tomlinson spoke to me actually, and said she wished she'd known sooner, but I didn't know myself about the First Aid test till Monday, and couldn't ring her before. Anyway I do need to spend the evening working, even though I know the Dancing would be good fun.

We had great excitement last night – a man (who escaped) broke in to the top floor in an attempt to burgle. Apparently he came up the Fire Escape and in through the door on the 5th floor at about 10.15pm. He met one girl on the 5th floor and hit her with something that has scratched her head very badly – somebody suggested it was a lavatory brush! She dashed down to Sick Bay – or staggered I should say – and from there they rang the Police. Detectives came, and Matron and all the Sisters in creation appeared apparently, and they all scraped down the building from the 5th floor.

But the man had escaped without doing much damage. I had a bath about 9.45 and got into bed at 10.15 unaware of all this drama. About 11.15 somebody came into my room and woke me up – apparently (according to the others) it was a Staff nurse who came to see that I was alright. I thought it was just somebody coming into my room by mistake.

At the same time there was an <u>awful</u> din outside my room, and I thought it was a party of inconsiderate people returning from the theatre. I was furious, but couldn't be bothered to get out of bed to tell them to shut up! The row subsided for a few minutes and then started up again further down the corridor. I thought I heard Paddy's and Bish's voices, but was only semi-conscious and couldn't understand what was going on. In fact I just turned over and went to sleep again.

This morning the others were most alarmed that I hadn't known what was going on! It was those idiots themselves making all the noise, so scared about the burglar that they didn't go back to bed till 1am. And they slept all night with their windows closed. There was I blissfully ignorant of it all, and with my window wide open!

The poor girl who was attacked was questioned all day long and is fed up, but alright. So you see what happens in our part of the world! We think the men concerned were drunkards – it was just after the pubs closed.

Strong and I have been setting up for our steam tent cross for tomorrow morning, so it's now 7 o'clock. I broke off writing the letter of course when the lecture began, and continued later.

4th May
Yesterday we had jolly good fun over the opening of the Festival of Britain. We were allowed an hour from 11-12 in the morning to watch the service in St. Paul's on television. It was wonderful I thought, and we had a much better view of it than we should have had if we'd been there! Then we watched the King and heard his speech from 12 till 10 past and we all agreed that he seems to be improving in health.

In the evening we watched the end of the Festival Concert, and saw the King and Queen and Princesses again. The Queen looked wizard, but apparently she was wearing a pink crinoline – a bit unusual for her. But still why shouldn't she wear pink?! There were floodlit planes going over the Nurses' Home – they looked wonderful.

During the service in the morning a plane flew over St. Paul's in the middle of the prayers – you may have heard it. The sound of it had hardly subsided on T.V. when the very same plane made the very same noise as it flew over the Nurses' Home. It made us all laugh.

By the way I've actually made an appointment with the dentist for May 21st. We shall be back on the wards then.

Last night we thought we had a fire here. I was working, and suddenly thought I could smell smoke. I opened my window a bit more and it simply poured in. You couldn't see through it. Anne came out of her room too, and we told the others and ran to Sister Clarke and told her there was a fire. She sounded the alarm and came dashing along to our rooms saying, "Oh hell, what next?!" It took ages to subside – at least 5 minutes – !! – and when it did, we saw that it was only the chimney on the house over the road! (Not over the road – I mean those backing onto us from Cleveland Street.) Sisters were appearing from all directions and everyone was in a panic! Bish had been in bed and appeared in her <u>coat</u> all ready! Paddy soaked her face towel and wrapped it round her head and started crawling along the corridor! (First Aid lectures!) We were just in hysterics! It was like a thick fog in my room – I thought I would choke when I went to bed, but it cleared quite quickly. What things do happen here! What with men breaking in and fires and goodness knows what. There's never a dull moment. Now I must buzz off to the post.

PS: My growth of bugs from the door handle of the W.C. was very disappointing! There weren't any worth having! But Paddy grew quite a colony from sweeping her bedroom floor!

7th May
This time it will really be short, and I'm terribly sorry I've been so neglectful in the past day or two. On Saturday afternoon I had an urge to do some work! So I worked till tea-time. Then after tea four of us went swimming for an hour. Then after supper Elizabeth Jones and I went for a long walk in Regents Park and ended up in a Milk Bar on Oxford Street with a frothy Horlicks! We got back here about 9.30pm. Then I did some of the craziest things imaginable. I got into the bath and found I'd left my soap behind (the bathroom is down the corridor from my room). So I had to dry myself, throw a dressing gown round me and go and fetch it. Then when I'd had my bath I put my pyjama top on and put my dressing gown on and forgot the trousers! And then the third thing – I got into bed without doing my teeth and had to get out again. It must be all this revision going to my head!

Yesterday morning I went to Communion at 8.15 in the chapel – there were only four of us there, and then when I came back I started a letter to my lovely boyfriend which I didn't have time to finish. I left here at 10.30 and went to see Ivan and Eileen Starke in Buckhurst Hill, leaving there in the evening at 9.15. The baby is due very soon. When I got there, Ivan was peeling potatoes so I helped him and then helped Eileen. She looks a bit tired but quite well. The baby is actually due on June 22nd and she's coming to the London Hospital for the birth, so I'll be able to visit her.

I did some gardening with Ivan in the afternoon – there were weeds all over the place, so I weeded while he put in plants. Ivan took me to the train at 9.15 and I got back here about 10.30. All evening we'd chatted while I knitted, and we listened to the wireless.

This evening I've been over to the hospital to arrange to do a Vaginal Douche for a cross, so that's why I'm late now.

TOMORROW, MY DEARS, AT THIS TIME I SHALL BE A 2ND YEAR NURSE!!

9th May
Here we are – now 2nd year Nurses and tonight's the night to celebrate! We're going to the "Blue Cockatoo" in Chelsea. It fell to my lot to ring up and book a table. Barnett came with me and we couldn't find the A-L Directory. So I had to dial "O" and ask for the number of the Blue Cockatoo, which sent Mary into hysterics! And then when they answered I said, "Is that the Blue Cockatoo?" it really finished us off! I couldn't say anything for laughing and the man must have thought I was quite mad! In fact he fetched a woman to speak to me. Fortunately by the time she came I'd recovered so I could speak more plainly!

Yesterday morning – our "anniversary morning" – Barnett got up and made us all a cup of tea and brought it to us in bed to celebrate. It was real luxury. We've been trying to discover what the others are doing. Two or three of them are going to the cinema but apart from that we seem to be the only ones who are doing anything to celebrate.

The new PTS started the day before yesterday (the 7th) and three of them came up here to Foley St. for supper last night. I asked if Quinelda Clegg was there, and they said she was in Sickbay with measles! She developed it the very night they arrived! So when I came off duty I wrote her a little note saying that if there was anything she wanted she should let me know. I bought some tulips quite cheaply the other day and thought Quinelda might like them – they're so beautiful I thought they might cheer her up a bit. I couldn't go to see her of course. I had a letter from her today and she's certainly taken me at my word! I've got to ring her boyfriend and somebody else in Cambridge, and also buy some things for her.

I couldn't do the "douche" cross yesterday after all, which was such a nuisance. We had a lecture in theatre added to the timetable, so it will have to be done next week.

A week on Saturday (the 19th) we have an exam on Surgery, Materia Medica, Bacteriology and Anatomy, lasting 2½ hours. We didn't hear about it till yesterday so haven't had much time to revise.

We had a film yesterday on Bronchoscopy – I don't blame the patient for being terrified. I hardly dared to watch. They have to have an enormous needle jammed into their trachea through the front of their neck, and the procedure that follows is too awful to talk about. The boy, who must have been about 20, and was the patient in the film, looked simply petrified. But it was a very interesting film nevertheless. I must stop now and study for this exam.

10th May
I had a telegram yesterday from Ernest telling me that you had agreed to our engagement, and I want to thank you both, more than I can possibly say, for being to loving and helpful. There was also a letter from him this morning explaining the discussion in detail, and I'm so thrilled because now I feel that you're really happy about it.

Every day I realise more and more how lucky I am to have such genuine and devoted parents, and the more I realise it the more I want to repay you for what you have done for me. I think the best way is by always trying to live up to the example you have set. I should never forgive myself if I did anything against your will. My love for Ernest can <u>never</u> alter my devotion for you both, which grows continually. In the next two years I hope we shall be able to prove this, and that any doubts remaining in your mind because of the 14 years age difference are groundless. If the announcement of our engagement on Saturday makes you feel <u>half</u> as happy as we are, I shall be content.

We all had a wizard time at the Blue Cockatoo. It was quite cosy and we had a delicious 5/- meal for 3/6! We were very good and were back here by 11.15pm.

Three things went wrong. First we were held up for about ¼ of an hour in a traffic jam on Oxford Street and thought we would be terribly late. Then we had to change at Sloane Square and got the wrong bus, so had to walk miles to the Blue Cockatoo. Then Bish picked up one of the candlesticks to light her cigarette and the bottom fell onto her coffee cup with an obvious tragedy!

We left there about 9 o'clock, having arrived at 7.30, walked some way through the streets of London until we decided to get a bus back to Leicester Square. There we had Banana Splits in a Milk Bar, and from there back to the Nurses' Home for tea and chocolate! So altogether we had a thoroughly good time, and didn't stop to have a single alcoholic drink!!

Thank you again from the bottom of my heart, and I'll see you about 6pm on Saturday. Ernest will be meeting me of course!

16th May
It's 6.30 so I have half an hour to write to you before supper. Bish wanted me to go for a walk with her but I was firm and told her I didn't neglect my parents! Now she's moping on her bed reading a sloppy story called "After the Ball". She says her parents will have to "lump it" if they want a letter!!

By the way my preliminary exam is on 5th June, the day before Mummy is supposed to be coming to London, so if I can get the day off, at least I shan't be worrying about work.

When I arrived back here on Monday the others were all up waiting, so I told them the whole story of the Engagement weekend! They thought it was a great joke that the ring was too small and that I had to wear it on my little finger! I drew diagrams of it for them! Ernest said yesterday that Perry's were closed but that he would take the ring in today so I hope to have it for the weekend.

Thank you so much for an extremely happy weekend. I'm afraid I didn't see as much of you as usual, but perhaps it was forgivable just this once!! The stockings have saved my life because I have laddered my last decent pair and haven't had time to mend them.

We've got tickets for the Dance next Wednesday, but can only find about 2 males, and we're supposed to take partners as it's 7/6 for two people. We thought we would have too many men at first. Mary has just gone out with the male she met at the last social. She's heard a rumour that he's married so is rather disturbed!

I haven't done an atom of work for Saturday's Block exam yet, so had better get a move on. I am going to miss getting up late after next weekend! Paddy, Anne Key and Di Willis have all got their new caps and epaulettes. About three others of our set have as well. They look smashing. I wish I could just get my last crosses – it's so annoying when the opportunities don't arise.

20th May

I've received lots of letters of congratulations, and a funny one from the Nottingham Journal saying that they would be pleased if I would inform them in due course of the date, time and place of the wedding, so that they can arrange to report it! I haven't replied yet! I'm going to write and tell them to contact me again in 2 years!

The exam yesterday wasn't bad. The results come out in 2 weeks. Prelim is on June 5th (the two written papers) and the Practical a few days later.

It's lovely and warm here today. I went to Communion at 8.20 and then took the other 4 their breakfast.

I don't know which ward I'm going to. Paddy says she's simply dreading it. I've now washed my hair and done a few other jobs that have needed doing for ages.

Up at 6.30am tomorrow. Oh dear! We've been spoilt in Block! But it's lovely not having to worry about tests for a little while. There is a prize awarded at the next Prize Giving for the best Nursing Paper (the exam is in July) plus the best ward reports. I'm jolly well going to try for it, though there's not much hope with 70 of us!

22nd May

I've had more letters of congratulation AND THE RING! I'm so thrilled – I was beginning to think it would never come! I've got a half day today as well, so I'm wearing it and showing it to everybody. It's simply beautiful with the 3 diamonds sparkling, and it fits perfectly now.

I went to the Dentist yesterday. It's a lady and she's very sweet. She says my teeth are in very good condition, so I'm glad I went when she could say that! I had to go for an x-ray of one tooth though, in case there was a hole beginning in it.

I've gone back to Meyerstein Ward again! They are quite a decent crowd of men on the whole, and I feel quite at home again now. Yesterday it was a bit of a shock to go back to really hard work after the easy time we had in Block. Sister Hammond is a bit of a terror usually – freezes at the sight of a nurse! But she actually managed to give me a lovely smile when she saw me, and she said: "Hello! Are you back again?!" She seemed quite pleased to have an extra nurse. It cheered me up quite a lot.

The only snag is that I haven't got my list of off duty yet and have to take it from day to day. But I expect I shall have it settled quite soon.

Anne Key is free tonight so we're going to the Physiotherapist's production of "Miranda" at 8.30 in their gymnasium. It should be good and we don't have to pay!

Tomorrow is the Dance so that means I shall be very late to bed – it's from 9pm to 1am. But it should be good fun. We're still hoping we'll have enough partners for the 7 of us! Mary has bought herself a new evening dress – it's quite plain and it's cotton. Elizabeth Jones is very good at needlework and has altered hers beautifully. I've taken the net off the shoulders of mine, and put two narrow black velvet straps on, and made a stole out of the pink net I had left. I've twisted four of my paper anemones together too, and am going to wear them in my hair – won't it be posh?! Ha! Ha!

24th May
I'm enjoying Meyerstein, though I'm scared stiff at some of the things I have to do sometimes. There are two pros beneath me now! So I'm not looked down on now! I do like Sister after all – we get on quite well together. The end of my crosses is in sight at last – I've done some recently. And I'm making appointments on other wards to do the surgical crosses. Oh what a relief it will be when I get my epaulettes! Only 6 out of 40 of us have them so far (3 of them are in our gang you know!) so I'm going cross-mad for a week or so!

The Dance last night was good fun. 6 males turned up in the end for 7 of us and poor Bish didn't dance at all. We started off by going to a nearby pub. The male creatures had beer and we had cider. The dancing was quite good – there was a fairly decent band. Refreshments half way through were delicious. It all started at 9pm and finished at about 1.30am so we got to bed soon after 2am and had to be up at 6.30! Some of the others went out after the dance finished and didn't get in till 4.30am! Our partners were quite nice but not outstanding! <u>How</u> I <u>wished</u> that my lovely fiancé could have come – I felt lost without him.

27th May
We had a thunderstorm yesterday morning and had to have all the lights on in the ward, it was so dark. And then when the storm passed over we had a baking hot summer day.

I'm beginning to think more of the idea of Ernest becoming an army chaplain. I'm afraid I tried to put him off because I thought it would mean being away from him the whole time if we were married, or not being able to be married for several years, and I couldn't bear that. But if I could follow him about and it would enable us to save more money it would be better. It would be rather an unsettled sort of life, but no doubt it could be good fun.

I'll let you know as soon as possible when I can come home. Sister has given me a half day today and day off tomorrow, but I don't quite know what I shall do yet. There's plenty to do here – all my letters, and knitting and television, and piles of anatomy and physiology etc for the exam. But I think I must go out somewhere and get right away. My exam is a week on Tuesday (5th June) from 10am-1.15pm with a break of ¼ hour at 12 o'clock. Then the Practical is a day or two after that – we don't know <u>when</u> until the 5th.

I've been feeling rather fed up these last few days – there have been times when I've been tempted to give it all up. I have such a lot more responsibility now and I'm so scared of doing anything wrong. Sister blew me up sky high this morning because I'd thrown away a dangerous drug phial which should have been kept. I gave the Premedication to one man yesterday before his dental extractions – an injection which had to be made up from tablets. There were only 2 left and Sister checked them with wet hands, so the first tablet dissolved in her hand and was wasted, and I had to use the last one. One always does throw away empty phials usually, and I didn't think anything of it till Sister told me about it today. Apparently you have to produce the empty phial for dangerous drugs if you want any more. I apologised profusely to her and said I hadn't any <u>idea</u> it was the wrong thing to do. Had there been any tablets left I should naturally have kept them. It was my bad luck that the blinking thing was empty.

Also yesterday I threw away the contents of a bedpan which should have been saved. That <u>was</u> my fault because I knew about it and forgot.

Then I spend my life doing crosses which worry me to death. It's a relief when each one is over and the agony doesn't last long, but beforehand I feel like crawling up the wall.

The others often come off duty feeling the same way, so I suppose it's only natural to feel a bit scared about these things. But sometimes I feel like screaming – I realise that nothing worthwhile can be achieved without effort, and try to laugh about the things that go wrong, but I still worry.

Perhaps Harefield T.B. Hospital will be more restful. I shall have my epaulettes by then I hope, and more off duty probably. I've now heard that we have to do Night Duty for the last of the 3 months there. I've only just finished Night Duty. Oh dear!

We've also got a <u>woman</u> in our side ward with Scabies of all things. I had to wash her this morning – none of the others wanted to and they know I always say yes! So I had a very itchy ½ hour! She's <u>covered</u> in scratches and is terribly self-conscious about it. Can you imagine me trying to look for these beastly bugs without her noticing?

I didn't find any but I've been itching since!

In the other side ward we've got our precious composer – Manning Sherwin – and <u>he</u> keeps me alive! He calls me "Sally-Ann"! He knows lots of film stars personally and is always talking about them and he says that I am like Sally Ann Howes. Yesterday he rang his bell because he had hiccoughs so I gave him a drink and they stopped! In his Yankee accent he said, "Sally Ann, I think you're <u>wonderful</u> to work such a miracle for me! You're beautiful and I love you very much!" He babbles on all the time and is so funny. He had a cerebral catastrophe a week ago, and is paralysed down one side, and his speech is all on one note, more or less. One of the doctors came into the ward yesterday, and asked who the heck Sally Ann was because Mr. Sherwin wouldn't stop talking about her! So the nice things <u>he</u> says and the fun I have with all the other patients help to make up for the things I do wrong! The men say that when I take their pulse it goes up 20 and all sorts of ridiculous things!

30th May

You now have to address my letters to "John Astor House", Foley St, not the "Nurses' Home!" Matron's latest idea!

When I go to Harefield 20 of our set are going to Woodside. I should have preferred it to Harefield I think. I've heard say that Harefield Nurse's Home is lovely, but some nurses have to live in prefab huts and they're horrible!

I'm most upset because Ernest is to have another two weeks holiday in the summer and was coming to stay with the Lewises in Edmonton. If he goes there it will take him an hour each way when he comes to see me at Harefield.

We've all had to be measured for 2 new uniform dresses. I also went to the Dentist on Monday to discover the result of the x-ray, and I've got to go and have one of the fillings redone on 11th June. Another delightful thing to think about!

Our Scabies patient has gone into the Women's Ward now, and we've got a woman who is dying, and is completely "up the pole". The relatives sit outside the ward all day long.

Manning Sherwin is still as large as life and progressing very favourably. <u>On my day off</u> (note) Sheila Sim and Richard Attenborough (film star husband and wife) came to visit him and brought some lovely flowers – John Mills <u>was</u> to come but sent a nice wire to say he couldn't. So I might see him yet! Michael Wilding is in Hollywood – Mr. Sherwin says he would have been the first to come otherwise.

I went down to fetch some things from the x-ray department the other day and who should come but Raymond Glendenning! He said, "Good morning – are you in charge?" So I directed him to the proper person. I wonder what sort of an x-ray he had? So you see I'm meeting all the celebrities! He had a very made-up foreign-looking female with him!

There's a great "to-do" on the ward today over the Derby – all the patients are betting and they've put money on two horses for each of the nurses too. I'm not sure which two I've got yet. So this afternoon we shall all have our ears stuck to the headphones! I wish I could win!

On Monday I should have a definite off duty list so I can decide when to come home. I'm fed up with not knowing.

1st June
I'm thrilled to think that you're coming up to London on Wednesday, Mummy, but so far I can't say what off duty I shall have. I will have to ring you up on Monday or Tuesday when I know definitely. It would be super if I could come home with you on Wednesday night and have a day off Thursday. I hope Sister doesn't make me have my day off on Tuesday so that my 3 hours exam comes out of it.

So glad you've tracked down the noisy ghosts in the loft. Di Willis had been telling us that the "Grey Lady" walked again on their ward the other night. She's a nurse who contracted cancer (it's supposed) and she suffered a great deal and was nursed on their cancer ward – Queen Mary, where Di is working. She comes back to comfort the sick and dying, and when Mrs. Hewson was dying the other night, she walked again. Only the patients see her, and one of them asked Di who was the Grey Lady who gave her an injection. Isn't it horrible? It scares me stiff.

We were paid yesterday and they've given us an extra £1 for our second year. Isn't that generous of them?! Mine was £7-0-1d so the men in the bank said, "Don't forget the penny!" I want to put some into the Post Office Savings Bank and have got a form so that I can get a new book. But I have to fill in the number and Post Office of any other books I have. I'm sending the slip to you – would you mind filling it in for me, because I seem to think I have a book in Daddy's safe. I <u>must</u> start saving in earnest.

I'm feeling a bit relieved now – I've launched myself on doing reports with dear Sister.

3rd June

We're having a spell of simply heavenly weather. I'm feeling jolly homesick because sunny Sundays seem to remind me of sitting in our lovely garden. As it is I'm sitting on a pillow on my windowsill (being on the ground floor) with my feet on the swimming pool roof! – very convenient! The sun is shining this way, so it's lovely. I think I'll get a magic carpet to sit on and fly home! If I was a typist I'd be able to do all these things and be at home to enjoy the lovely weather, and save lots of money, and not have a Sister to badger me all day long! The only trouble is I'd HATE to be a typist – how boring! I'd much rather be a nurse. There are one or two of our set who are fed up and homesick at present. The sooner I come home the better – you must be sick of my moans and groans in my recent letters. I'm sorry – I suppose it's bound to happen occasionally. What pluck men in the forces must have had, to keep up their spirits when they're away for <u>years.</u>

The Block test results haven't come out yet – I've only got 3 crosses left to do so I'm feeling better over that. Sister is off this weekend so I feel freer. I can work so much better when there's nobody hovering around with an eagle eye all the time!

I must go and wake Elizabeth now as it's nearly 10 o'clock. I expect you're launching on the washing up, or maybe still having breakfast. I had my breakfast at 7.45 with the intention of going to Communion in the hospital Chapel at 8.20. Then Bish came into my room in her dressing gown with a streaming cold and no voice, asking my advice on whether she should go on duty or not! So it was too late to go to Communion then. I'll go to the service this evening instead.

4th June

This is just a hurried note with final arrangements for meeting Mummy on Wednesday, that's if it's OK for you to miss the afternoon session of your meeting. I come off duty at 1.30 and will see you in the front hall of the hospital. There are plenty of seats for you to sit on if you get there first – I expect you will because it only takes about ¼ hour to get to Bourne and Hollingworths from the Albert Hall on the 73 bus. A 73 takes you from right outside the Albert Hall to just past B & H's. We can get lunch at B & H's Restaurant, or there's always Jo Lyons open if we were too late.

Then if it's nice we could go for a walk in Regents Park and get back to my room for some tea before I go back on duty.

I will arrange with Sister Clark for you to come to my room afterwards if you want to. You could come round to the hospital with me when I go back. Oh I <u>do</u> want to see you, but of <u>course</u> I shall quite understand if you can't miss the afternoon meeting.

It's nearly tea-time so I must change. Bish is in sickbay with her cold and laryngitis. I don't know if she'll be taking the exam tomorrow. But she's only got one of the papers to do because she and Barnett and some others did Part I at school. Now I see why I would have benefitted by taking it at school – i.e. anatomy and physiology instead of French or History. Bish hasn't <u>any</u> anatomy or physiology to do for this exam.

9th June
Just to let you know I'll be home tomorrow. My fiancé (!) will meet me, and we'll be there in time to help you with your supper party.

One of the patients gave me a whole basket of strawberries on Tuesday! I ate them <u>all</u> for supper! Another female gave me some bath cubes, and a gent who was visiting one of the patients gave me 20 Players cigarettes! I DO NOT SMOKE!

So I'll divide them between Papa and that man Ernest Sheeran!

There's really no news at the moment. Life is quite good again you will be pleased to hear. Must have been examitis. I only wish the sun hadn't disappeared just when I'm coming home.

Sister has put a notice on her Bunk door saying "Please open gently". When I opened it to ask if I could go off duty there she was nursing a big brown fluffy puppy! It was so sweet. SEE YOU TOMORROW!

When I'm at Harefield it will cost me another 5 shillings to get home and take another hour!

11th June

Once more thank you for my lovely days at home. It's always hard to leave again, but once back I really do enjoy my work on the whole.

We've got a male nurse now for Manning Sherwin in the side ward. He got too much for us, ringing his bell so often. Now we can walk past, knowing there's someone else to answer it!

Bish greeted me when I returned last night, and the first thing she asked me was, "Got any grub?" I think she was quite astonished when I produced six hard-boiled eggs!

I'm just off to the Dentist's torture chamber now. My appointment is at 3. I'm sitting on the roof in a deckchair at the moment. Practical is at 10.40 tomorrow morning and lasts 40 minutes, so please keep your fingers crossed for me! I'm <u>not</u> looking forward to it. It's really hot again today.

14th June

The exam wasn't bad at all, and now yesterday and today I'm sitting back while the others shiver and shake! I'm feeling on top of the world now – only 2 crosses left (I did one yesterday) and Prelim <u>over</u>! I've been to fetch my Block exam paper this afternoon and I came a "cropper" on the last question as most people did. It was Bacteriology and Materia Medica and I couldn't do it at all, and got only 8/25. But I'm pleased with much better marks for the two surgery exams and Anatomy and Physiology.

The Dentists was OK and I had the tooth refilled. I'm to go again when I come back from Harefield for an "examination".

I've been quite annoyed recently – we're so short-staffed on the Women's side that I've had to do my ordinary work on Meyerstein and then go over at 8 o'clock and help on the Women's ward. So it's been 8.45 by the time I've gone for my supper. And we don't get paid overtime. And <u>now</u> they've moved me permanently to Vaughan Morgan (the Women's ward) and I <u>don't</u> like it! Bedpans every 5 minutes! Men are so much more pleasant to deal with.

Last night I took out my first 7 stitches from our Borstal boy. He kept screaming (or pretending to) while I was doing it, and saying he was having an abortion!! The men were in tucks of laughter.

Must fly and have tea now. Bish has gone into her Practical. She's been dreading it. Mary will have just finished. She has been feeling sick all day and couldn't eat anything. And I've had a day of bliss! I can't tell you how relieved I feel now it's all over, and with the thought of having my epaulettes next week!

15th June

I simply must tell you the good news. I'm feeling on top of the world and as happy as a sandboy! I'm not going to Harefield till August 7th – 6 weeks later than I should have gone. There's been a hold-up somewhere, and 8 of us can't go till August. We shall only be there 6 weeks instead of 3 months, as we have to come back the same time as those who are going on 27th June. Unfortunately the other 6 of our gang will be in Harefield all the time, but I don't mind about that so much – all I want is for Ernest to have his fortnight's holiday while I'm in London. I'm the luckiest person in the world – my prayers are always answered. I couldn't see any way out of this difficulty and was so miserable, and now it's all turned out to my advantage.

I've worked it all out. I shall change my room to one facing the tennis court when the others go and I shall have a wonderful chance to do lots of 2nd year crosses for my strings too.

I'm almost signed up for my epaulettes, and this morning I had my first taste of Head nursing on Vaughan Morgan. We had two emergency patients, and I had to get two extra beds for them, and I had to put up a milk drip. I got in a bit of a mess finding all the drugs from the Poison cupboard, but Sister was perfectly sweet. I don't know what's come over her – she's so nice now. It seemed so strange to be ordering the pro about but I tried to be decent and to joke with her when she did anything wrong.

It's wizard weather, and I've got an evening off, day off tomorrow and ½ day till 1.30 on Sunday. Last week I was like a duck out of water, and now I've been blown to the other extreme! Paddy is off tomorrow too, so we're going to go out in the afternoon. The rest of the time I'm going to sunbathe and have a jolly good time!

16th June

Thank you for the lovely photos of the house and garden. They're really beautiful. I've got a new idea – I've framed that postcard size one of the house, and now can look at it and wonder in which room you all are, and what's going on. It's wizard – I never thought of it till 2 days ago!

I'm thoroughly enjoying my time off. Last night at supper time Jessica Niblett said she <u>must</u> go out somewhere to get away from the hospital, and would I like to go with her. So we set out for the Festival. When we got there we discovered we had to pay 4 shillings to go in, so decided to go for a trip on the river instead! But we couldn't find our way down to the boats, so we didn't do that either! It was nearly 9 o'clock when eventually we found a little pier. By then we thought we ought to be going back, but feeling hungry we stopped at a Forte's café and had two enormous egg and tomato sandwiches and a doughnut each – costing us 1/10 each. Jessica is at Soho hospital, so I went back with her as I'd never been there before, and then got back here about 10pm. I <u>had</u> meant to go to bed early!

This morning I got up for breakfast at 7.45 and then changed into my uniform and went over to the hospital to watch some clips being taken out on Rosalind Chetwynd ward. Sister was <u>very</u> nice. There were 2 patients with clips to be taken out so I watched her do the first, and then she let me do the other for my cross. There were 16 clips altogether so I was jolly pleased with myself. The only snag is that I wanted stitches, not clips, though clips are a 2nd year cross and rarely used in the hospital now, so it's as well to get them done.

I got back at 11am and changed back into mufti and came up onto the roof to sunbathe. I've spent the whole afternoon sunbathing – I've written a letter as well – and honestly I'm beginning to wish I'd been a bit more careful. My arms and legs are bright red now, and so <u>sore.</u> My knees are the worst – they look like beef steak!

It's now 6.15pm and much cooler and I must fetch a cardigan in a minute. I've been to tea, and then out to finish off Barnett's and Key's sweet coupons. It's lovely to have such a lazy day and nothing to worry about.

Our hospital will soon have a bad reputation. Yesterday a Physiotherapist fell, from the landing window on to the floor below Meyerstein in the same wing onto Cleveland Street and was killed outright. It happened about 5pm and I had gone past that very window as I went off duty ¼ hour before. It obviously couldn't have been an accident and it is so <u>awful</u>. One of the strings nurses saw it happen – I don't know which one though. The girl was only 23 and was the Chief Physio on Bond St and Dressmakers wards. It is in the papers today. Last year two patients did more or less the same thing if you remember. Let's hope it's the 3rd and last.

I think I shall wash my hair tonight and then go to bed early. Tomorrow morning I shall have breakfast at 7.45 and then go to Communion in the hospital chapel at 8.20. If it's fine after that I'll come up here onto the roof again. It will soon be Friday and I shall be coming home again.

19th June

I don't know whether or not I shall be changing wards again before I go to Harefield. It's quite likely, but we're so short of nurses on our floor that I may have to stay. Yes of course there are several women who are good fun, but in general they are terrible fuss-pots! – always wanting B.P.s at the most awkward times, and whining if their injections are half a minute late!

I've had an afternoon off today. I took out some stitches this morning for a cross – the lady is to have a baby in 3 weeks' time. It's a wonder she didn't have it then and there from shock! Now I have only <u>one</u> cross left and am hoping to do it tomorrow morning. So I should be signed up for my epaulettes tomorrow with a bit of luck.

I had a crazy dream last night that I had to give a talk on marriage for a cross! I wished I'd read up about it beforehand. All I could think of was that marriage should be a partnership – there should be no quarrelling and all difficulties should be discussed! They shouldn't worry about money – if ever one was short they shouldn't be afraid to ask to borrow some! I'm sure I didn't get my cross!!!

I also dreamt that I jumped onto a railway engine while it was moving and Princess Elizabeth was driving it! We rode all round the countryside together!

Yesterday Bish and I went to take her shoes to be mended. On the way back it started to rain so we went into the News Theatre for an hour. It was great fun for a shilling.

On Sunday morning Paddy and I went to Communion, and then from 11.15 to 12.45 I lay on the roof and sunbathed. And now it's agony to have a bath or anything. My nose and my knees seem the worst. SILLY ME!

25th June
Many thanks again for a lovely weekend. I did enjoy it. Bish was waiting for me when I arrived back, and she had arranged some flowers for me. They look simply lovely.

Enclosed is the stocking for Shirley. They seem to have mended it quite well, and they've oversewn the hole in the toe.

Yesterday evening I had to go to Charles Bell Ward (a men's surgical) to help while one of their nurses came to take temperatures on our ward for a cross. I took half the temperatures, and gave three penicillins and then returned. So I quite enjoyed the little exchange.

We now have a very bad case of T.B. on our balcony – a woman (quite young) who is a waitress. Just think of how many people must have had germs breathed all over them and their food for the past few weeks. She's rather nice though and it seems a shame.

I haven't had to go to Matron yet for my epaulettes, though one or two girls went this morning. Maybe I'll be going tomorrow.

28th June
I'm sorry I didn't write yesterday but my gang have gone to Harefield and they've left all the belongings they couldn't take in my room. They got the maid to open my door, and now I've got coats, hats, gramophone records, flowers, lemonade, teapots, a rug, cups and saucers, powder, an umbrella and goodness knows what, So I had to do a big tidy-up of my room. I've told them I shall make use of all these things till they return to collect them.

The girls who came back from Harefield yesterday say how nice it is, but they seem a bit doubtful as to whether I shall go after all. Apparently 6 of their set were told it was postponed and then never went at all. The trouble is lack of accommodation.

I still haven't got my epaulettes. Elizabeth Jones and some others had to go to Matron because they were going to Harefield and hadn't finished their crosses. They got their crosses done and got their epaulettes all on the same day. And I've been signed up for a week now, which makes me cross!

It was Di Willis' birthday on Tuesday. She and I had coffee together in Bourne and Hollingworths in the morning, and then went to try hats on in C & A's sale! In the evening she had a party just from 9 till 10 and produced chocolate biscuits, birthday cake, chocolates and goodness knows what. I dressed up again. I put my curlers in and then put a piece of pink net over my head and fixed it on with my bathing cap! Then I put a Sprig of May in the top and some more net over my dressing gown, hanging from the waist. Barnett had packed her dressing gown so she put her cape round her, back to front, put a flower in her hair and pinned her clock to her cape!!

Dr. Yellowlees (the most smashing doctor in the hospital and who is R.M.O. at present) was doing his round and saw me going into Di's room. He came in to see who it was! I nearly died! We asked him to have some coffee but he said he didn't think Matron would approve!

I'm now going to bed early – I was awake from 3am onwards on Monday night. I woke up at 3 to hear a girl screaming, and then I thought I heard someone out on the roof outside my room. I jumped out of bed and looked out of the window and the door, but there was no sign of anybody, but I couldn't settle down and go to sleep again. By 4am it was so light that sleep was now out of the question, so I just tossed and turned till the buzzer went.

1st July

If you want to give me a birthday present you could give me 5 shillings towards my next train fare home. I honestly can't afford to come home every other weekend though with all my heart I want to. I shall never be able to save anything. I went shopping yesterday morning – took my coat to be cleaned and bought birthday cards, notepaper, stamps, soap etc and I could hardly believe I'd spent so much. I'm keeping a record of what I spend.

3rd July

The exam yesterday was quite decent for a change. I finished the paper and was jolly lucky. The compulsory question was on the nursing care of a patient with heart failure, and of course that's my speciality at the moment. Meyerstein and Vaughan Morgan are full of heart failures!

Am sunbathing on the roof again this afternoon. It's lovely and warm with a slight breeze.

10th July

I've had a postcard from Bish from Harefield to say she's coming tonight to collect her bits and pieces. What a blow! I was hoping to have the loan of her coat and umbrella a little while longer!

I got my "flappy cap" made up today and sewed on my epaulettes after I'd had lunch. It took me a long time. I'm very thrilled about it and my females seem to like the flappy cap better than the other smaller one. The Houseman said to me yesterday "Am I right in thinking you've been promoted?" When I said he was, he replied, "Well congratulations!" I was so thrilled that he should have noticed and bothered to remark on it. He's the one (Dr. Acheson) who went to the dance with the Staff nurse when she presented the bouquet to Princess Elizabeth.

Yesterday afternoon I was off – I collected my coat from the cleaners and it really does look clean! Then I washed, dried and curled my hair, and then wrote two letters. Don't you think I did well for one afternoon?

I'm so fed up that a stye seems to be appearing again on my right eye – I can't think what I've done to deserve it! I just keep hoping it won't be a bad one, or better still that it will go without developing into a proper stye.

We've been hectic on the ward today. I came off half an hour ago late for my morning off. The pro had to go for a medical about 8.45 so there was only me to do the cleaning while the Head Nurse did the temperatures.

I'm sitting outside my bedroom window again. It's a bit dull and cloudy but quite warm. I'm wondering what you are all doing now. I hope Mummy has a lovely birthday tomorrow. I must do some washing of my "smalls" now and make my bed up with the clean linen. I was in bed by 9.20 last night having had a bath!

22nd July

I had a lovely birthday I never really thought much about it till the day itself and then I had so many cards. Ernest bought me some super tablemats – Vernon Ward bird series. So we are starting a collection for our future home. I had cards from the ward maids on Meyerstein and Vaughan Morgan, Mrs. Farina and Mrs. Hadley (two patients) Jean Davis (one of the nurses on Meyerstein). Mrs. Farina and Mrs. Hadley gave me ten shillings to buy some new stockings because I laddered mine. Ernest here – we went to the Festival, toured the Dome of Discovery, examined the Skylon, watched the fountains and the lights and then spent 7 shillings on a pot of tea, ham sandwiches and ice-cream.

Yesterday we went to Harefield. Bish had a day off and she showed us round. It is a super place but she says the work is boring. We went for a picnic afterwards in the lovely countryside. It has been a most wonderful holiday, though it has been hectic fitting in work with seeing him. Barbara Sebire and Gillian Woolveridge brought some breakfast for me this morning, as they thought I would be feeling "cheesed off"!

As for the Nursing exam! The one I'd wanted to do well in and thought I hadn't a hope! 80 of us took it (2 sets) and I've come top with 80%! I'm just keeping my fingers crossed for the rest. The prize is for the best nurse of the year. There are two other sets competing and I don't know if my 80% is higher than their top marks.

24th July

I've felt so lost without Ernest around for 2 weeks, but at least I've been able to go to bed early and catch up on all the sleep I've missed while he was here. And the swimming bath is closed for 2 weeks, so it doesn't wake me up at 6 every morning when they start cleaning it out.

I've just had to write a surgery essay in preparation for the exam on Monday. My Prelim results are due on Friday and I have to address them <u>home</u>. So if you see a very forbidding sort of envelope in the post on Friday you might just keep it on one side for me. I daren't think what might be inside. Probably a blank sheet with "Try again Chum" on it!

THE GENERAL NURSING COUNCIL
— FOR —
ENGLAND AND WALES

TELEPHONES: LANGHAM {2819 3375 3411}

TELEGRAMS: GENURCOUN, WESDO, LONDON

REGISTRAR:
Miss M. HENRY, S.R.N.

23 PORTLAND PLACE,
LONDON, W.1

2 7 JUL 1951

Dear Madam,

I have much pleasure in informing you that you have been successful in passing Parts I and II of the Preliminary State Examination held in   June   1951.

Yours faithfully,

M. Henry SRN.
Registrar.

Miss N.A. Bryan.

31st July

The Surgery exam yesterday was <u>AWFUL</u>. We all agree that if we'd been working solidly for a fortnight we wouldn't have learnt what we were asked. One question was on drugs – hardly a Surgery question. Sister asked me afterwards how the exam was, so I told her it was LOUSY! Later when I went to collect my paper after she'd been looking at it, she said, "You can take it – I don't like it at all!" And <u>she</u> examines for the State exam!

Last night we had a tremendous thunderstorm. The lightning wasn't just in individual flashes, it seemed to be continuous. I shut my window at the bottom and then covered my face up with my sheet!

Sister has been terribly nice to me this morning. I've been Head Nursing on Meyerstein and Vaughan Morgan. Two Meyerstein nurses have gone on holiday and are not being replaced, so yesterday I was on the Men's ward all day. Sister remarked how nice it will be for me at Harefield. I shall have to pack my trunk this weekend. My address from Monday onwards will be The Nurses' Home, Harefield Hospital, Nr. Uxbridge, Middlesex.

5th August 1951

Harefield T.B. Nursing very soon now. A big change. Apparently we're going to have about 2 months there according to Sister Bird yesterday. I'll let you know as soon as possible about my off duty, but I haven't got any money to come home after buying Ernest's birthday present! It was a lamp with a Vernon Ward bird picture on its shade and stand, to match the table mats we've bought for our dining room. But it cost me £ 2-15-0 with asking Bourne and Hollingworths to pack and send it for me. I didn't want to take it to Harefield and back. Money, money, money! The plague of my life!

I had a little lie-in yesterday, one this morning and will have another on Tuesday morning. We go to Harefield by coach leaving here at 9am on Tuesday. Our trunks go by van, and we go in full uniform taking one case with us. Sister Clarke has asked me to take the envelope containing our records for the Matron at Harefield. I wish I could look at them en route!

I've had a very lazy but rather dull day off. It rained nearly all day yesterday so I couldn't sit on the roof as I'd hoped. I slept till 7.30am

106

when Gillian Woolveridge came with some breakfast. She's so sweet to remember me, but I was annoyed to be disturbed! This morning she brought me some again, but I was awake so was quite pleased. Yesterday I went out to buy a birthday card for Ernest, and some shampoo, and I got SOAKED – caught in a really heavy shower.

In the afternoon Strugnell and I were going to go out, but the only free tickets from Matron's Office were for "Kings' Rhapsody" which Anne had seen. And we couldn't afford the cinema. So she cut out a dress she's making and I stuck photos into my album and did a bit of clearing up. In the evening I went to see your friend Mrs. Shaw, on Campbell Thompson Ward, and so enjoyed her telling me how she met her husband on the train coming back from Denmark, and how she refused him the first time he asked her to marry him, and then wrote to say she'd made a mistake and would like to after all!! She seemed very cheerful and has been having injections and lots of examinations, but no results yet. After supper I washed my hair, and was in bed by 9.45pm.

On Friday evening I did some ironing of blouses and things I'd washed, and then just as I was going to bed early, Jessica Niblett arrived to ask if she could leave some things in my room, as she's coming back here from Soho tomorrow. She stayed talking to me till 10.15pm and although she was screamingly funny about her experiences with Sister etc – I wanted to get rid of her and go to bed! She was telling me how she was serving suppers the other night, and thinking that Sister had gone to supper she decided to taste the soup before she sent it to the patients! She was just standing holding an enormous ladle in her hand, sipping soup out of it, when a voice said "Nurse Niblett! What do you think you're doing?" And poor old "J" replied: "Having some soup, Sister!" We laughed till the tears streamed down our faces – I could just imagine it all! I haven't been caught yet eating up leftover bits, but I shall be one day if I'm not careful! Oh – once the staff nurse caught me eating blancmange, and asked me if I had nothing better do to, and I said "No" without thinking! She nearly fell through the floor!

Elizabeth Jones rang up the other night to say she was coming over from Harefield to collect some of the stuff they've left in my room, but she didn't come so I've still got to pack it somehow!

Miss Balcomb – our misery patient – gave me a lovely traycloth the other day as a farewell present. I thought it was wizard of her.

We're having a big problem with Mrs. Smith – another patient who has carcinoma of the oesophagus, the second worst thing from which anyone can die. She won't eat, and we have to stand by her while she drinks her milk. I asked her to drink some the other day and she was so annoyed with me that she picked up the saucer and threw it on the floor. Otherwise my ladies are quite well behaved and it will seem strange without them all. They're chronically busy on the ward at present so I'm leaving at a good time from my point of view! I shall miss dear Sister Hammond though – I've grown to like her very much indeed. I <u>must</u> stop and start packing now, and rush to the post before it starts raining again.

6th August
Well I feel quite on holiday now what with my last day on Vaughan Morgan and going off to Harefield tomorrow. And there's a strange atmosphere about – everywhere's so quiet. Sister has been very kind and given us all an extra hour off, so I'm enjoying a blissful <u>long</u> afternoon from 1.30 to 5.30 instead of 4.30. I've done some very useful jobs – 1) been to the classroom to copy down the list of 2nd year crosses 2) mended about 10 ladders which appeared in my nylon stockings when the whole of the toe gave way. Where the crosses are concerned – now that exams are over and I've got my epaulettes – I can start afresh on the 2nd year ones. There are only 22 of them (whereas there were 96 1st year ones) and I've done 4 already, leaving 18. I did an intramuscular injection for a cross – I've been putting it off for weeks and at last decided that I'd be a fool to go to Harefield without it. And I was just lucky – the needle sailed in at the first jab, just about the first time that's ever happened!

Since then I've had a fond farewell with Sister. She will be off when I go back at 5.30. I thanked her for all she's done to help me and said I'd be sorry to leave the ward now, after being there so long. And lo and behold! – I could hardly believe she was the same person who used to tell me off left, right and centre in March – she said: "I'm very sorry to lose you, nurse, and hope one day you may come back here." Then she said that if she had to write another report for me she'd write a good one because I've been "a very good girl!"

Hammond, my dears, said that!! Then I asked her where she was going on holiday on the 20th, and said I hoped she'd have a lovely time. She's flying to Italy and says she can't really believe it yet! So you see my farewell with the "foul fiend" (as I once imagined she was) was really quite touching. And I find myself quite genuinely sorry to leave her. But I'll be glad to have some new surroundings and glad to get out of the Head Nurse's way. She annoys me beyond words.

And now I'm about to launch on my packing! I don't intend to let it take me long because I HATE packing. Turner says they ask you at Harefield what day you want to be off, so if that's the case I'll say Thursday shall I? Now I really must start packing or I'll have to be up all night and I don't want that! I went to chapel last night for the last time for 2 months – I wonder if there's one at Harefield – or perhaps I shall be able to go to the village church.

8th August at Harefield
Sorry you've had to go two days without a letter but it's been a bit awkward for writing yesterday and today, especially as we're not free till 5pm and the post goes from Harefield village at 5.30. However I hope I'll be able to tell you a bit about what's been happening and get it into tomorrow's post.

Many thanks for your letter. The others are always disgusted when I have so many letters and they have to come away disappointed. I've had one by each post today!

It's perfectly heavenly here as you will see for yourselves next Wednesday if you manage to break your journey to the South coast. We spend a great deal of time in the fresh air, and it's wonderful to be able to sleep with my windows wide open, and feel real fresh air instead of London's dirty smokey stuff!

I feel I have been here much longer than just since yesterday morning. I stayed up till 10.30pm packing on Monday night having had a hectic last evening on Vaughan Morgan. It was quite appropriate that I had to Head nurse and write the report on my last evening, but it was the first time I've had to Head nurse in the evening there, and the first time I've had to write the report there. There were so many drugs and injections and all the temps and charting of course, but I quite enjoyed it really. Then the farewells and several little gifts of chocolates and nuts etc.

Yesterday morning I got up about 7.30 and went to breakfast at 7.45, then finished clearing up my bits and pieces and moving them to the hall. We were told we could take one suitcase each, and there were several ideas of what was meant by <u>one suitcase!</u> I had a suitcase, a carrier bag full of the gang's and my hats, a carrier bag full of crockery, a string bag with food and knitting and shoe-cleaning stuff (what a mixture) a coat and macintosh, a handbag, and the precious envelope from Sister Clarke containing our records and she also gave me one with clean caps for us all. The others were in the same sort of state, and we wondered as we waited how the <u>bus</u> would carry it all! Then the shooting break turned up for us! The driver nearly had a fit, but he managed to squash us all in, and we had Simpson's wireless on to take our minds off the squash, and ate chocolates. The wireless faded out when we went round corners and up hills, so Simpson then proceeded to take out and re-arrange the batteries, and off we went again!

We hadn't gone very far when Sebire wanted a "Ladies" and we had to keep making suggestions to her for comfort! So the hilarity was terrific all the way! We arrived at 10.15 – I didn't feel right in uniform – it seemed so like a holiday, and in fact has done all the time.

We had coffee and biscuits and then went to our rooms to unpack. My room is just the same as all the others, but lends itself to all the little individual nick-nacks much more than the Foley St. ones did. I'm thrilled to bits with it, and the bed is lovely. We had an interview next with Home Sister and one with Matron (a much more friendly little soul than Marjorie M. of the Middlesex) and then lunch at 1pm.

The marvellous thing is that all our gang of 6 are in Hut Q which is the Middlesex hut, and all my crew are here so we're re-united. It is <u>wizard</u> to be with them again – I did miss them so much before.

Lectures all afternoon and an interview with the assistant Matron, tea, and off duty at 5.30pm. We changed, and four of us went for an hour's walk through fields and country lanes and gathered wild flowers for our rooms. It was so warm, and so lovely. Supper at

8.10pm and then coffee and biscuits and a chat with the gang till 10pm. Then bath and bed.

The food is decent as far as I can see – though the others complained to Matron about it. We have milk with every meal, and there is Bemax on all the tables. Grace is said at lunch and supper. The female in charge of serving meals appears and starts tying her apron strings, which is the signal to stand and say Grace! Paddy says she often goes on tying the strings through Grace!

Will finish off now for a little while, as Paddy and I are going for a walk through the woods. Then we're all going to see the film "The happiest day of your life" in the hospital cinema. There's a film every Wednesday at 8.30pm for villagers and everybody.

Thursday 9th August – lunch hour
We had a wizard walk last night, first through the woods and then down a country lane to Black Jack's Mill and back through the fields. The film was <u>wizard</u> – I'd seen the play before. It was free of course.

We got back about 10.15 and had coffee and biscuits and cheese and another late night! That's what happens when the crew are around. Tonight I <u>must</u> be early and I have a day off tomorrow.

We started lectures yesterday and today at 8am, off from 9.15-10 for "elevenses", 1-2pm lunch, and finally 4.30 for tea. Yesterday morning we all had chest x-rays and on Saturday we start on the wards.

It seems very likely that I can be off next Thursday and will therefore have a 4.30 evening, but we never have ½ days after days off. We have to be back here by midnight.

There are lots of male nurses here and we <u>all</u> have meals together in the dining room. There are no restrictions about mixing with them as there are at the Middlesex.

The Sister Tutors – especially Sister Edwards – seem a bit annoying. "In <u>our</u> hospital" they say, "we do so and so", and seem to look down their noses at us when we say what <u>we</u> do! We have dreadful arguments sometimes, trying to stick up for <u>our</u> hospital! We've been told anyway that although we're working amongst the most infectious disease in the whole world, this is considered the most renowned T.B. Hospital in the whole world, and it's a privilege to be here. It certainly is a marvellous place.

5pm
I'm off now for the evening and day off tomorrow. I'm borrowing Barnett's bike and two of us are going cycling and picnicking.

I'm going on "D" ward – a women's surgical "open TB" ward. Bish has just been working up there and adored it, and Barnett and Powell are there at the moment. Barnett says somebody else has asked for Thursday off so I'm wondering if I have any hope, after my hopes for Thursdays off had been raised so high.

21st August
Everything here is much the same. On Sunday evening Pam Sellicks and I went to Evensong in the little village church and thoroughly enjoyed it! I cycled there in the afternoon to discover the time of the service, and then we went together at 6.30. The parson is very young and lives in a most super Vicarage, fairly near the church. The church is a quaint old place, with very ornate tombs and things, and armour hanging on the walls. It's so homely after London. In London you don't feel you belong anywhere in particular, but here it's so friendly and intimate. We've made friends with the people in the little shops and hear all the latest village gossip! – it's lovely!

On Monday Barnett and I went for a most wizard cycle ride. I wanted to explore, and we found a lovely little lane that took us past a deserted manor. The road branches off from Ruislip to Harefield almost at Harefield Village Green. This afternoon I have a long afternoon (till 5pm). How I wish it were tomorrow. When you come tomorrow do make yourselves a cup of tea if I'm not back. I'll leave the things out, and if the kettle isn't boiling it soon will! Don't forget it's Room 12 in the hut nearest the road. Nobody will mind if you just barge in! I shall look forward to hearing all your holiday news.

24th August
I do hope you had a good journey back to Nottingham and that everything was in order when you arrived home. You certainly both looked very brown and well. I do hope you feel that the holiday did you good. Ernest has asked for at day off on Saturday, and is coming

up to London this evening – leaving this afternoon and arriving here about 6pm. He ordered me to have my things ready to dash straight off, but goodness knows where we are going! It's rather fun not knowing where I'm going to land up for the night. I'll let you have full details later!

Miss Caunt has sent me another nightie she's made for my trousseau – a flowered one this time! She says it's for coming top in my nursing exam! Isn't it kind of her? And such a nice surprise too.

I was hoping to go down to theatre this morning to see an operation – I hadn't heard that I was going but thought I might as I was disappointed last time. But somebody else was told to go. This is my lunch hour and I must go back to the ward now.

27th August
Another rushed lunchtime scribble I'm afraid because I'm not off till 6pm when the post will have gone.

Ernest had a bit of a crash on his way here on Friday – nothing too bad – careless driving I expect! He was going too fast and went through a gate into a field and nearly into the canal instead turning the corner on the road. The only damage was some squashed tomatoes and two broken eggs! Ernest and I had a simply wonderful weekend. He arrived in pouring rain on Friday evening about 5.45. I was ready waiting with my case packed (as instructed by him!). We went straight off to Windsor and booked two rooms at the Old House Hotel. It is an enormous place and rather expensive, but simply lovely. I was lucky – I had a beautiful little room in the new wing. Ernest had to go into the old oak drawing room where there is a bed made up when all the other rooms are booked. He couldn't sleep for traffic, and the night porters cleaning with a hoover! Then two bricks fell down the chimney etc. etc!

We had a lovely breakfast about 9.30am and then spent the morning looking round the castle grounds and the state apartments. Then we came back in this direction and on to Chapel St. Peter for the rest of the day. We picnicked on a little narrow lane. Ernest brought me back about 7.45 and departed about 8.

On Friday evening we had supper in a restaurant in Windsor, and on Saturday morning we had coffee in another little café. So it was all simply wizard.

29th August
One of the nurses on D. Ward dreamt last night that she and I were fighting the Germans together!

I'm having another long afternoon today till 5pm. It's beautifully sunny and quite warm but there's a terrific wind. Yesterday was so cold that I wore my winter coat! English summers!

We've been paid today instead of Friday. And we've been given our Prelim. money, so I've got £11-9-8 altogether! I feel quite wealthy! I can't begin to work out how much of the Prelim. money they've taken off in tax, but I don't think it's as much as I was originally told. Our normal pay is about £7 a month so they couldn't have taken more than a pound, and probably only ten shillings.

I've had a note from the Insurance people saying that I'm six contributions short and will I pay them. Elizabeth Jones had one the other day, and sent a letter back saying that she refused to pay because she was unemployed before she started nursing. I don't know whether to do the same or send the whole thing to the Middlesex and ask them to deal with it. What do you suggest?

I haven't done anything very interesting since I last wrote to you. On Monday evening I came off very late – 6.30 instead of 6pm. Barnett and I were both in bed by 9.30, and both of us were mad because Biddy Luck and one or two of her crowd were making such a row. They were singing at the tops of their voices. I couldn't be bothered to get out of bed and shut them up, and hoped it wouldn't last long. But they didn't stop till 10.30! So yesterday Barnett and I told them off, but they weren't much better last night. The sound echoes so much in these huts and it's hopeless to try and go to bed early.

About 2 days ago one of the administrative staff came round our hut – looked in all the cupboards that were unlocked, and took all crockery that looked like Harefield crockery. Then a large notice went up on the outside door to say that a great deal of crockery and cutlery had been found in our rooms, and "would Middlesex nurses please refrain from depleting the dining room equipment"! Barbara

114

Sebire had some of her <u>own</u> plates taken away, so she went and complained, and the female was <u>not</u> very pleased!

Ernest brought me another nightie that Stella Caunt had made. It's for doing well in my exams she says. It's the same style as all the others but white with pink and green flowers on it.

Dr. Young says she would book for us in the Whiting Bay Hotel in the Isle of Arran, where she stays. And if we want a honeymoon in 1953 we shall have to book not later than next June! Apparently it's a wizard place and she knows the dear lady manager there would look after us very well.

2nd September
The six of us who came here on 7th August plus some new nurses from Watford and Charing Cross are supposed to be going to visit a Chest Clinic on Wednesday afternoon. I'd like to go, but I don't see why I should give up my day off, so I'm going to tell them I shan't be there.

We've all got a craze here for embroidery, so I bought a little tablecloth for 8/6 which should be rather pretty when I've finished it. On Friday evening I bought 5 blooms of gladioli from a garden opposite the hospital gates. They were 2/6 for 5 and are simply super.

Yesterday afternoon I wandered round the village shops, and then sewed up what I could of the bed jacket I've knitted. I was going for a cycle ride but then the rain came. After supper I washed and dried Bridget Luck's hair, and then went to bed by 10.

This morning I had breakfast at 9, and then went to the hospital chapel with Jean Wright at 9.30. The vicar from the village church takes the service every Sunday and they have Communion once a month.

Now the op! It <u>was</u> exciting! Sister Guy had said on Thursday that she wanted me to go down with Mrs. Parker on Friday morning, and just as I was going to "Elevenses" at 9 o'clock they came with the trolley. Sister Lichter didn't want anyone to go and watch the op – she's a bit high and mighty since she married her surgeon apparently! But Sister Guy insisted that I should go. She told me afterwards that Sister Lichter didn't want me to go, and she said,

"Really that woman infuriates me sometimes!" Two sisters working on one ward you see! (Incidentally Sister Guy has gone to Switzerland today for a fortnight.)

Anyway I went down, and got all dressed up in gown, cap and mask, and then had a drink before I went into the Anaesthetic room. Sister told me I ought to get one. I felt a bit shaky at the thought of actually going into theatre – especially after Anne Bishop had nearly fainted. But there was poor Joyce Parker lying on the trolley scared stiff before her op, so I had to pretend I wasn't at all afraid.

They had a lot of difficulty administering the anaesthetic – they couldn't get the needle in the vein, but eventually she "went under". Then they got the airway down the wrong side and she went all blue in the face. When I watched Mrs. Hiskey having her anaesthetic she just sailed under with no bother at all – so I saw how different cases vary.

Then in we went to theatre and they lumped her onto the table. About 6 men trying to put her in position, and two Sisters getting the instruments ready. I just stood and waited and watched! She was a very heavy person and had to lie on her tummy. So they had a bit of difficulty getting her off the trolley, and turning her over. Everyone had gowns and masks and caps on of course.

It seemed dreadful to bump her around so much – she lay with arms hanging down at the side, and head hanging face down on the end of the table. All I could think was "Gosh! Thank goodness her husband can't see all this!" Honestly I think he would have had a fit.

Then they covered her with sheets and sterile towels, even over her head, so that there was no part of her showing except her back where the wound was to be. She had a towel tied round her eyes too. Of course she knew nothing, but it seemed pretty dreadful to me!

Then Mr. Mallard (the surgeon) came in, and he and Mr. French (the House Surgeon) scrubbed up together, and put their gowns on. I was standing behind the Anaesthetist at first, but one of the chaps told me I'd see better behind the surgeon, so I moved around. He'd made the first cut before I'd had a chance to realise what was happening, and then he continued with the whole op. just as calmly as if he was taking somebody's pulse!

They have a needle which works by a sort of machine and burns through the tissue. It wasn't bad to watch but the smell wasn't too good!! Then three ribs came out – click click and he threw each into the Kidney dish in turn! Barnett told me that it was horrible hearing the surgeon breaking and sawing through the bone, and I hated the thought of it, but there was no sawing and nothing horrible at all. He used an enormous clipper thing, and just clipped through each end of the rib. French mopped up the blood all the time! It was wonderful to see the lung – getting bigger with each inspiration and then smaller as she breathed out. At 11.45 I had to go to lunch – they were still cutting bits of lung out, so I didn't see the sewing up. But to tell you the truth I was a bit bored after 2 hours of the same old thing. The best part was watching the first part and the ribs coming out! One of the chaps gave me a stool to stand on, so I had the best view of anybody, and I never felt a bit like fainting. The worst part was the sort of "idea" of it all – the butchery – just like chopping up a cow for market! Theatre was crowded – about 8 men besides the surgeon and House surgeon, and two sisters and me.

Now I must stop as time is flying so if you want to hear more I'll have to tell you when I come home on September 11th.

4th September
It's lovely to be off again for another day so soon after my last day off. I'm rather wondering where I shall be next Wednesday. Miss Dewer (the Senior Sister Tutor – they call <u>all</u> the Sister Tutors "Miss" here!!) said she was going to arrange for "our six" to move to another ward. Whether it will be this week or next I don't know. If I go to another ward before next Wednesday I can't be sure of getting that day off. But anyway I'll come home next week whichever day it is.

Barnett and Elizabeth Jones have gone on night duty now, so there's only our six left on days out of the Middlesex nurses. Last night was quite extraordinary – all the night nurses had gone on duty, and the other 5 of our 6 had an evening off and had gone to the flicks in Uxbridge. I'd had an afternoon and when I came back to the hut after supper the place was deserted! No lights on and nobody to be seen. So I crept along to my room having turned on all the lights, and took the opportunity of the remarkable silence and went to bed early. I was asleep by 9.30 for once, but the old "so-and-so's" woke me up when they came clattering in at 11.30! But really I've never known such quiet at bedtime since I started nursing!

Now that Barnett has gone to D. Ward I'm the senior nurse apart from the Staff Nurse. Sister Guy is in Switzerland on holiday, so we have a Staff nurse in her place, and there's still Sister Lichter and Staff Nurse Béné – who is French and very sweet.

In the evenings if I'm on duty I have to do the injections, and three times a week there are 14 to be drawn up and given. Gosh! I told Béné I quite enjoyed doing 2 or 3 but when it got to 14 I felt like throwing it at them! To make matters worse one has to wear rubber gloves for giving Streptomycin, because the Strep. can cause a skin disease which takes ages to cure. Yesterday I was giving the injections – a day with 14 – and twice the syringe blew out of the needle and the Strep. squirted all over! I nearly had a fit – especially as it went on my face and practically in my eye. I could imagine getting this deadly skin disease in a second! I still can't think how it happened, and of course I wasn't exactly pleased to have to mop up the patient's pyjamas before I could proceed. Béné says it's good for the character (in her broken English) – she says it teaches you patience and self-control! Boy! I should be good after a few more evenings of injections! The injection round and the medicine round both take an hour on these wards. I've certainly learnt quite a lot while I've been here.

This afternoon has been hectic. Sister has been sending me here, there and everywhere to do jobs for her till I was nearly scranny. I went down to theatre about 7 times – the last time one of the male nurses (the only decent one in Harefield incidentally!) said, "Well if she's not satisfied this time tell the woman to stew in her own juice!" Now that Lichter is married to a surgeon she thinks she's the cat's whiskers! All our nurses seem to be scared stiff of her – if she sends for them they're petrified, and they're scared to go and fetch anything if she's in the room. Either I'm very strange, or I'm learning how to handle Sisters – but I can't for the life of me see any point in being scared of her – it only makes her worse! If I want anything I just march in regardless as if I own the place, and nobody says anything! The trouble is that as a result I have to fetch everyone else's equipment now! Twice today people have said: "Bryan go and get... for me – Sister is in the Consulting room and I daren't go in!" So in walks Bryan, and out walks Bryan in one piece, and they stand amazed!!

Sister blew me up at lunch time for starting to serve lunches without her permission! She was busy in the Consulting room and it was getting late so I got on with it! She walked into the kitchen and said in her very slow distinct manner, pronouncing all her vowels and syllables and consonants and everything else in the most elocutionary manner – "Who started to serve the lunches?" I said I had and told her exactly who I'd sent them to. Unfortunately for her she couldn't find anything wrong so all she said was, "In future you will please obey instructions. Please go and give an intramuscular injection of Pethedine to Mrs. Watson. You will sign it in the diary and in the drug book." So off trots Bryan at the double and obeys instructions! She's not a bad old stick really – when I say she blows you up I don't really mean any more than a gentle ticking off. It's just her to be very precise and emphatic about everything. She is an excellent Sister and knows exactly what she's doing and what she wants. I admire her very much, but she amuses me so much sometimes!

So much for the ward – I haven't really done much in my off duty – at least nothing exciting! I washed my hair yesterday afternoon, and dried it in the sun while I wrote to Ernest. Then I mended a pair of stockings and that was about all. But I felt I had done something worthwhile. Then I went for a cycle ride to the church to pick up a magazine and back for tea.

One of the other nurses on "D" ward is engaged, and funnily enough on the same day as we were – 12th May! And what's more her ring was too small! Her fiancé lives in Gillingham, so she sees quite a lot of him when she's at the Charing Cross Hospital.

One of the patients has got a very pretty traycloth for me to embroider from the Occupational therapy department. Strictly "wicked" but I fell in love with the one she was embroidering, and asked her to get one for me as they are only 4/7 each, with silks supplied.

Ernest was telling me in his letter about the pranks he and the Youth Fellowship played on some friends after their wedding recently. Somebody said to Ernest: "This is <u>nothing</u>! Just wait till you and Nina are married!" Lucky couple, but I suppose time is passing quite quickly. I've been here almost 16 months now, so it's only 21 months till I take my finals in June 1953.

Blow! I've just had a maddening telephone message from Sister Fox. Last night we had a meeting of visiting nurses to decide on a representative to put forward suggestions at an inter-hospital catering committee tomorrow morning. I – (my dears) was chosen as the representative! Miss Fox has just phoned up to say that there's a preliminary meeting this afternoon in the Board Room, and she's terribly sorry to ask me to go on my day off, but could I possibly go?! Then I shall have to go also to the meeting tomorrow morning at 10.30 and meet Matrons and Dieticians and put forward our suggestions – i.e.

1) Cakes for tea more often than once a week
2) More fresh or cooked fruit instead of the eternal milk puddings
3) Salad as an alternative on fish and sausage days
4) More variety in vegetables
5) More variety in method of cooking potatoes!

So now I had better stop and write to Ernest and meditate on <u>food!</u>

9th September
I've really quite a lot to tell you now – I've been so busy this past week. Old Bryan gets around you know and makes herself known!

I felt quite worn out after my day off on Wednesday. I rang up to Godmother Joy to say I couldn't go for lunch as I had to attend the Dietary meeting. She was so disappointed because they've got special Roast Beef from Canada, so I said OK I'll come for lunch and then come back. It was hectic! I cycled there arriving at 12.30, had lunch and then left again at 2. When I got back it was nearly 2.25 and I dashed into uniform but couldn't find my cap. Blow me – Biddy Luck had taken my clean cap because hers was so bedraggled, and she thought mine was respectable! I prowled around and found

Biddy's and I looked <u>awful</u> but I was desperate and didn't care as long as it was a <u>cap</u>!

As it happened I was early for the meeting so it was OK. It was the preliminary meeting, with the Harefield Catering committee alone. There was Dr. Stokes (the R.M.O. and one of the leading Physicians here) the Assistant Matron, the Chief Dietician, two Sisters, a Harefield nurse, and me – 7 of us. The meeting started at 2.30 and finished at 3.45. We said exactly what we thought, and it's surprising how things have altered in the last day or two. People, patients and nurses keep saying "This food committee must have done something!" We said we wanted more fruit – yesterday morning we had grapefruit at breakfast for the first time in history almost, and the day before we had apples for lunch and plums for supper! The patients had chips the other day, and we <u>all</u> had roast potatoes with pork today!

Anyway I changed again after the meeting and cycled back to Ruislip. There was a little boy called Timothy playing with Joanna. We looked round the garden, played the piano and what not, and I left again about 7.45 to get back here for supper. I enjoyed going there, but it would have been better if I hadn't had to rush about so much.

On Thursday morning at 10.30 we had the food committee proper – the "Regional committee for Northwood and Harefield". There was our little 7 and 4 visiting bods – 2 men and 2 posh females – one of whom took the Chair. As soon as I walked into the Board Room I was handed a cup of coffee, and we had biscuits too! It was worth being on the Committee for <u>that</u>! There was I drinking coffee and chatting to the Assistant Matron! Unfortunately the meeting only lasted ¾ hour because there wasn't an awful lot to say.

Since the meeting a report of the meeting has been put up in the dining room and it says "Student Nurse Bryan was elected representative for the seconded nurses"!!! My name will go down in history yet!

The other day somebody came to me and said they'd heard that I played the piano, and could I play the organ for the morning service in the chapel today? It was one of the male nurses but how he knew I can't imagine. I suppose one of our girls had mentioned it. Anyway the deputy assistant Matron (who usually plays) rang up the ward and asked me to go and see her when I came off duty on Friday evening. We went to the Chapel and she showed me where everything was kept, and this morning I did my stuff! It wasn't too bad, but I had to pump with my feet and at the same time use my knees to push out the swell! I spoke to the vicar and he's very nice indeed – nicer than I thought he was at first.

I've now got a half day and several of us are going to church in the village this evening. Toole-Mackson is the vicar, but there's a visiting one this evening. It's Toole-Mackson who takes the hospital services too.

Yesterday afternoon Christine Jones and I went for a lovely walk – it was warm for once so we couldn't miss the opportunity, and it was wizard. Today is bitterly cold again.

Tomorrow morning we have another lecture from Dr. Stokes (who is on the food committee) and it should be very interesting. We had one last week and it was very good.

12th September
Just to say that Ernest will be meeting me tomorrow evening and I'll be home about 9.30. I'm longing to see you – I'm fed up with not being home for so long.

What's more, I'm just about "up the skylon" – to say nothing of "up the pole" – the pole just isn't in it. I'm on the children's ward – only I prefer it to be called the <u>Kids</u>' ward. They're not children here – they're just <u>hooligans</u>. I'm on the boys' side, and I've been doing <u>baby</u> boys so far. If you're doing boys you do 'em alone, and nobody 'elps yer! They scream an' 'owl all day long, and as fast as one throws his bricks on the floor, another one pulls his restrainers undone, and another wets his bed and another throws his pillow on the floor! I once said I'd like a large family, but now there's only one consolation – that I shall not have 52 at once! Diane is on the baby girls' side and Bish is on the girls' side but hers are older, and they're both going as crazy as I am!

17th September

Thank you so much for my wizard day with you. We were lucky to have such lovely weather, and I did enjoy it so much – if only it hadn't been so short.

On Saturday morning I spent most of my 10-12.30 off duty practising the organ. I really quite enjoyed it. Sister Smith (the 3rd assistant Matron) was preparing the chapel at the same time, so we chatted together about the hymns and so on. She's very nice.

On Sunday morning I was free till 12.30. I got up about 8.45, breakfast at 9, and then went to play the organ at 9.30. It was Holy Communion. They administered the Bread and Wine together in the form of a piece of wafer – I couldn't understand why everyone got up after they'd had the wafer! I did likewise eventually. I suppose it was my fault, though, for not noticing that the Vicar said "The Body and Blood..." together. Barnett and Paddy were a bit stunned too. I was told afterwards by two of the male nurses that they'd never heard the organ played so well before! Good job, because Matron and two of the assistant Matrons were sitting on the front row!

I was quite pleased to go back to my baby boys again – once you've got used to them all they're very adorable. There's a baby girl in a separate cubicle – she's 14 months old and perfectly lovely. I've been feeding her since my day off and love looking after her.

Well now I must go and do some shopping. I'll be phoning you before long. I've finished eating the brandy snaps, and the peas are delicious. I haven't eaten the eggs yet.

19th September

After a rather dull and cloudy morning the sun is now shining and I'm sitting outside on one of the wooden seats. It's terribly easy to waste one's time isn't it?! I feel I've done nothing much today. This morning I went into Uxbridge to try to get some shoes for a patient on D. Ward, but had no success. I did get two bunches of Asters though, for my room – at 6d a bunch! And three little hankies for Paddy's birthday and a book with photos of beauty spots in England for Ernest's mum's birthday. Then I caught the 12.30 bus back and arrived back here in time for lunch. I took Bish's bike to the bike shop on my way to the bus to Uxbridge. I think the part I enjoyed most was going to town on a green double-decker bus. It made me think of my childhood days.

We return from Harefield to the Middlesex by coach at 11am on Wednesday 3rd October, and have to be prepared to go on duty when we get back. I think I shall have only a week or two on Day duty, then go on Night duty till my holiday in January. Then Block in February. Then after Block I shall nearly be due for my Strings!

This afternoon I've done absolutely nothing but read magazines, write to Ernest, eat, listen to the wireless, and play duets with a male nurse for about 20 minutes. And now you'll have to excuse me while I move from outside back into my room, because I'm being bitten my midges!

The hospital film tonight is about "Lassie" but I don't think I'll go because I've been so lazy all day that I really must do some mending.

Yesterday afternoon I went to theatre again – this time with one of the boys, who went to have a Bronchoscopy. It was strange that the news about King George's bronchoscopy should have been made yesterday too. I know just what happened to him now. It isn't terribly interesting though because there isn't much to see. There were several doctors there. The surgeon allowed me to look down the bronchoscope, but I don't think I got near enough because I couldn't see very much. We've decided now that the King hasn't got TB, but he might have Carcinoma. How dreadful. I do hope it isn't anything too serious after all.

The paper today says that there is to be a General Election on October 25th. Can you remember the last one? – flying to the wireless every time a result was announced. I think Daddy and I had lunch alone in the kitchen that day but we were so busy putting down the results that the pudding went cold!

After supper. Well we've just had sliced hearts for supper – just the size of a human heart! The Ventricles and auricles were very plain, and the papillae for the attachment of the Cordae tendinae were also visible. It was thoroughly delicious??!!

Elizabeth Jones, Cecile Simpson, Mary Priest, Pamela Sellicks, Paddy Gee and Diane Willis are all convinced they have TB now.

We've had a conference tonight (between ourselves!). Paddy has a Malar flush this evening, Elizabeth has had a lot of sputum for days and days, and now has developed a cold and <u>terrible</u> cough. The others either have a pain in their back or chest – oh yes, and Anne Key gets a pain in the top of her chest when she runs. <u>My</u> TB cleared up a few days ago, but I still have a pain just about where my heart is, so altogether we're in fighting trim!!

Cecile is so worried that she's asked if we can all be x-rayed before we go back, so next week we are all going for x-ray! They'll need to open up a new ward for new suspects!!

Bish is in a bad mood tonight – she's worried because she's cold from head to foot. So what <u>she's</u> got I don't quite know! She left her wireless with me for her day off, and she's just taken it back. We're <u>all</u> too tired to go to the "Lassie" film. I got up late but I'm terribly tired now – at 9pm!

I've asked Sister about being off on the 30th, and she says it's quite out of the question being off on a Sunday. So that's that, and I'm having my day off on Wednesday. Then for my <u>next</u> day off we'll be back at the Middlesex – Hurray!

22nd September

I'm playing the organ again tomorrow morning. Miss Arthur – the deputy assistant Matron – came to speak to me about it the other day – came to <u>me</u>, my dears, didn't <u>send</u> for me! She thanked me for all I'd done so I said, "I haven't really done <u>anything</u> Sister!" To which she replied that she'd like to think I'd be there longer than another fortnight. She asked if I'd enjoyed being in Harefield so I said I'd <u>loved</u> it! Well I <u>have</u> enjoyed it.

I had a blowing up from Sister yesterday – the first I've had from her. She's been perfectly charming to me apart from that. But it was just a bad day for her I expect – they're all like that occasionally. I didn't worry about it because it wasn't my fault at all. She asked me to start bathing the kids and putting them to bed, so off I went. But the first child I came to was sitting in a puddle on the bed, so I proceeded to change his sheets, while the going was good. While I was doing this one of the other boys trapped his finger in a door and yelled, and Sister went to him. According to her he'd probably broken his thumb because I hadn't done what I was told! Well if I had done what I was told and shut myself in the bathroom with one of the kids I would have been even less likely to be at hand in case of such an accident. It's a wonder all those kids haven't broken their <u>necks</u> by now, never mind their thumbs! Anyway blow me up she did, and I couldn't do much about it. Next time I had to speak to her I did it as though nothing had happened, and so she has been charming to me ever since.

Well I <u>must</u> go to bed now – it's 10.15. I've had a 6pm evening off. First I went up to D. Ward and saw Sister Guy and she gave me 5 crosses! Then I practised the organ till 8pm. The weather has been lovely but rain is forecast for tomorrow.

30th September 1951
I'm sorry I haven't written for a day or two. I must be getting lazy! Thank you for your two letters and for the newspaper cutting about the King at Westminster Hospital and the nurses. We <u>had</u> read about them already, and we'd been wondering who had to rub the King's back, and who gave him his bedpans, and whether he'd vomited, and who had to "cough him" etc. etc. I wouldn't have liked to do all that!

I've just been looking at my Surgery paper again and I just can't believe I came top! I hadn't revised a <u>thing</u> that was on the paper and hadn't an inkling what to write. I've never felt so much like walking out of an exam before, but I thought I <u>could</u> write a few lines of waffle! I worried no end about it the day after and then I asked myself what was the use of worrying, because <u>just supposing</u> I had passed I should feel so mad with myself. I shall never worry again.

Well this is the end of Harefield and I'm going to Soho Women's Hospital – a part of the Middlesex but the other side of Oxford St. in Soho Square.

But first I have another Harefield meeting tomorrow. Matron's office rang me up to ask if I would be the representative for the seconded nurses at the representative Council meeting since I'd been the rep. on the food committee! So I've had to quickly draw up an agenda and hand it in, and the meeting is tomorrow at 10am. The main thing is to show some interest by <u>being present,</u> because last time there was no representative for the seconded nurses.

This evening I'm off at 6, and Elizabeth Jones and I are going to Uxbridge to see "Showboat" – you can get a good seat for 2/3 there, so I don't mind.

Tomorrow I must <u>pack</u> and we leave here at 11 on Wednesday morning. I played the organ again yesterday morning – for the last time – and the vicar asked me if I'd had some experience of organ playing. I said I'd had lessons from our church organist before I started nursing. He said he wished I could be there longer! I told him about Daddy being a vicar and he seemed quite interested. Matron and the assistant Matron were chirruping away on the front row at the service!

Must fly back on duty now. I shall only be a few <u>days</u> on duty at Soho and then I go on nights there on Monday. I suppose I shall be on duty in the morning till 1.30 and then be off till 8 when I go on for the night. Bish said she would arrange for us to share a room at York House. I expect I shall have to move there on Monday afternoon. I shan't be able to sleep much on Monday. After I move, my address will be The Middlesex Hosp. Nurses Home, York House, Berners Street, London W.1. Two others of my set are going to Soho on night duty on Monday and one is already there. Bish will be on nights at the main hospital. Anne Key is also going on nights on Monday, but not the others.

8th October

Just a hurried note to let you know that our Prizegiving is on Thursday 18th October at 3pm, and Field-Marshall Montgomery is coming to present the prizes! I hope you won't be disappointed but someone else has got the prize – a girl from a set or two above me. Another girl in my <u>year</u> has a prize because she stopped a patient from throwing herself over the balcony. I'm disappointed – but then I didn't ever really expect to get the prize.

But Monty should be rather interesting so maybe you'd like to come. I don't suppose Ernest will want to come now that I haven't got a prize, do you?

I'm loving Soho. Sister came back from holiday today. Everyone said how strict she was but I think she's quite nice.

10th October

I've just come back from Soho for an evening off, and it's now 6.30. We've had wonderful weather ever since we returned from Harefield, so I've been very lucky for walking to and from Soho. But I'm looking forward to moving to Soho quite soon – <u>not</u> York House – it will save a lot of rushing about, and the rooms are lovely. What's more, my dears, on days off the maids bring breakfast to you in bed! I simply can't say how <u>wonderful</u> it is at Soho. I've never been so happy in all my 18 months nursing, and I've been on some fascinating wards. But this is just perfect, and I realise more and more how I love <u>surgical</u> nursing. I know that theoretically it's just as important to give a hot drink to a medical patient as it is to take out a surgical patient's stitches, but one feels so much more as if one is <u>doing</u> something worthwhile when there's plenty of treatment. On Meyerstein and Vaughan Morgan there was no organization – no definite routine, and one just muddled through cleaning and Beeps and meals and so on, not really getting anywhere. But on Queen Mary we're occupied all the time doing tremendously interesting work. And Sister is <u>wonderful</u>. Before she came back from her

128

holiday I kept asking the others what she was like, and they gave me the impression that she was rather an old bully of a battleaxe. But she's nothing of the sort, and we get on famously together. She's a woman after my own heart – she knows exactly what she wants but she doesn't <u>dictate</u> – she <u>suggests</u> and is always ready to hear suggestions from others. Her organisation and efficiency are A.1, her courtesy is A.1, and she's got a terrific sense of humour. In fact she's A.1 altogether! Gynae is so fascinating and I'm as happy as the day is long.

Today we've been quite busy – Wednesdays and Fridays are op days for us, and we've had 6 ops. Two were emergencies – incomplete abortions, and they went up to theatre for evacuations. One of them came in on Sunday, and I had to prepare her for theatre. It took me over an hour because she was aborting all over me. Just when I thought I'd finished she started losing with added gusto and I had to get help. Both girls had lost their babies before they came in.

Of course it's the sort of ward where one gets even more vulgar than ever! Somebody was asking one of the nurses if she would be sorry to leave the ward and she said: "Lord – <u>no</u> – I'm sick of seeing vaginas all day long"!!! The nurses are all charming without exception and I've no doubt that girl didn't really mean that she disliked the ward. Maybe after 3 months it becomes a bit monotonous.

As for the Prizegiving – I've applied for invitations for you, but you'd have to pay 30 shillings, and I'd have to leave you not later than 4.15. It won't matter if you decide not to come.

Did I tell you that I'd bought 2 yards of dark green wool and rayon material to make a dirndl skirt? – and a new white blouse. The blouse is smashing and it should look rather nice with the skirt when I've finished it.

Now I must dash to the post and then have supper. I've just been listening to the "Archers", thinking that you were listening too. "Two sides can play that game and they'll soon find out the cost!" <u>You see</u>!

129

12th October

I shall be writing later to let you know the detail about the events of the weekend, but I simply <u>must</u> tell you to listen at 7.45pm on Sunday evening to the service which is being broadcast from <u>our hospital chapel</u>! It's on the Home Service and you <u>must</u> try and get back from church in time. I shall be at the service because I have an evening off, and I should love to think you were listening to it. I'm sure it will be lovely and we'll all sing at the tops of our voices! It would be a pity to miss it. Daddy will have to cut his sermon short! 7.45 <u>don't forget</u>!

I've had a wizard morning on the ward. It's op day again – about 6 ops again. We've been busy this week. And now I have a ½ day and day off and am looking forward to the Reunion tomorrow at the Grosvenor Hotel!

14th October

I'm so sorry I didn't get a letter off to you today, but the post went before I came off duty so it was no use.

I do hope you're going to listen to our service this evening. You should get back for the beginning because I notice from the Radio Times that there's a conversation to start with, with 3 medical Missionaries. Mr. Chapman is apparently taking the service, and there is a visiting preacher. Several of us are off this evening and are going to the service. I'm quite excited to think that it will be going on all over the world.

I did enjoy my ½ day and day off and really felt that I hadn't wasted my time. On Friday afternoon – apart from writing two letters – I was lazy and listened to the wireless and looked at newspapers and magazines. Then I departed about 5.45 (after tea) to see your friend Miss Russel – Marjorie Russel was there too. She is staying first with one relative and then with another. They really seemed pleased to see me, and Miss Russel seemed delighted with my flowers. I took her some very beautiful white chrysanthemums edged with a very delicate pink. I got a bit of a shock when I first saw her – she looked an <u>ill person</u> and looked older and thinner in the face. Her hands were a bit shaky too, but oddly enough her mind was as alert as ever. She carried on a perfectly rational and intelligent conversation. Miss

Russel was saying that she has an area of "<u>inflammation</u>" in her head – that is obviously all she knows.

Last night we had Paddy's birthday party. She was 20 yesterday – about 6 of us sat in her room after supper, and ate chocolate biscuits and drank cider and coffee and so on and talked till about 11.15.

This morning I discovered that the King didn't have a Pneumonectomy which was an op. I watched at Harefield. He had <u>part</u> of the lung removed – a lobectomy I imagine. We have very definite ideas on the subject now, which I'll reveal to you later.

17th October
I'm so glad you enjoyed the service from our chapel as much as we all did. I was so thrilled with it all I simply <u>had</u> to ring you up afterwards to see if you'd enjoyed it too. There were microphones dotted about down the aisle and in the chancel, and we had a special parson to conduct the singing, and it was really all quite exciting. We had supper at 7, and then went straight over to the hospital before 7.30. It was a good job we went early too, because the place was <u>packed</u> and <u>Matron</u> had to sit on a chair at the back!

At about 7.40 we all practised the first verse of the first hymn, and were given a few instructions, and then from 7.45 till 8.15 we listened to the discussion from the <u>studio</u>, which was relayed to us over a loudspeaker. Then after the service we had to sit still for 5 minutes and listen to the appeal made by the Sister from Papua. I thought she was very good.

During the service I stopped singing from time to time to hear what it would sound like to <u>you</u>, and it made me quite proud of the hospital. I imagine it must have sounded quite impressive over the air. Ernest managed to listen too. During supper I kept saying I hoped you were both keeping an eye on your watches, and cutting your sermon short. There was a suggestion "May the words of my mouth and the Meditations of our hearts not run on too long tonight"!!

Soho is as lovely as ever. It's op-day today so it will be a pretty hectic afternoon, though we only have 3 today. I'm having another morning off.

I've bought about 30 Christmas cards already! The first time I've ever bought them so early – 2½d and 3d each at Woolworths and very nice ones.

21st October

Many thanks for two letters received last week. I say – I must be sadly neglecting my correspondence since your first letter is headed "Wednesday". Surely I must have written to you since then. Oh I know! – I had an evening off on Thursday after I'd received the letter, and sent a hurried p-c to you about Friday.

On Friday I had a ½ day so went for tea with the Tomlinsons in Chelsea. Jo was home early from college. I arrived about 4pm having been ¾ hr on the bus owing to a traffic diversion because of road mending on Tottenham Court Road. We had tea almost immediately because Mrs. Tomlinson had to go out at 5.30 and then I talked to Jo for ½ an hour after that and left at 6pm. I had promised to go out somewhere with Paddy. She tried to get theatre tickets from Matron's office but had no luck. So we went to the Odeon, Marble Arch, to see "The Mark of a Renegade" and "The Lady Pays Off". They weren't striking films, but it made a change and was a bit of fun. We got back for about 11pm. We'd had supper before we went.

Yesterday morning I had to get up at 7.45 because I'd forgotten to ask Bish to bring me some breakfast, and I couldn't have survived without it! So I had a lovely long morning listening to the wireless and knitting, having first washed my hair. In the afternoon I darned stockings and now have some really decent pairs of stockings to wear!

Quinelda was bobbing to and from my room yesterday afternoon. She had a ½ day and wanted to go somewhere. So in the evening, immediately after 4.30 tea, we went to the Academy Cinema, Oxford St. to see "Edward and Caroline" – a French film with English subtitles. It was charming and very amusing. The story was good and we both enjoyed it very much. We got back about 9 for late supper. By then I was jolly tired, and it was a lovely feeling when I got into bed at 10 to put my watch back an hour, and actually turn out the light at 9 o'clock! Of course having gone to bed so early I woke up before 6 this morning, but that was really because there was a terrific gale and my door was rattling.

The weather has turned quite cold now and I notice it's just started to rain, so I shall have to wear a mac when I go back to Soho.

In a week's time I'm "taking over" the Private Patients. We have a special nurse for the private ward (there are three private patients to each ward) and the present nurse is going on night duty on the 29th. As the special nurse must be either epaulettes or strings I've been looking after them when Williams has been off. It's quite good fun – except that everything has to be "just so" and proper, and one has to be fearfully polite!

We've had a terrible crew in there since Wednesday – one was called Gloria Perkins née Angel! She's been married 3 months and is 20. She was <u>dreadful</u>. She wanted such a lot of attention and made a perfect nuisance of herself. All three had bags of money but <u>no</u> education! Gloria couldn't even read properly – I heard her trying to read something to the others from the newspaper. The others aren't too bad – one is still there and gave me two eggs, some butter and an orange today. Mrs Daniels went out today as well as Gloria, and gave me 6 shillings! For which I was very thankful! I hope the next ones will be a little better! But that's the trouble with private patients – you have to be <u>very</u> careful with them!

I had to cope with them on Thursday morning – preparing all three for operations. They had their pre-med injections within ¼ hour of each other, and I was flying round getting them onto the trolleys, going up to theatre etc. etc. I hope to <u>see</u> an op here before I go. Meanwhile we just go as far as theatre, fill in the details in the theatre register, and hold the patient's hand during the anaesthetic. Sister is off this weekend. She's been a bit "ratty" lately.

The Prizegiving was good apparently but I didn't see anything of it as I was on duty.

23rd October – Soho Hospital for women, Soho Square
I've moved home! I'm now in what is more or less a "flat" at Soho! You could never imagine the luxury, my dears! A little sitting room with a gas fire, gas ring, mantelpiece, two armchairs and another chair, two lovely oak tables, a bookcase and mats on the floor. <u>And</u> a lovely <u>little</u> bedroom through a door from the sitting room, with cupboard, mantelpiece, dressing table, dirty linen basket and

WIRELESS! I'm sitting by the fire now and can easily hear the wireless. It's wizard. The bathroom is just next door. I had a choice between two rooms. The other is just a single room overlooking the street, so it's noisy, and not nearly as comfortable because there are no armchairs. And there's no wireless either. The only thing that's better is that it's lighter than this, but I don't mind that. I prefer the comfort!

I'm planning to catch the 3.20pm train on Friday from <u>Marylebone</u>, not St. Pancras, so I'll see you about 6.30pm I hope. I come off duty at 1.30 and will be able to have some lunch before I leave.

Soho is a bit <u>hectic</u> at the moment as far as work is concerned. Four of our staff have moved and one has gone off sick. So we're down to the bare minimum.

Last night, 5.30 until 8, I was on <u>alone</u> with Sister. I thought I should die! I had the ward <u>and</u> the private patients to do. But I'd more or less finished by 8 o'clock, and Sister told me I was to leave everything then to the night staff and go off duty. I thought it was very sweet of her. Usually we have about 5 nurses on in the evening, and still have plenty to do, and there's always a Special nurse for the private patients.

Mrs. Haring, private patient, has given me eggs, butter and fruit, and now says her husband is bringing some nylons for me this afternoon. Isn't it wizard?!

Yesterday morning, to add to the atmosphere with a depleted staff, one of our sweetest patients died. She was 61 and obviously the op was too much for her. But it must be the first death here for months and months, and I was actually with her when she died. It was pretty dreadful but fortunately didn't last long. She had a clot on the lung to put it in basic English. A "pulmonary embolism" if you prefer!

Well I must get ready for lunch and going back on duty. I've had a long morning – 9-1.30 – and have had to move down from Foley Street and do all my unpacking. My trunk isn't here yet so I shall have to unpack that this evening. It's been great fun arranging all my bits and pieces, and the furniture to my liking. I can imagine the fun we shall have arranging our house when we get one! It seemed <u>miles</u> to carry all my things from Foley St. – my arms nearly broke! I brought my crockery and my coat and dressing gown before, and still had two enormous bags full to bring today! How I shall get home in January I don't know! Incidentally I've heard that our holiday starts about 27th January, which means I shall just miss Daddy's birthday – we must have a party for him when I get home! See you on Friday!

30th October

Thanks again for a lovely time. The train didn't get to St. Pancras till 11.15pm and I hadn't the strength of will to catch a bus so got one of the many taxis that were buzzing about the station. I unpacked and put up all my new pictures before I went to bed! Aren't I crazy? But I don't like waking up to a muddle – I like to think everything is straight before I go to sleep. The flowers look wonderful on the mantelpiece – just what I wanted to add a bit of colour to my mansion drawing room! It was horrible going back on duty on Sunday – I'd had such a lovely time that work seemed like a nightmare. I was off on Sunday afternoon – what a relief! I'd been doing private patients all morning and it was just hectic. Only two of them but everything that <u>could</u> be done to them <u>had</u> to be done.

One of them had an enema too, so I had to run for a Beep every 5 minutes! I was very glad to go off duty at lunch time. I'd asked Bish to come and visit me in the afternoon and she brought Barnett with her. We sat and talked and they'd brought knitting and embroidery with them. As soon as they came I made Nescafé for them and we had apples with it, and then about 3.30 I fetched bread and jam and biscuits from the dining room, and we had them with more Nescafé and thoroughly enjoyed it. They departed about 4pm to go back on duty at 4.30. It was great fun. I can imagine what fun it will be acting hostess when Ernest and I have a house of our own.

By yesterday morning I had recovered from my "post day off" feeling, and settled down to routine again. It's always the same when I've been home. In the afternoon I was off again and went up to Foley Street to discover some train times. Bish and Anne Key are having a joint 21st party on 10th November – a week on Saturday evening – and have sent an invitation to Ernest. Of course he must be back for Remembrance Sunday and didn't want to drive back to Nottingham through the night. I've found a train at 10.45 from Marylebone which gets to Nottingham at 10 to 2am. I rang him up last night and he's quite willing to come for the party and go back by train. He's planning to come up on Friday afternoon as I have a ½ day and day off. I expect we'll go off somewhere for Friday night.

We've had another hectic day today. I should have had a long morning off today but it would have left only the junior pro to do all the treatment, so I'm having to have an evening instead. So you see – for all Sister's nagging she couldn't do without me this morning! I felt like telling her so!

I had to give somebody a Soda Bicarbonate bath this morning – a great scream because I hadn't the vaguest idea how much to put in! I know you use a teaspoon to a pint of water but I could hardly measure the bathwater in pints! The patient – an elderly doctor's wife – quite casually told the sister afterwards that she'd never heard of a Soda bic. bath and that "the nurse didn't know what to do either!" Of course that was a fatal thing to say in front of Sister, and Sister gave me a little lecture later on about it! Fortunately the Staff Nurse (Sister having spoken to her about it first) warned me that a lecture was in the air, so I was prepared and I treated it as a joke! The thought of putting the bathwater in pint by pint seemed rather amusing to <u>me</u> and so Sister didn't bother to go very deeply into the matter!

This morning – as every Tuesday morning – we had our weekly service on the ward. A piano and hymn books are brought into the ward, and a dear old white-haired parson plays the piano for the three hymns. He takes the prayers and gives a short talk. We can't do treatment during that 15 minutes so the nurses and Sister join in. The patients chose the hymns and it was really lovely. Afterwards the parson did a round of the ward. I think it's a very good idea. I've always been off duty before on Tuesday mornings so have always missed it.

Now I have some ironing to do and am going to listen to "Over to you" on the wireless at 9.30, I think. The apples are delicious – they really are very sweet and nice. We ate crisps on Sunday afternoon. I shall come home again on the 16th or 23rd November. Which do you think is best?

1st November

Thank you for your letter and for the simply beautiful <u>leaves</u>. They look perfectly lovely under the glass top on my table. Please don't apologize for forgetting the brandy-snaps! I'm sorry I didn't bring them – indeed! – but it was my fault if anybody's. I did pick them up off the table and saw what they were. I knew you would give them to me in any case if I asked! But I didn't know if they were really meant for me so I didn't <u>ask</u>!

Only one person has had a day off today, so we've been quite well staffed on the ward. Everything has run very smoothly and Sister has been perfectly charming again. I think it must be when we're so rushed that she gets fidgety and nags. I don't blame her, and I've been much happier again. One patient said to me: "You're the only one who can do this without hurting me," and another said, "I hope <u>you</u> take my stitches out – you're so light-fingered!" So that cheered me up immensely too.

I'm going up to Foley Street this evening to see the others and collect my laundry. Must fly – !

4th November

I'm a bit late starting this letter today – I washed my hair first, then feasted on chocolate and apples and pears, and then when I'd just nicely settled down in my old armchair by a glowing fire, the buzzer went and the porter said there was a friend to see me! I had my curlers in of course – doesn't it always happen that way?! It was Di Willis and John Somebody, and they couldn't think where to go because it was raining! I suggested Madame Tussauds, but whether they will go there or not I don't know. John waited downstairs thank goodness and Di came up to my room for 5 minutes or so.

You seem to have been having a lot of fog lately. We haven't had <u>any</u> in London. Today it's pouring with rain, but yesterday for my day off it was sunny and quite warm.

Anne and Bish are having their party at Marlborough Court from 8pm to midnight, and then some mad jaunt down to the Strand or something. But Di tells me that Mrs. Key has just written to Bish saying that as most of Anne's friends can't come, wouldn't it be better to call the whole thing off?! Bish is furious at this "11th hour" suggestion – after all it's less than a week till the party and all the arrangements have been made. So she's written to her father asking what she should do.

I had a lovely day off. A <u>maid</u> brought breakfast to me at 8.30 yesterday morning – cornflakes, bacon and tomatoes and fried bread, toast and marmalade and tea! I was most lazy! Really I shall have forgotten how to work soon, being spoilt like that! I turned on the wireless and sat eating in bed to music! The bacon and tomatoes were a bit cold but I'm sure I wouldn't have had the heart to complain!

I went out shopping in the morning – buying a few Christmas presents, and some honey, and salt, and Dreft!! – and a box of matches from a poor old man sitting on the pavement on Tottenham Court Road. After lunch I buzzed off to see the Starkes at Buckhurst Hill. My Godson Jonathan Simon was in his pram by the front door, crying away!! He seemed to have a bad day yesterday, crying quite a lot, and usually he's quite good apparently. He's got his Pa's long legs and the same shaped face, but his Mama's colouring – he's quite a gingery auburn colour (his hair I mean!). Eileen has been quite run down but is better now. We went shopping and I pushed the pram which was lovely. Then I made the toast while Eileen did the rest of the tea. Ivan came in from the garden, and tea lasted from just after 5 o'clock till nearly 7! The babe was yelling, and Eileen had to go and feed him in the middle of tea. It was a scream! I couldn't help laughing – Ivan giving orders, and suggesting what was the cause of the crying, and Eileen saying, "Don't be silly, Ivan, it isn't that at all!" I washed up after tea and then helped to put Jonathan to bed and then the three of us chatted. I left there about 10.30 after listening to Saturday night theatre with them.

Well time is flying and I must get ready to go back on duty. We're going in search of Bonfire night activities tomorrow!

6th November - the morning after Bonfire night!
Yes! It poured cats and dogs here yesterday and we thought our arrangements were going to be washed out. <u>BUT</u>, my dears, we had FUN, we had FUN!

About 8.30pm Jetta Willmott (who is down here at Soho and is one of my set) and I decided we were going to see the fireworks, rain or no rain! I rang up to Foley Street and after about ¼ hour Bish answered and said she was ready, and the rest of the gang were coming with us to see the fireworks. We met Bish, Paddy, Mary, Di and Elizabeth about 5 to 9 at the appointed spot on Oxford Street – Anne Key didn't want to join in, so the 7 of us set off walking. Di and somebody else saw the Medical Students Rag as it passed the hospital when they came off duty, but we didn't know where it was going after that, except that it was supposedly ending in the Albert Hall. We walked in the rain to Piccadilly, to and along the Strand, past Green Park, along Park Lane to Hyde Park Corner. This walking – note! – saved seven pence!! A 1½d ride on the bus from Hyde Park Corner took us to the Albert Hall, and still not a glimmer of a sparkler had we seen!!

Nothing doing at the Albert Hall, so we stood at the top of the steps behind the hall, in fits listening intently for bangs. We thought we'd decided from where they were coming so we set off walking in that direction. We stopped and listened, and changed our direction several times, and eventually landed at a bombed site where the glowing embers of a bonfire were only just sufficient to light the remaining two or three fireworks of some lads of 14 or 15! Washout! But we'd seen ONE FIREWORK!

On we walked, to save cash, to Knightsbridge, admired the window decorations in Harrods, on a tube then from Knightsbridge to Piccadilly, and then walking to Leicester Square. We were so hungry by now after walking so far that we went into the nearest Corner House, and spent about 3 shillings each on cheese and bread rolls, ice-cream, meringues and orangeade!! I had the most of course, and the others got so fed up waiting for me that they helped to eat part of it! They told me they didn't own me because I had by then got a fit of the giggles such as only comes on those occasions, dropped my cheese on the floor and was generally unladylike! But who cares?! I didn't know the people in Lyons Corner shop!

When we came out of the Corner House we saw the crowd waiting outside the Odeon in Leicester Square. A Bobby said the Queen and Princess would be out by 10 to 11 and it was then 20 to 11. So we joined the mob and got soaked! WELL! – we got more and more squashed, and more and more wet, and the time got later and later, and at quarter to 12 – after we'd been there an <u>hour</u> – there was still no sign of Royalty! But then they turned on the floodlights and we saw the Queen and Margaret looking <u>very</u> beautiful, and then other guests. It wasn't very easy to see much of them, but at least we did see them. At midnight we "hopped it" and got back about 12.15am and to bed soon after 12.30! So much for our fireworks! Next year we are definitely going to buy a programme – we think it might help us quite considerably!

Tonight and tomorrow I must go to bed early because on Thursday – the 8th – we're having an eating and bottle party in Bish's room, to celebrate 18 months bedpans and sweeping floors! Then Ernest comes on Friday and we'll be away in Westcliffe for Friday night, and Saturday at the party.

I'm looking forward to the party very much, especially after Ernest's letter today. Mr. Richardson has given him Sunday morning off, so he's coming by car which will make things much easier, and he can go back early on Sunday morning, and therefore stay to the end of the party. I must ask if he can stay at Marlborough Court, where the party is, on Saturday night. He won't get to bed till early morning anyway! The party has to finish at Marlborough Court at 12, and then we're walking down to the Strand Corner House according to Bish!

Today I have a long morning and have lots to do.

You say you watched "Saturday Night Theatre" too. I didn't like it very much either – I was just glad that the horrible man got killed! I don't like those sort of shooting plays, and afterwards I dreamt that some thugs were trying to take <u>you</u> (Mummy and Daddy) away, and I was trying to save you and couldn't. So I won't listen to any more like that!

Must go to a shop to match some wool for a patient now for something she's knitting.

9th November
I'm just waiting for Ernest to arrive – originally he said 2.30pm, but today in his letter he says it will be later. So I've had time to do some

ironing and other odd jobs meanwhile. I expect he called on you on his way, I asked him to collect my evening bag for me. I hope you managed to find it without too much trouble. We're going to stay in Westcliffe tonight – I expect Ernest told you. Tomorrow we're going to Southend to have lunch with David and Betty Thurley and family (Ernest's college friend David). He wrote to Fairhaven Guest House in Westcliffe too, and they said they'd be delighted to put us up again for the night.

Last night I went up to the Nurses' Home at Foley Street for supper, prior to our Bottle Party. It was Anne Key's 21st the day before yesterday. She went home and had a little party at home with a lovely birthday cake – of which she brought the remains for us to try. So we had cake and Australian something or other beginning with "S" – a sweet wine a bit like cider. Not very potent but quite nice. We talked about the party plans and Bish and the others were thrilled that Ernest needn't go back till Sunday. I managed to get a room for him at Marlborough Court. Bish demanded that Ernest should take her and Anne from Foley St. plus balloons and things, to Marlborough Court in the car – to save them having a taxi!! I didn't dare to suggest it, but that's Bish all over! And it will give Ernest something to do while I'm changing. He is changing before we leave Westcliffe.

Bish has got a new evening dress – pale yellow taffeta covered with sort of chiffon of the same colour. Elizabeth has a new black and pink dress too, but she won't let us see it till tomorrow! Anne Key has a new one which I haven't seen.

I asked Matron this morning if I could have a late pass till 2am after the party and she was very obliging!

Sister has been quite good humoured of late. Yesterday she and I were serving lunches together, and I had to take away a Beep in the middle. I washed my hands in the sluice, knowing jolly well she would ask if I had! When I got back the first thing she said was "Have you washed?" So I triumphantly said, "Yes Sister – I knew you would ask me that!" She replied that she didn't think what I said was quite the thing to say but nevertheless quite justified! And then she hooted with laughter! I think I made her feel rather silly!

141

Op. day again today – I had the preparations this morning for them, but shall miss the trial of coping with them on return from theatre.

One patient gave me a pen and pencil in a little box when she went out the other day, and another gave me chocolates. We're always being given stuff here.

We've had miserable weather here for several days. I hope it cheers up for tomorrow. Thank you for the flowers and Nescafé too. I love to sit down in my armchair by the fire on my morning or afternoon off, and sip a lovely sweet milky cup of it.

12th November
We had a wonderful weekend with Bish's party. Ernest arrived about 4.25 on Friday afternoon and we went more or less straight off to Westcliffe on Sea. We unpacked our things and then went out for the evening, and had supper in our usual little café. On Saturday morning we went for a walk by the sea in the sunshine for about an hour, then went off to Southend for lunch with Ernest's college friend and family. They are charming people and we thoroughly enjoyed our visit. The kiddies – John aged 7 and Jimmy aged 4 are adorable – noisy but obedient! We left about 3pm, had a ride around and then went back to Westcliffe for tea. Ernest changed into his evening gear there and then we left at 5.30 back to the Nurses Home, where he had promised to pick up Bish and Anne in their finery and take them to Marlborough Court to prepare for the party, while I was changing into my evening dress. The party was very good – mostly dancing, and I thoroughly enjoyed it. It was so marvellous to be there <u>with Ernest</u>. We have so little chance of going anywhere together. He was a brick to come all the way and spend more money. You see how much he loves me!!

Ernest brought me back to Soho after the party, about 2am. I had a late pass till then. Then I saw him at 9.30 yesterday morning when I came off duty to coffee. I sat in the car with him for ½ hour. I think we both had a "morning after the night before" feeling. But his room at Marlborough Court was OK. Last night I was in bed just after 9 o'clock and went to sleep almost immediately, so I'm feeling a bit better today! Incidentally it's 6 months today since our engagement!

I must now go out and get some wool for a patient. I'm contemplating whether to come home again this month. I'm thinking I shan't survive till December! But I can't really afford it with Christmas coming soon, and I shall be home twice in any case before Christmas, once I go on night duty.

On Tuesday, one of the nurses from Queen Mary and I went out straight after duty – with the idea of trying to get into the Middlesex Annual Variety concert at the Scala Theatre. But we didn't manage it of course, so we went in the "Gods" at the Dominican Cinema for 2 shillings to see "Oliver Twist". It was simply marvellous and we had a very happy unexpected 2 hours out. The cast consisted of several of the same people as "Tom Brown's Schooldays" which I saw some time ago and loved.

Sister has been charming just lately, and we've had quite a lot of fun discussing Christmas decorations. I knew she was thinking of making paper flowers, so I bought a little book I happened to see in Bourne and Hollingworths for 2 shillings and 6 pence on how to make them. When I took it to her she said she already had one herself but added, "Never mind that will come in useful for you when you're married and in your Vicarage!" I just exclaimed "Sister! How do you know?" She says she knows a bit about everybody! The Houseman knows too because the other day he said, "You won't be able to fool about when you're sitting in the pulpit"!! I told Sister I'd had good training for life in a vicarage and she asked where Daddy was vicar. Blow me if she hadn't lived in Bramcote for 21 years and knows Aspley and Nottingham very well. She was very chatty after that!

Then she told me she'd changed her mind about making paper flowers and would have to exchange the paper she'd bought at B & H's for some little balls for the Christmas tree. She asked me if I dare go and tackle them as she daren't! Dear Nurse Bryan dare do anything! She told me she thought I'd be able to plead rather well! So off I go and change the paper, and come back on duty with little balls, and Sister was THRILLED! "You clever girl," she said, and Nurse Hood (Staff nurse) told me that Sister told Matron what I'd done!! So you see I'm in her good books now, touch wood! I only hope it lasts! She told me off yesterday for not paying enough attention to a visiting surgeon who came in her absence, but I know I was to blame and she was quite reasonable about it.

She gave me 2 shillings and sixpence for the book I'd bought, and said she'd give it back to me on the Christmas tree!

Saunderson, another girl from my set is working with me, and today Sister took her into the Bunk for 20 minutes, and told her she wasn't pulling her weight. Saunderson is to go to Matron what's more. So for all my spell of being told off I've been luckier than that, so far!

Ernest and I gave Bish and Anne presents together. I bought two little china brooches in the shape of a flower, for ten shillings each. They're very pretty. Ernest gave me half the money and I really am quite pleased with them. One was in the shape of a pink rose, and the other a primrose I think.

I'm getting on fine with my Christmas shopping. I think I must have enough cards by now – I must make out a list and decide if I need any more. I keep buying odd things from time to time too. It's more fun than leaving it all to the last minute – that's too harassing then.

Soho. 5th December 5am

As you see I am now on night duty at Soho. AND I'M COMING HOME FOR CHRISTMAS!! Isn't it wonderful. Night Sister has explained to me tonight just what I shall be doing on night duty and when my nights off will be. The first lot begin on Monday next, so I shall be coming home on Monday morning 10th December, have nights off 10th, 11th, 12th and 13th and return to London 4.30pm on Friday 14th. Then I shall have 24th, 25th, 26th and 27th at home – and return on 28th. The third lot will fall on 7th, 8th, 9th and 10th January 1952 and then 21st, 22nd, 23rd and 24th January. All of them Monday to Friday of course. After the last lot I shall come back for four nights on duty and then pack up my bags and come home on 28th for A WHOLE MONTH! Can you bear it?!

As for work at the moment – the 10 nights should go quite quickly because they are divided up. I'm not going to be on Queen Mary after all, but the ward immediately above – Queen Alexandra.

I do 4 nights pro-ing there, then 4 nights head nursing on the same ward, and then 2 nights extra-ing. Tonight and probably until

Saturday this week I'm extra-ing which means I roam all over the hospital throughout the night relieving other nurses. It's jolly good fun although there's no real nursing attached to it. There's one thing, it means I don't have to do any B.P.s or backs!

First when I come on duty I take the drink list from the pro on each ward in turn, make the drinks and then take them to the pro to distribute. Then between 8.30 and midnight all I have to do is all the washing up for the whole hospital, tidy all the kitchens, make a pot of tea for Night Sister, wash all the masks, and fold and sort into piles all the dirty laundry. The latter takes ages. Actually tonight I didn't make the drinks because I had to chaperone Dr. Jolly while he examined 4 new patients on Queen Mary. While I was there one of the patients gave me a nailbrush and a toothbrush for a present!

12 midnight	Lunch.
12.30am	Relieve Staff Nurse on Cubicles ward for lunch.
1-2am	Cut, and butter bread for whole hospital's breakfast.
2-3.45am	Rest and tea. Tonight I had my tea when I got back from rest – in the solitude of Cubicle's kitchen.
3.45-5.30am	Relieve Staff Nurse on Cubicles for rest. That's now. I've been making Christmas decorations for the ward till 5am and now I'm writing to you!
5.30am	Make tea for night Sister and wake her up!
5.30-6.15am	Prepare and make early morning tea for all wards, and take to pro to distribute.
6.15-6.30am	Do round of waking up maids, orderlies and day staff (Boy oh boy I shall shine my torch right on them!)
6.30-7am	Wash up throughout hospital and generally tidy up kitchens.
7-7.30am	Help Staff nurse on Cubicles to make beds. She's always alone you see.

Then I suppose I go off duty as soon as possible!

After you rang on Monday (and thank you for a lovely surprise!) I rang Ernest at 7. He hasn't been feeling very well – has had a pain in his tummy due he thinks to a cold. He had 18 babies to christen on his own!

Then I went on duty at 8 and the night went very smoothly. I was pro-ing on Queen Alex and enjoyed it very much. I had supper at 8am and then Bish came to collect me. I finished packing with her assistance and then we got a taxi to York House because there was so much luggage! There is another girl in Bish's room till Monday, so I've got a single room till she goes. I'd rather like to stay in it because it's a lovely room, but Bish's double room is just as nice and has a bathroom of it's own!

Bish yanked me off to Elizabeth's room when we got to York House, for a cup of tea and I got to bed about 11.30am and went straight to sleep! I woke at 5pm and couldn't go to sleep again, but I consider it was pretty good for the first day.

In my rest time I had about an hour's sleep I should think, so I haven't felt tired all night. In the morning at 10am Bish and I and several others are going to see a trade film opposite Bourne and Hollingworths's somewhere – a film about the hospital. It's free and only lasts 20 mins. I didn't know anything about it till Bish told me yesterday morning that she'd booked for both of us! Good job it was free!

It's now 5.30 so I must pack up my things. Swales will be back in a minute and I shall have to go and wake old Fanny Clarke out of her beauty sleep in Sister's bunk on Queen Mary.

7th December 12.45am
I'm so enjoying this Night Duty at Soho, even more than Day Duty here. There's so much freedom, less rushing about and no nagging! We just get on with the job with nothing and no-one to worry us.

I'm managing to sleep very well too – I think perhaps this second Night Duty isn't such a strain as the first, when everything was new and odd. I haven't been in bed before 11.15am, but I always go to sleep straight away, and sleep till 6.45 when we're called. The noises outside sometimes wake me. Yesterday I woke at 4pm with hammering and sawing outside. There are workmen not far from my window. But it didn't disturb me for long.

I have no difficulty in eating either! Last night duty I often had no appetite for my meals, especially for lunch at 11pm. But now, as usual, I'm always hungry – and terribly thirsty always too. I drink the

146

cream from all the milk bottles as I go from ward to ward! No consideration for the patients of course! I just like it!

4.15am
Came back from rest ½ an hour ago. I went to sleep for nearly an hour I should think – on the floor! I put cushions and a blanket on the floor, and cover myself up with a blanket, and I'm "as snug as a bug in a rug"! The worst part is waking up afterwards – that's when I really long for my little bed!

I must get down to some sewing in a minute or two. I'm making a Donald Duck out of felt for my Godson for Christmas.

I'm wearing my special Night Duty stockings again. They're lovely and warm when I'm sitting still for so long.

Yes! Wonderful experience all this is! You'd think I'd be an expert packer by now. Several of the girls remark that they've had to pack so often that they now have a little corner for everything, and know just exactly where everything should go. I don't think I can have a packing mind though! – I hate packing so much that I just throw the things in as they come out in drawerfuls, and then get someone heavy, like Bish, to sit on the lid!! The trouble is that the situation seems to get worse every time, and I find I have more carrier bags of oddments each time I move. This last time there were cotton reels and jars of hand cream and hats bobbing about all over! The taxi man asked me if I was going to Bournemouth! I hardly liked to say I was going just across Oxford Street to York House! Talk about expanding brains – all I want is an expanding suitcase! The whole of Sutton Bonington village will have to meet me when I come home on holiday in January! – there'll be so much to carry!

Thank you, Mama, for all your letters. They are always so wonderful – I look forward to reading your newsy tit-bits so much always.

Yes we'll make the Christmas puds when I'm home, and try to get a few Christmas jobs done. Do you need any more Christmas cards? If so I would advise you to get them pretty soon, because I've noticed there really aren't many good cheap ones left now.

I believe I gave you the telephone number of my little room, but that will be altered when I go into Bish's room. York House itself has no telephone number. Museum 8333 is the hospital number, so don't be put off if you hear "Middlesex Hospital" when they reply. Just ask for York House, extension whatever it is.

My dears, we really are in the thick of Soho here! There's Bateman's Alley one side, and Frith St. the other, and both are pretty awful about 11 o'clock at night. Tonight we had an awful scare – there was suddenly terrific screaming as though someone was being murdered or something. I flew to the kitchen window and there was a man beating a woman with an old boot or something. Sister came in while I was there and asked what it was all about. She says she gets the police to that sort of thing. She leaned out of the window and shouted "Now clear off the pair of you or I'll fetch the police"! The woman was making such an <u>awful</u> row. It leaves me quite cold to see the things that happen. Why people can't be content to live peaceful and respectable lives I really cannot imagine.

Well now I must go and see old Donald Duck, or he won't be ready for Christmas. See you on Monday morning. Can you possibly meet me? I'll be catching the 10.15am from St. Pancras, arriving in Loughborough at 12.34pm. If you can't meet me perhaps you could ring up to Ernest. I've suggested he doesn't bother to come on Monday but I daresay he'd manage to meet me if Daddy can't.

4th January 1952
I'm so sorry I haven't written for 2 days, but last night it was just impossible. My first night on the new ward and I was terribly busy. I'm writing this in my lunch hour – we have an hour here which is much better than the ½ hour at Soho.

I'm really quite glad I didn't manage to write till now because last night I was feeling so utterly fed up with everything. I'm on the Woolavington wing, 1st floor, permanently till my holiday. It's the Private wing and all the patients are in separate rooms. There are two night nurses, each in charge of 8 patients, and each nurse does <u>everything</u> for her patients. I have 6 men and 2 women, but one of my women has a <u>special</u> nurse. It's terribly hectic after Soho, and last night I nearly went mad because I knew nothing about the patients, the work, or where anything was kept, and I just had to struggle on and hope for the best. I <u>hated</u> it and longed to be back at Soho!!

But tonight is much better and I'm much happier about it. I'm more organised, thank goodness. I don't yet know how I'm going to get through in the morning though. I've got a stomach washout, a skin preparation, two patients to prepare for theatre, an eye to bathe and dress, penicillin to give, a female to change because she's old and has no control over her waterworks – a man to blanket bath – all this morning in addition to temperatures, morning teas and cleaning etc! We can't start till 6, and have to be finished by 7.30am! Never mind, only 16 more nights of work after tonight. What a glorious thought!

9am
Well I'm off duty anyway. I had to <u>run</u> everywhere I went and still I didn't finish till 3 minutes past 8. Then there was the report to give to Sister. There were so many odd <u>little</u> things to do, and although I'd carefully planned what I was going to do, I got all <u>dis</u>organised. The stomach washout took me nearly ½ an hour. It takes such a long time to get the tube down into his stomach through his nose to begin with. Anyway I'm on good terms with Sister at present, and hope to remain so. It makes all the difference.

Details on one of the patients were in the paper yesterday. "In Middlesex Hospital now, to save the life of one eye, is Sir Humphrey de Trafford's younger brother Raymond. He was injured in a hunting accident in Ireland. A burr flew into his eye. After some time in a Dublin hospital he flew to London and will remain another two weeks. De Trafford, 51, lives at a country house near Dublin... etc. ..." He told me last night that he "rather fancies me"!! He gave me a bunch of enormous grapes on my first night. I'm going to keep in his good books! Think of me helping to "save the sight of one eye" for him. Quite a responsibility! The care I take over bathing it, and putting drops in, and giving his penicillin!

Another patient is brother of the Lord Chief Justice. My goodness! And there's just "little me"!

My new nights off are next Monday and Tuesday as expected, come back for <u>3 nights</u> then 4 nights off beginning Sat. 12th Jan., then work 10 nights and have 2 nights off on 26th and 27th January. So it will mean 2 more days added on to my holiday.

Bish has just washed her "wig" and I've set it for her. Now I must wash mine! Sorry my writing is so terrible but Bish and I want to get to bed, and unfortunately I didn't have a <u>minute</u> to finish this letter after my lunch. I didn't even have a rest last night.

10th January

Back once again. I had a good journey back this afternoon. I had tea on the train in the dining car, so the time seemed to pass more quickly. I read the church magazines from cover to cover, then snoozed! The only snag was I had a pain in my tum all the way and it didn't please me very much! I felt dreadful when I came on duty and I've been sitting in the office doing my charts and books with a hot water bottle on my tummy! I was very sorry to part with it when I came to lunch at 1 o'clock!

The train was on time this evening and I got back to York House at 6.45pm. It made such a difference to me catching the later train and having those extra 3½ hours.

Now I'm longing for my rest hour. I'm beginning to feel sleepy. I did enjoy my two nights off, and it was lovely that Ernest came all the way to London to fetch me, especially when <u>he</u> was feeling rotten.

9.30am

Off duty now and I'm going to bed. I didn't go to rest in the end during the night, I had so many odd bits and bobs to do. I do love Woola now that I've really settled down there.

18th January

Thanks for your letter. I was feeling a bit fed up this morning after rushing round in circles on the ward this morning, and now, after reading your letter I feel much better!

What wonderful news about Ernest's move to West Bridgford to a second curacy. And curate to a Canon too! And to have a curate's <u>house</u> will be amazing. I must go and see it next time I come home. It's all so exciting especially as Ernest will be moving in soon. We've been looking at furniture and we already have a very nice china cabinet, and I've been thinking what I shall put in it. I told Ernest we have a tea set from his mother, and a coffee set from <u>you</u> and I've got 3 plates, two ninepenny spoons and an orange squeezer from Woolworths, so we should be alright!!

Fancy you having snow! We haven't had any but it's <u>bitterly</u> cold. I'm so thrilled that I have only 7 more nights after tonight! I'm so looking forward to 4 weeks' holiday. Mr. Trafford went out yesterday – we now have 2 kiddies who had their tonsils and adenoids removed yesterday. Richard and Nicholas aged about 4 and 6. Nicholas is American and talks with a marked accent. I love going in to them to see if they're asleep, and pretending they're <u>my</u> children! Nicholas cried several times last night – I was very pleased with myself because I managed to soothe him and send him to sleep each time, and quickly too!

22nd January – 12.45am
Bish has gone off today for 4 nights so I shan't see her again till February 25th! Woola is quite quiet at the moment, but I seem to have been terribly busy all the same. I've been doing crosses as fast as I can, having left them till the end of night duty. But I shall be due for my strings 2 months after my holiday, and I've still got 7 to do.

24th January
I've had rather a disappointment this morning. The first time anything has ever gone wrong in my nursing. I had to go to the office because I had a bad report on night duty at Soho. I'm rather upset because I've been so lucky so far with all my reports, but I think I know the reason for it and I'm sure it didn't warrant the remark that I am "too thoughtless towards my work and the patients". It said that I was "quite pleasant and appeared interested" but that I was thoughtless.

At least I didn't have to go to <u>Matron</u> so it couldn't have been <u>so</u> bad, but it's pretty humiliating to have to be told even by the assistant matron that you have a bad report. Sister Bird was extremely nice about it – she knew that I hadn't signed the report, which meant that Night Sister at Soho hadn't <u>told</u> me she would give me a bad report. She asked if Night Sister had even mentioned anything to me about my work, and I told her how much I wish she <u>had</u> said something when she first noticed it because then I could perhaps have done something about it.

Sister Bird said, "Well don't worry, nurse, this happens to most of us at some time or other. We can't get on with <u>every</u>body, and I'm sorry that Sister Clarke didn't mention it to you before she wrote it in black and white. Nothing can be done about it now, and it will naturally go against you to a certain extent, but I should go and see Sister Clarke to discover exactly what she meant."

I'm not unduly worried – in fact not at <u>all</u> worried because Sister Bird didn't sound as if she had much esteem for her. But it's a bit upsetting when everything has been so wonderful so far. There were 7 others besides me who had to go about bad reports, so at least I wasn't the only one! I think what bothers me most is the thought of an interview with Sister Clarke at Soho, to discover what she meant. She'll think me awfully rude demanding an explanation – though I suppose I'm perfectly entitled to one since she didn't ask me to sign the report.

There's one thing – bad reports, as far as I can see, really only affect nurses who may need references and testimonials for other hospitals. It won't hinder <u>me</u> in getting State, and that's all that really matters to me.

Bish has gone away now and I shan't see her again till after our holiday. I had an awful palaver this morning trying to sort out a muddle over her luggage. The <u>clot</u>! She told me her trunk and case would be collected today by the railway, to be taken to her home in Maidstone. She left me a passenger ticket for 12 shillings and 4 pence which she said had to be given to the man who came for the luggage. But when he came this morning he refused to take it with the ticket and demanded 8 shillings and 8 pence instead! I couldn't lend 8/8 so the office had to pay! I get a bit annoyed with the way Bish goes off all bright and breezy and leaves you to do all her jobs! She doesn't care! <u>I</u>, being soft, have been "left with the baby" a bit too often. But she would just <u>laugh</u> if she knew!

Well – home on Sunday! I shall go to bed early on Saturday night because I've been sleeping rather badly these past few nights, thinking about the bad report episode I suppose, although I'm <u>trying</u> to keep calm! But hey ho! A whole month at home will cure me! x x x x x HOLIDAY.

25th February 1952 – Study Block
What a wonderful holiday – being with you all and friends for a whole month. But now back to work! I had a successful journey back

yesterday. I completely finished knitting the bedjacket and did some embroidery on the train. I arrived back in London on time and got a taxi and was back by 10 to 4. I didn't have time for tea because we had to be in uniform in the lecture room by 4.30pm, and I had to "fish" my uniform out from my trunk and cases, attach the epaulettes, put in the buttons and goodness knows what! You should have seen my room! I just threw everything out on the floor and bed till I found what I wanted! I should have planned my packing better!

The "gang" were round about all the time. Bish nearly didn't come back – she's not been sleeping throughout the holiday, and consequently has had lots of dizzy bouts and fainting.

We started at 4.30pm – believe it or not – with a Medicine lecture by Professor Keswick. What a way to begin! There's nothing like breaking us in gently! And we worked till 8.30 too!

I got unpacked by 9pm last night then we had coffee and eats in Barnett's room till 9.45.

Today is a fairly easy day – hence this letter in study time! We have the afternoon off on Tuesdays and all other evenings.

We are planning to go to the theatre with free tickets tomorrow night. Block will be hard work, but much better than coming back from holiday to the wards. You can phone me any evening, any time, except Tuesday. Just let me know beforehand so that I'm sure to be here.

I played the organ for chapel again this morning. The other two organists are cowards! They said they couldn't possibly play at such short notice! That is nonsense because I was in exactly the same position. We had "O God our help"!!!

Pancake Day today and we had pancakes here what's more! I bet they had fun in the kitchen frying 500 or more!

I'm so excited about our little house – how lucky I am marrying a curate! It's so thrilling to think the house is our very own. I'm just longing for September so that we can paint and furnish it, when Ernest moves in.

28th February

I think I'm settling down to this very different routine. The first day was <u>terrible</u> to say the least, but since then there's been so much to do that it has helped to make me forget to miss home!

Several of the girls in Block have got engaged recently, and they're all waiting till they've finished their training to get married. One poor girl is engaged to an Engineer in Eastbourne, who is going out to Australia soon for 3½ years. So when she finishes here she is going out there to marry him, and then come back to England, and wait for him to return. Think of that! I'm more fortunate than that!

We couldn't get theatre tickets from Matron's office yesterday so we went to the Curzon, Park Lane, to see the French film "La Ronde" with English subtitles. It was jolly expensive too – 4/11 for seats at the front! I had some idea that it was a bit disgusting, but it was far worse than any of us anticipated and we were all rather horrified. It was a series of very "hot" love affairs, joined together by the story teller. People disappearing into bedrooms, then the door closed and you were left to imagine the rest! The scenery was good, and it was quite well done, but for the first time ever I wished it would end! Thank goodness the supporting programme was good.

It's nearly supper time now so I shall have to stop. Paddy, Bish and Mary have gone to the News Theatre, but I've got a bit of a swollen gland and sore throat, and feel a bit feverish so I decided not to go. I shouldn't think it means anything – I shall probably be alright tomorrow. Must be the reaction of my poor brain to a bit of work! It's so un-used to any effort after the holiday! On the other hand it's perishing cold outside, and then stuffy in the News Theatre, and I don't want it to develop.

I've just realised that we shall be married in Coronation year! We shall always remember that!

2nd March

I haven't anything very interesting to report – we just have lectures all day. Don't worry any more about my sore throat. I knew I could cure it myself!! And now the sepsis has disappeared, the soreness gone, and my glands are no longer painful. I only hope nobody else has picked up my old Streptococcus!

Yesterday afternoon five of us (Bish and Mary having gone home) went to the Odeon, Leicester Square to see "The Card". It was expensive but very good. We liked it so much more than "La Ronde". Afterwards we had tea in a Fortes Café – a shocking place on a Saturday.

We had our written question yesterday morning and it wasn't too bad at all. We didn't get the question we all wanted, but then one never does!

In the evening we intended to do so much, but in the end told silly stories about our schooldays until we were all in fits of laughter, especially over Paddy's antics! She was always getting into trouble!

This morning I got up about 9.15am, boiled 2 of my 4 eggs for my breakfast, and didn't get dressed till about 11! I had a good shoe-cleaning episode, and then did piles of washing. I just about finished that by lunchtime, with a few other odd jobs thrown in.

It's now 4.15 – nearly teatime – and all afternoon I've been in Paddy's room eating nuts and listening to the wireless, and writing to you in between chatting to Paddy.

Paddy and Anne Key and I are going to St. Martin in the Fields to Evensong tonight. We're planning to do quite a lot in Block – sightseeing and so on. It's so lovely to have our off duty together. Block is great fun – I shan't want it to finish. I love Medicine too – it's much more interesting than Surgery. I thought nothing could beat Surgery at one time, but I'm not so sure now. I think I would still rather <u>work</u> on a Surgical ward though.

4th March
Last Sunday we went to St. Martin in the Fields to Evensong as intended. It was lovely. The verger used to be at Christ Church, Lancaster Gate, where I used to play the organ for PTS Evensong. He recognised us, and as the church was packed he allowed us to go in the Vicarage pew! After church I went down to York House to see Pat Sturtivant who has come here to do Midwifery. But they've put her on night duty so I left a note for her and had one back this morning. She has nights off today and tomorrow so I'm going down to see her again tonight. This weekend I'm going to stay with the

Ginevers (my Godfather) in Seale, Surrey. I've been meaning to go so many times and have never managed it.

6th March

We came off duty at 5.30 after lectures all day, and Paddy was feeling very fed up and wanted to get out, so I said I'd go with her to the News Theatre. It was interesting and made us laugh and was only 1/-!! We've just got back and had supper.

I've got so much to do before Saturday. We're having Gynae this week for our written question. They put a list of 10 questions up each week for us to prepare, and then we are given one of the ten to write on Saturday.

This week we're having a speech-making contest. There are 60 of us in Block this time, and we're divided into 6 groups of 10. We've got a common subject, which each group has to work out, and then one person speaks from each group. We've pooled our ideas, and I'm speaking for Group 3, so I've got to work out the speech, as I want it, now. I shall be glad when Saturday morning is over – with the test and the speech!

Our gang have had our little coffee session now, so I must go to bed.

Friday morning

Now it's 9am and we have study at 9.30, then a paediatrics (children) tutorial. We had a most marvellous lecture by Dr. Hart, the specialist in paediatrics yesterday. He started right from the beginning and explained how an expectant mother can help to ensure that her baby will be a healthy one. Very useful information!

I saw Pat Sturtivant on Tuesday evening. She doesn't seem to like Midder very much because they have to do their lectures in off-duty time. She came with three others from Sheffield so she has got friends here. We had a little chat. She wanted to know when I'm getting married etc.

I really must do some work now – I have a heart attack every time Sister comes in, for fear she should see me writing a letter.

By the way – my mild attack of tonsillitis only lasted for 2 or 3 days, and I am now COMPLETELY RECOVERED, so don't WORRY! I had an examination by the R.M.O. recently, and he told me my tummy felt nice and soft, so he didn't think anything was wrong. I didn't actually <u>faint</u> in one of the lectures, I just went giddy, and he says that is often an effect of standing for any length of time at that time of the month. He gave me a detailed account of the physiology of what happens, and said he didn't think it would happen again. I was in Sick Bay for 2 hours, during which time they took my name and home address etc. which they do as a matter of routine. But I thought they only wrote to one's parents if one had to be in Sick Bay for several days. I was furious that they should write to you just for that, and worry you so much.

I had a lovely "weekend" at Ginevers. They are all so charming and made me feel so welcome. Peter was home from school for the weekend. He is 16½ and quite the nicest of 16-year-old boys I've ever met. He's hoping to take a degree and then do Theological training in preparation for being a naval Chaplain. Maureen is 14 and very kind and friendly. In fact they're a very happy family altogether. They all accept their "duties" without grumbling, and I never really heard either parent raise their voice. Seeing them so happy made me long to set up a happy home of my own. I couldn't help noticing how "pally" the Ginevers were towards each other, and I'm sure those sort of families can be a great example.

We had lantern slides in our "skin" lecture this evening – there was one of a man's arm and another of a man's face. I feel so tired tonight. I <u>must</u> go to bed early. Did I tell you that the speech contest was jolly good last Saturday? Six of us spoke and Jean Marles (group 5) and I tied for delivery, but their group had many more marks for subject matter. They'd done so much research work that they really deserved to win. They'd written to the Ministry of Health and the District Nursing Association and the General Nursing Council to ask their opinions on the increase in the number of bedsores, and our group hadn't done <u>anything</u> like that. I stayed up till nearly midnight on Friday preparing the speech though, so at least it was worthwhile. The other 4 groups had very low marks I'm pleased to say! Next Saturday somebody else will have to do the speaking, so I shall be able to sit back and enjoy it instead of trembling in my shoes!

We're wondering what the Budget has in store tonight. I hope there won't be too many increases. I shall pass out if train fares go up any more.

We had a Gynae lecture by Doctor Roques this morning, and he was discussing abnormalities – relationships before marriage etc. – that women often get disabling pains and general discomfort in relationships with a partner before marriage. I was quite interested to hear it because obviously that could have been what was wrong with me last week.

10th March
We have a study period first this morning, and then we're going to have a film of some sort. This morning I got my notes completely up to date, so I'm feeling on top of the world. Tonight we're going to see "Miranda". We saw the trailer last week and can't resist the temptation!

Could you possibly phone me this week as I simply haven't enough money to phone <u>you</u>. I'm not off till 8 on Friday, though I should have finished supper by 7.15pm and don't have to go back to a lecture till 7.30, so 7.15 would be a good time.

Sister Fawkes was telling us the other day that as we have to work an extra month above our 3 years till we take our State in June, we can have an extra month sick leave, above our ration of 3 weeks, without having to stay on after State to make it up. So I said, "Oh that means I can have another 5 weeks!"

By the way, Bridget Luck seems to have become attached to our little group, making an 8th "man". How long she will last I don't know. She went away with Anne Key to Germany during the month's holiday, and they've stuck to each other for this week. So she goes with us everywhere now.

Thank you so much for the <u>wonderful</u> parcel of flowers. They arrived quite fresh and looked so beautiful that I had to show them to everybody when I opened the parcel. I've divided them up into three vases for <u>myself</u>. I'm very selfish you see! I couldn't bear to part with any of them so they form a little sort of half circle round the photo of the house on my table and look very attractive. The catkins are lovely still – buds are beginning to come out on them.

12th March

Sister Fawkes – our senior Sister Tutor – is in Princess Alice Ward having had varicose veins done. Several of us thought it would be a good idea if we took her some flowers. So I got up on my hind legs yesterday before one of the lectures and told everybody I'd like 2d per head this morning from those who were willing. We collected 12/- altogether.

In the dinner hour Paddy, Mary, and I went and bought pink tulips, blue iris, and Mimosa which, when they were arranged, looked super. The three of us went up to the ward to leave them, and Sister Bennett-Evans asked me if I'd like to take them in. The other two were waiting on the landing. Anyway I went in to dear Fawkes and she was <u>delighted</u> with the flowers, and said it was worth being ill, to receive such a lovely present! She said she was feeling very much better and chatted for a few minutes and then I departed.

We had a super thank you letter from Sister Fawkes this morning saying she was "very thrilled and touched when Nurse Bryan arrived yesterday with the bouquet of spring flowers". I don't quite know whether she was thrilled and touched to see Nurse Bryan or the flowers!! Ha Ha!

There seems to be a non-sleeping bug going around our gang. Bish and Elizabeth haven't been able to sleep of late. On Sunday night Bish didn't go to sleep till 3.30am and at 5.30 she was awake and reading!

18th March

We thoroughly enjoyed "Miranda" last night – it was terribly funny. We were off at 5 o'clock. We dashed upstairs, changed and were sitting in the "Cameo" on Regent St. at 5.15! I don't know how we managed it but that is the truth! We were out by 7.30 and back for 8 o'clock supper. Now we can't go to anything but free ticket theatres! The trouble is there never seem to be any free tickets when we want them.

My study period is now over, and we have a Medicine Tutorial. By the way, I'm now having a course of <u>walking</u> lessons! The gang are very worried because I walk with my toes turned out! So I'm having to practise walking with the inside of my feet each side of a straight line. It's absolute murder, but it's better than walking in front of them and hearing their dirty laughs. The Medicine Tutorial is now over, you must have gathered, and we're in a terrible giggly state. Sister MacCullum has been talking about constipation of all things – we certainly go in for some delicious subjects in this place. She says she thinks one of the causes is the lack of "accommodation" in schools, houses, hospitals, hotels. So now we are talking in very polite terms of "going to look for accommodation"!!

We've just had our cocoa and this morning there was sponge cake as well! Now we're studying again and at 12 o'clock we have to listen to "diarrhoea and vomiting" for an hour. Sorry it's all so disgusting, but we've been in fits of laughter about it.

20th March
Thank you very much for this morning's letter and for the lovely little "first violet". I nearly didn't get the violet – something fell out of the envelope, by the tennis court, as I was walking along and taking the letter out. I looked and couldn't see anything, so thought I must have imagined it. When I read that you'd sent me the first violet, and I couldn't find it – I went back to the tennis court, and there it was! Somebody might even have walked over it and thought nothing of it. But it was a matter of life and death for <u>me</u> that I should find it! So now I'm keeping it very carefully!

What a hectic time you've had this week. When I'm in my Vicarage I think I shall put a notice on the door re-closing time! Anybody wishing to be admitted during closing time will have to pay £5!

No the Insomnia Bug hasn't affected me. I seem to go to sleep the minute I get to bed thank goodness.

I rang up to Eileen on Tuesday evening. She wants me to go to Buckhurst Hill for lunch on Sunday and then help her a bit in the afternoon to get ready for Jonathan's christening.

On Saturday evening we're going to Barnett's in Upper Norwood about 5.30, and have passes till 1am in case we need them.

Jo Tomlinson rang up last night and asked if I'd like to go to the next Square dancing class – next Thursday. She tells me it's 2/- a time now because the Instructress is Professional. I'm quite looking forward to it – the dancing I mean, not paying 2/-!!

There is some talk of being off from Friday evening till Sunday evening over the last weekend of Block, so that would be nice.

Our Gynae test is tomorrow afternoon and so far I haven't been inspired to work very much. I feel fed up with work today, and am longing for a long walk or something. I feel bored with lectures! It's just tea-time now, and then we have another hour of study before we are off.

We have had another Gynae Tutorial today and Sister said that every nurse should know how to deliver a baby on a <u>train</u>! She asked for suggestions as to what we would do, so we said (in fits of laughter)

1. Pull the Communication Cord! (Sister said that wouldn't be much good in the middle of the Derbyshire Hills!)
2. Go and fetch the Guard! (what could <u>he</u> do, she asked!)
3. Throw everyone out of the compartment first and then raid the Restaurant car for dishes and hot water etc. etc. – slightly more sensible she thought!

8th April

I was completely wrong with all my guesses about my new ward after Block. I'm now on Charles Bell – a men's surgical, and a very big one too. But I settled down quite quickly for <u>me</u>! – though I was petrified at having to do all the new treatment at first. But the men are very cheerful and helpful and I'm VERY HAPPY!!

I'm not Head Nursing – perhaps just as well when I'm strange to the ward. I'd be even more frightened.

Sister Rees is very sweet. She's young and quite attractive and charming. I'm told she <u>can</u> be horrible when she chooses but I have that pleasure still to come!

My days off are ½ day Sunday afternoon and day off Monday this week, and then next week evening on Monday and day off Tuesday. So I shall have ½ day Easter Sunday and day off Easter Monday. Which day do you think it would be best for coming home, when I do come? The Sunday/Monday would give me a bit more time but

I'd have to come home on the bus. But that wouldn't matter – I'd just be in time to meet you out of church.

My room looks absolutely lovely with all the flowers and the other two pictures I brought back from home last week. I wish the sun would shine and make it even more cheerful!

Bish has gone to Soho. She moved down there this morning and is enjoying it very much so far. Mary of course is on Night duty and Di on holiday, so our little gang is a bit split up. Elizabeth Jones is on the children's ward – Bernhard Baron – with Sister Fuller. She says she stampedes into the ward umpteen times a day and raves at everybody.

Must fly to tea now and back on duty at 4.30.

17th April
Isn't the weather wonderful? I heard on the wireless that the Midlands had had thunderstorms. We had rain during the night but no thunder or lightning. I hope it holds out till my next day at home, though heaven knows when that will be. I'm a bit fed up with everything at the moment, and haven't the energy to think out when it will be!

On Tuesday evening it was <u>10 to 9</u> when we came off duty, we were so busy. If I'd had three sixpences and three pennies I'd have phoned you to say I couldn't stick it any longer. But I hadn't got the right change, so I told myself what an idiot I was to be so weak about it all, and that it was perfectly obvious I couldn't give it up.

Yesterday was a much better day. There were three of us on instead of two, and Sister wasn't so bad because everything was more organised. But in the evening we were just going off duty at 10 past 8 when we were told to expect another emergency. Our emergency week is supposed to be over! So we had to prepare to admit him, as the two night nurses were new to the ward.

I was so tired I thought I'd go to bed immediately after supper, and then I remembered that I'd promised to set Boyle's hair for her. Thankfully it didn't take long, and I was in bed by 9.45. I had an awful night. I had nightmares all through the night about setting up intravenous drips and people having their legs amputated and Sister yelling! I woke up at 3am having just dreamt that you three had all come to see me because I was having nightmares! I think I was at home in that dream, and you took my temperature and it was 102! I had to get up and have a walk round at 3 o'clock to try and stop myself dreaming, but the minute I got back into bed it started all over again!

Today I feel as if I'm going to have flu or something but I shall have to stick it out because there are few enough nurses as it is. It's just crazy to leave two nurses to cope with 21 patients – 10 of them really ill, and a T.B on the balcony.

You'll have to forgive me for all this grumbling. No doubt I shall get over it. I'm not the only one who feels like it though. Bunyan, who has been on with me most of the time feels just the same. Elizabeth Jones is on Bernhard Baron – the children's ward – and she's so fed up with Sister Fuller that she keeps pricking her fingers with nappy pins to try and get a septic finger so that she can go off sick!!

At Soho Bish says they've got so many nurses that they've nothing much to do, and here on Charlie B we're just going up the pole.

I've been on with the pro once or twice – on Tuesday for instance for morning treatment. Nobody told me that Bunyan had gone off and that I was in charge – I discovered <u>myself</u> half way through the morning. Tuesday was the day when there was so much to do – 5 people on intravenous drips, one on a continuous stomach suction, and three people to be aspirated and fed hourly. To say nothing of 5 dressings, umpteen enemas, and the usual ward routine. It's a bit disheartening when you're in charge, and trying to get everything done, and Sister comes and says, "<u>Why haven't you started the dressings?</u>" I told her I hadn't a free minute but that I was about to do them. So she snapped, "What you need is a little speed and organisation, my girl!" I felt just like walking out! If I'd gone any quicker I shouldn't have been walking on the floor at all. And what was <u>she</u> doing? – going round the ward with Professor Ascroft at the speed of 1/1,0000000 of a mile an hour, enjoying life to the full. It makes me so mad! And yet in the evening when she came back from an afternoon's riding she was as sweet as pie – telling me about riding through the mud in Epping Forest, and having to groom the horses afterwards.

163

Now I must stop as it's nearly lunch time again – how one's off duty flies!

21st April

Many, many, congratulations and tons of love for your 22nd wedding anniversary, my darling Mummy and Daddy, and many more happy anniversaries to come! I'm sending you a card with this letter, but I've been so busy that I haven't had time to put your little parcel together – I hope you don't mind waiting a day or two for it.

I suppose you will have had another of those charming letters from Matron today, telling you that I had to give in and go to bed. Isn't it silly? I was quite sure I should be able to shake it off but I really did feel rotten again on Saturday morning, and when the Staff Nurse remarked on it and took my temperature it was 102. So I came across to Sick Bay about 10am and here I am still. I'm in solitary confinement – not being allowed any visitors and no sign of being able to get up.

Yesterday morning my temperature was down to 98° after 4 doses of Chloromycetin capsules, but it shot up again to 100 last night. This morning it's down to 98 again, so let's hope it stays on the downward trend. Meanwhile I continue with the Chloromycetin and have to drink so much that my visits to the loo are rather frequent.

My cold and cough are much better, but I seem to have a general sort of ache, and my throat is sore and my eyes ache, and today I just feel I could throw something at anyone who comes near me. They're very kind in Sick Bay though. Sister and the Staff nurse are sweet, but I feel all the time that I ought to be "up and doing" instead of being waited on. Though I must say I appreciate a bit of peace after Charlie B.

So you see the question of whether I should come home today was answered for me! Nobody has brought me any letters this morning but maybe there'll be one later. Sorry this is such awful writing. I don't know what's the matter with me. I feel as though I'd love to squirt the ink from my pen all over everywhere, or scream the roof down!

Thank you for ringing up on Friday evening – it was lovely to speak to you, though I'm sorry I was so grumbly and silly.

I hope Sister Rees enjoys going back after her weekend off today and finding she's another nurse short. When I came off on Saturday morning there would have been <u>one</u> nurse on duty. I felt so guilty leaving her single-handed. Still – whether she meant it or not – from what Sister Rees said to me last week I'm only a menace when I'm there. If I didn't care, it would be a different matter, but when I'm Head Nursing I'm so "on edge" to do the right thing and so worried stiff lest anything should go wrong while I'm in charge – especially with all those drips and suctions and things – that it's little encouragement to be told you're no good. I think some of these Sisters expect us to be perfect from the start. But of course <u>they're</u> under a lot of pressure, I know.

Well last week apparently Sister told Haworth that <u>she</u> was no good, but she says she didn't take any notice. And one or two others who have worked on Charlie B. say that Rees is a tartar, and might say <u>anything</u> when she's in a bad mood, and then be as sweet as sugar the next minute – which is just my experience because she's been terribly nice to me since that awful blowing up – probably because she had a weekend off in view! Still, why worry? What does it matter who blows me up as long as I get State? No blowings up can prevent me getting it.

After another lovely sunny day yesterday it's pouring with rain today, so perhaps I'm in the best place here in Sick Bay!

By the way you've no idea what a dirty trick they have here! I have to have my pills 6 hourly – 6am, 12, 6 and midnight. It's not so bad being wakened for temperature and pills at 6am, but Sister wakes me at midnight to give me them! The first night I wasn't asleep, but last night I was and it's jolly annoying. Now I know how my patients feel!

We've got wirelesses in our rooms here so I can listen whenever I want to. Yesterday I listened to Wilfred Pickles and "Take it from here" and "Down your way" and several services. In the morning there was "Songs for Sunday morning" and I imagined you listening over breakfast in the dining room. There was a most lovely setting of the Lord's Prayer and I could just imagine Daddy adding a bit of harmony to it as he looked at the Sunday Times and drank his tea! I must listen at 1 o'clock and hear how Stafford Cripps is.

It's 10 to 1 now and I finished my lunch about ¼ hour ago. Since then the Lady Almoner has been in to see if I want anything, and Paddy just poked her head round the door and threw a note in to me. She came out of Princess Alice ward yesterday and is going to Norfolk for 10 days. She says she's lost nearly a stone while she's been ill. She thinks Bish is off sick too. I wish she could have come in and talked to me but the notice "No Visitors" on the door is large enough to scare anyone off. Even the Lady Almoner said, "I'm not a Visitor"!

Oh I've just heard the news that Sir Stafford Cripps is unconscious and sinking fast. What a terrible thing when not long ago his family were so thrilled to think he was cured.

Well I think I'll stop now. There's nothing to tell you besides moans and groans and I'm sure you've heard quite enough from me recently in that direction. Don't take too much notice of me. I daresay I've just got in a rut and I'll be alright again when I get out of it!

28th April
What a lovely surprise it was to be allowed out of Sick Bay and to come home for a day! I now feel uplifted and ready for work again!

Sister Rees is as different again. Yesterday she <u>welcomed</u> me back to the ward, and at elevenses time she <u>asked</u> me if I'd had my coffee, and presented me with a large tin of biscuits to go with it! It was then that I took the bull by the horns and asked about my day off. She said of <u>course</u> I must have my day off. It would be a new week and I must have my full off duty. But she changed it to evening, day off, ½ day, instead of the usual ½ day, day off, so it's even better.

When I went to ask permission to go off duty I said, "It seems too good to be true, Sister – coming back after a week's sick leave and then going for a day off!" It's almost as though she thinks she might have been the cause of my going off sick. She smiled and said, "Don't worry, nurse, the ward is much quieter now and we'll be alright." The other nurses have noticed her good temper as well and everyone is thrilled to bits!

So I had the evening off and was rather sad that no-one else was off at the same time. I wanted to go to church but I wasn't keen on going alone. I spent ages staring out of my bedroom window trying to decide what to do, and in the end I said, "Well, girl, this won't do! Time flies and you've got to make up your mind!" So I came out of my trance, put on my church clothes and went to St. Martin in the Fields alone. I got a very good seat at the front again but the lovely curate must have been preaching elsewhere! The organ broke down just before the service too, so they had to use the piano by the chancel steps. I got back for supper at 8, and after I'd phoned you I went and had coffee in Beth Howarth's room with Helen Bell as well. Beth told me that the very ill man on Charlie B. has been moved into the side ward as Sister thinks he's near the end.

Then I went round to Boyle's room as she was feeling "mis" and wanted someone to talk to. She's getting married in September and I think these last 4 months are proving to be rather trying. Consequently she had a bit of a row with Ian yesterday and was very upset afterwards. She asked me to go to her wedding on 13th September at Swiss Cottage, near Hampstead. I must get the day off when I've changed wards.

I got to bed eventually at 11 last night, and slept till the hooter went at 6.30am and then on and off till 9am. I boiled two eggs and had Ryvita and marmalade and Nescafé, got dressed and went to collect my pay from Matron's office. Then I went round the shops and bought shampoo and soap and a new pale-blue and grey suit with pleated skirt. I liked one at £9 but then found this one at Richard Shops on Regent Street at £7.19.3. I met Elizabeth Jones in Dickens & Jones. She was looking for black earrings to go with her new evening dress, so we continued to search together. Elizabeth liked my suit and she has excellent dress sense so I'm sure you will like it. Now if anyone wants to buy me a handbag for my 21st "say navy blue" please!! And should anyone feel like it I'd like a white one too!

We've just had "John Astor House" placed in bronze lettering outside the front door of the Nurses' Home. Matron has decided it sounds better than merely "Nurses' Home" so if you happen to think about it in future perhaps you will write "John Astor House, Foley Street".

I'm sitting out on the roof at the moment as it's a lovely day. I hope to finish the pullover for Daddy tomorrow.

You should have heard the uproar when I walked onto the ward on Sunday morning. The men made very rude remarks of course and there were shouts of "Aye Aye Aye Aye"!! Thanks again for another lovely little break at home.

2nd May

Sorry I haven't written for a few days, but Paddy is back from her sick leave and we've had the same off duty together so we've been out shop window gazing and the like.

I want you to know that everything is wonderful on the ward at the moment, especially as I managed to do my "last offices". We're supposed really just to <u>help</u> the first time, but I did quite a lot with Sister last night, so it remains to be seen whether she gives me a cross when I take her my cross paper. But in future it won't bother me, at all. I was there when dear Mr. Page died, and there was nothing horrible about it because he'd been unconscious for some time anyway. We moved him out of the ward into the side ward at 4 o'clock and he died at 5 to 6, so none of the patients are aware of what happened.

I was Head Nursing again yesterday afternoon and everything went very smoothly for a change. We were very busy, but Sister Rees was extremely helpful and I felt quite happy. I can do <u>anything</u> when she's in a good mood! She will have gone for her weekend off when I go back after tea.

When I got back from home last Saturday night I found that the maid had stripped my bed for me on clean linen day, and made it up with clean linen. She's awfully kind – the maid on this corridor – and looks after me wonderfully. Yes please, Mummy darling, could you please send one summer frock to me as the weather is warming up (Famous last words!). I think I'd like the red one for a change.

Did I tell you that Bish has been to Sick Bay again? She fainted and was violently sick all day on Monday and was in Sick Bay for 2 days. She's back on duty now. Paddy seems much better except for having lost a stone in weight during the 10 days she was in Princess Alice Ward. I'm so glad she's back. I felt quite lost without both Bish and Paddy.

7th May

<u>I'm on top of the world!</u> I was so certain that Sister would only give me a <u>stroke</u> for my Last Offices as it was the first time I'd done it, but I went to her today and asked her to sign up the stroke and SHE GAVE ME A CROSS!! She asked if I'd know how to do it another time myself and I said yes (of course!) so that was that! I could have thrown my arms around her! Honestly I don't know what has come over her – ever since I came back from Sick Leave she's been marvellous and tremendous fun. I feel I can talk to her and joke with her now, instead of being scared of her and oh what a difference it makes to life! When it's like this I feel I can stick another year quite cheerfully. But goodness I feel so <u>mad</u> with myself because I've left my ear syringing and eye drops crosses thinking I wouldn't get my Last Offices. If <u>only</u> I'd done my eye and ear ones I could have got my strings on time. However I can go ahead and get them done within the next week and I should have my strings by the time I come home next time! Oh wonderful, wonderful, wonderful – I can't tell you what a relief it is to me!

The other very ill patient, Mr. Dowden, died at 6.30 yesterday morning. He was completely bewildered in his mind and we moved him into the side ward the afternoon of the previous day. So now we have been relieved of our two "difficult" patients and have about 6 empty beds. This morning we had finished all the bedmaking and cleaning by 10 to 9 and had very little to do till quarter to 10! Usually it's about 10.30 when we finish! We've never been so slack all the time I've been on the ward. Somehow I prefer to have a little more to do though. Time goes so slowly when you're not busy and I hate <u>looking</u> for things to do. I'm never satisfied! I really shouldn't grumble. I expect we shall have plenty of new patients before long.

Thank you so much for your letter with the 21st arrangements. I'm so thrilled with the party arrangements. You certainly have put your heads together and made "headway"!

I quite agree with you that it would be better to postpone the party till 27th September. My exams will be over and it will be much more fun because I will be able to help with the preparations. Now all I have to do is get a day off for my birthday so that I can be home for the actual occasion. I think it was quite a good idea to ask Margaret

169

to share my party. I'm sure expenses will be cut down. Just wait till you see my new outfit!

Now for the week's grumble. I've heard from Ernest that neither the 19th nor 25th nor Whit weekend are any good for him for me coming home. But I can't possibly leave it any longer than that. I'll have to stick to the 19th for the moment and hope it works out.

The <u>Block</u> results have come out at last, and they weren't worth waiting for! I've got a hopeless mark – 60%! Honestly, though, I hadn't learnt anything on the paper and it was pretty impossible to do well unless you're terribly brainy because there were 10 subjects to learn for 4 questions. I'm going to settle down and see what I can achieve for the medicine exam on 10th June.

Has Bish got a romance you ask? Oh yes – she's crackers on a male of 35 called John, who is a great friend of the family. She has rows with him every few months, but at the moment she seems to be quite happy and crazy about him. I met him when I went to stay with her and I met his father and brother. He is extremely nice – John Vallis is his name.

Sunday was Pat Ellerby's 21st party and she asked me with 5 or 6 others (Paddy included) to go to her room after duty. We had the most marvellous eats which she'd made herself, and champagne from the magnum or demi-magnum that her father let her bring back, followed by cake and coffee. It was super. As we ate she showed us her presents. She had <u>three</u> travelling clocks! That would be alright if she intended to get married soon – she could put one in each bedroom!

On Monday evening I was free and so was Paddy. We did a thing we've never <u>thought</u> of doing for <u>months</u> – went to see Buckingham Palace, and walked round St. James' Park. We took particular notice of the royal standard – that was Queen Elizabeth's <u>own</u>. When we got back we heard on the 9 o'clock news that the Queen went into residence at Buckingham Palace on Monday. So then we knew what had drawn us in that direction on that particular day! We can say that we saw Queen Elizabeth's standard flying on the first day <u>ever</u>! We also fed the pigeons in Trafalgar Square!

11th May
Do you realise that I'm now in my 3rd <u>year?!</u>

Tonight I'm going down to Soho, and Bish and I are going to St. Martin in the Fields for a broadcast service. Then I'm having a snack supper in her room. Tomorrow I hope to go to the Leonardo da Vinci exhibition at Burlington House in the afternoon.

One year ago tomorrow was our Engagement day. Ernest says he's sent me some pale pink carnations and a new navy blue handbag! He does spoil me!

We've had a lot of rain, and a thunderstorm last night woke me up. Today it's bright and sunny one minute and dark and pouring with rain the next!

I thoroughly enjoyed head nursing yesterday afternoon with the pro and it was wonderful! I had the utmost difficulty at washing time because the Arsenal v. Newcastle football match was in full swing and all the men were listening! I took bowls of water to the ones in bed, and bless me if 10 minutes later I found they were still calmly sitting there behind the curtains with their headphones on, and their washing water untouched! I had to be very cross with them! The pro went to tea at 4 o'clock so for ½ an hour I was alone. They thought it was a great joke! But one of them remarked that even though there were 20 of them to one nurse they were outnumbered!

I was off at 5.30 and intended to finish knitting the pullover and write letters, but I knocked on Elizabeth Jones' door and she happened to be there and was going with Biddy Luck to the flix, and I couldn't resist the temptation to go with them! We saw "Springtime in Italy" with another lovely ballet film of "Giselle", at the Rialto, Leicester Square. We got in about 6.15 and came out soon after 8.30. We hadn't put our names down for late supper so we went in search of a café or a snack bar. It's pretty hopeless finding anywhere on a Saturday evening though, especially around Leicester Square. It's quite a revelation! Eventually we landed up in the Brasserie, downstairs, in the Tottenham Court Rd/Oxford Street Lyons. It has red and white checked tablecloths and reddish imitation tiled floor. For 2/9 we had fried egg, tomato, luncheon meat and chips, and ice cream – to the accompaniment of the orchestra. I really did enjoy it –

an evening out, even though it meant spending 6/9. It was 11.30 by the time I got to bed but I had a lie-in to look forward to, so it didn't matter.

Tomorrow I have another evening off and a day off on Tuesday, so I'll go and see my little Godson for tea.

I've told you about Bish's romance, but not about the others!

1. Elizabeth Jones is very smitten by Biddy Luck's brother. She went home with Biddy one weekend and has been going out with Brian ever since! She always has been very interested in the boys, but now she says she's "through" with everybody else but him! I've never heard her say that before! I wonder what will be the outcome?

2. Anne Key, who has never been known to mention the name of a male, has met an artist somewhere, and has been out with him 2 or 3 times!

3. Mary Barnett is crackers about the Houseman on Obs. She's Head Nursing on Night Duty on Obs (my second ward) and more often than not she is there alone without a pro. The Houseman goes up there for coffee in the evening and stays as long as 2 or 3 hours!

I can see they'll all be married before me yet! Poor old Paddy seems to be the odd one out. She can't find anyone tall enough 'cause she's 6 foot! I'd better introduce her to Cousin Robin!

12th May
A year since our engagement. I remember how I was trembling with excitement at the thought of Ernest meeting me at the station, and then the ring was too small, so I had to wear it on my little finger all weekend! Also I remember it seemed so strange to read the announcement in the paper!

I've been working up on Meyerstein this morning because they are so short of nurses and we are really slack on Charlie B at the moment. I went up there the other evening too, and Sister Hammond was telling me all about what happened to all the patients I nursed there a year ago. She was so <u>nice</u> to me. This morning Sister Rees came to me to tell me to go up to Meyerstein, and she said, "These two nurses can manage without you." So I asked her whether that was an insult or a compliment! – Yes! I <u>dared</u> to ask her a thing like that! She's so entirely different now. And she replied that she thought it was a compliment because Sister Hammond had told her how pleased she was when I went up the other evening. When I came off duty this afternoon Hammond said, "Goodbye, Nurse Bryan. Come again <u>anytime!!</u>" So I laughed and said something about the "ever open door"! Why can't people always be like that? Everything's so much happier that way. But of course they must get very stressed sometimes.

Day off tomorrow. I'm not sure what I shall do. I don't really want to do anything special. It's just so nice to please myself and have a day when you don't have to rush about – on and off duty, to and from meals, and up and down the ward.

13th May
It was wonderful to talk to you last night. I'm sorry I was a bit late but Paddy did so want to go out, and I insisted that if we did go out, we had to be back for your phone call. We went to see Margaret Rutherford in "Curtain Up" at the Odeon, Marble Arch. It was screamingly funny and we enjoyed it immensely. I hope you didn't mind waiting those few minutes.

The new PTS are arriving on the wards this morning I'm told. Thank goodness I'm not starting my three years all over again.

14th May
We've been so slack on the ward that we came down to earth with a bump today. We had 6 ops, starting at 9 o'clock this morning, and not finishing till 7 o'clock this evening. Sister has been on all day, so she was feeling very fed up with it all, and saying how she longed for 8 o'clock.

A new PTS girl has just come onto the ward. It is so funny – can you remember when <u>I</u> started on the wards? I'm sure she's got much more confidence than I had though! She said this evening, "I should have been off <u>12 minutes</u> ago, and my feet are killing me!" She was upset because the Head Nurse had just asked her to do something else. So I told her to go for heaven's sake and <u>I</u> would finish the job. Of course it didn't occur to her that <u>I</u> should have been off <u>12</u>

minutes ago as well! Now I know what an idiot I must have seemed on Howard D. Only I'm sure I was far more clueless than she is!

15th May

I've been off this morning and have been an hour on Princess Alice ward practising eye irrigations and things, so that I can do my cross next week. They're the sort of things that look so simple when experienced people do them, but are not so easy when it comes to doing them oneself!

The ward is chaotic again. I knew we couldn't be slack for long. Not only was it op day yesterday, but it's our emergency week as well. We've had some odd sorts of cases in, and when I went on duty this morning an emergency arrived back from theatre having been admitted at 4am. He's very much on the brink at the moment, having oxygen and a drip etc. I had to stand by his bed from 8.15am, taking his pulse quarter hourly, blood pressure, aspirating hourly, keeping the oxygen going, and an eye on the drip and his general condition, and he still hadn't come round from the anaesthetic when I came off duty. Now time is flying it's nearly time for tea, and another hectic evening.

25th May

I'd just got settled on the roof when I discovered there was no ink in my pen, so I had to go and get some more. I was jolly cross! I've got a ½ day and day off at my disposal and next week I shall be home again. Oh blow! I thought I'd brought my sunglasses with me but I haven't! I shall forget my head one day! – but I don't suppose it would be a great loss!!

Our emergency week has been pretty awful this time. Most of our ill patients have been emergency ones. Yesterday a boy of 14 was brought in. He's still at school but works in a bakery on Saturday morning to get a bit of pocket money. Yesterday morning he was in charge of the bread-cutting machine and it stopped. He took off the guard (or glove or whatever you call it) and the machine started whizzing round, and cut his left hand clean off at the wrist. They brought him to casualty and from there he came up to us. His hand, if you please, came with him, though he didn't know that, and it was given to Sister. Sister says she nearly passed out on the spot,

174

Anyway he'd just come back from theatre when I came back on duty, so for the afternoon he was "my baby". He's so good, and when his parents came up to see him – nearly in tears – he wasn't at all disturbed, and telling them not to worry. He told them he'd left his hand in the bakery! Doesn't it sound awful? Sister has taken quite a liking to him, and seems to enjoy mothering him. You know I'm sure these spinster Sisters have got a strong desire to be married, and are frustrated because their desire and maternal instincts are not satisfied. Sister seems so thrilled to do things for him, and comfort and spoil him. But then – that's what nursing is all about!

The Spaniard here told me the other day that he thinks I'll make a good wife, because I'm so lively! He says that before he came to England he was told that all English people went about with long faces but that it can't be true because I'm always happy and smiling! One of the other men said he didn't know where all my energy came from, and yesterday Mr. Dean said that all the patients would get pneumonia from the draught I make when I'm rushing about! They are daft really! But we do have some fun.

The man who came back so ill from theatre the other day is as perky as anything now – quite as cheerful and well as the man who had a similar op the day before. The only thing is I don't think he's a very desirable character. He has a venereal disease. Fortunately it's in its non-infective stage because he's had it so long, but I didn't care for having to blanket bath him and so on before I was told it was non-infectious. I seem to get some horrible jobs – that's nursing.

Tonight Bish and Langley and I are going to the Albert Hall to an "all nations cavalcade of song and dance". It sounds rather good to me. We were originally going to St. Martin in the Fields, but last night Biddy Luck gave us these free tickets which she couldn't use, and we thought the opportunity was too good to miss. I'm really looking forward to it.

Friday was Elizabeth Jones' 21st birthday and last night she had a little coffee party in her room, with our little gang. I felt in a crazy mood and went dressed up in the most ridiculous things. Of course, as you might expect, to make matters worse Elizabeth tugged my skirt at one stage to ask if I'd have another biscuit, and the cup of coffee which was nestling in my lap, went over. Consequently I had a large wet patch on my uniform skirt. The others were in fits, and said they thought I knew better, and that I <u>might</u> have waited!! So altogether we had quite a hilarious gathering and got to bed soon after 11pm.

Tomorrow I must write my medicine question which has to be given in on Thursday in preparation for our exam. I went to collect my Block test paper yesterday, and <u>now</u> I know why I came down so badly. I got 18/25 and 19/25 for my two medicine questions and 17/25 for gynae which I don't consider was bad at all. But the <u>last</u> question I didn't know a thing about and got 6/25 for it. If only I'd known that as well I could have got a decent mark!

Dear me! These people who don't learn their work properly! But the medicine marks give me fresh heart for my exam on June 10th. I wish I could be top and surprise everybody!! But I couldn't possibly – there are so many others taking the exam who are far cleverer than me.

27th May

We've had good fun on the ward with our Russian man. One of his visitors brought him a teddy bear the other day and it sits on his bed table. He calls it "Cheeshka" and is always talking to it in a crazy way! We are continually in fits of laughter.

The man I had to watch all morning incidentally is the one with syphilis – the V.D. He's really quite a nice man although I thought he wouldn't be. He's 65 and his wife is 45. He is getting on wonderfully well too. He smokes like a chimney but is quite interesting to talk to.

The young boy is doing fine too. He knows he's lost his hand and is so cheerful about it all. He was showing me today the mark from a caning he had at school about a month ago. He said he had two strokes on each hand, "but of course," he said, "you can't see the other!" It sounded so terrible to me, and yet to him it seemed to mean so little.

It's funny how there are usually one or two outstanding cases, and the rest just quite ordinary. Some you forget completely, and others you remember for quite a long time.

29th May

You'll never guess! We had a sweepstake on the ward yesterday for the Derby, and I drew "Gay Time" who came 2nd! So I got 15/-!! That's a lot of money and the first time I've won <u>anything</u>!

On Friday two of us went to Battersea Park for the afternoon, and we did enjoy it. What's more, we saw Peter Scott there! He was opening a new thing "The Bird Song Walk". I was so thrilled to see the creator of the paintings Ernest and I love so much and the person who has inspired the dining room scheme for our new little house.

It's a frightful day today – as cold as Christmas, and the rain is pouring down. I do hope it clears up for my day off. Perhaps it will blow itself out today and then be fine for tomorrow.

I had an evening off yesterday. I came off at 3.30 for Whitsuntide. We all have an extra hour off duty. I wish it could have been added on to my evening tomorrow but there was nothing doing. Di and I went in the Gallery at the Apollo for 2/6 to see "Seagulls over Sorrento". It was an all male show about sailors, but was very good. We thoroughly enjoyed it. It started at 5.30 so we were out by 8.30 and back in time for supper. This morning I have a ½ day, so if I get a ½ day on Wednesday morning it will be in place of next Sunday's. I shall have been on Charlie B for 2 months tomorrow. And to celebrate we have two hind-quarter amputations this week. I'm <u>dreading</u> it.

1st June

Sister is still in an excellent frame of mind even though we're very busy. She's really a brick. She does <u>everything</u> for those hind-quarter ops. She's been working so hard with them – and I can't understand why it doesn't get her down. I can't understand her at all (i.e.) what it is that changes her moods. I wonder if she's having a problematic love life or something?!

7th June

Instead of feeling miserable returning from my day off at home, I seem to feel invigorated! I've been so happy as Sister has been such an angel, and the ward reasonably under control.

We have our medicine exam in two days' time. I <u>have</u> done some work. Paddy and I spent most of the evening yesterday discussing medicine questions, but I haven't done a stroke of work yet today. I must do some after supper. Often what I learn at the last minute is what I remember best.

9.45pm. Oh I am a naughty girl! I was quite determined to work after supper and then the wireless was so interesting I <u>had</u> to listen. I embroidered my tray cloth as I listened, but that didn't help me to learn any medicine. And now I simply <u>must</u> go to bed, so I shall just <u>have</u> to spend all my off-duty tomorrow working. I had fond hopes that I'd be in a really studious mood before this exam, so that I could try to get a good mark, but now I'm wondering if I'll get a mark at <u>all</u>!

Di and Paddy and Elizabeth have been in for coffee and a chat after they came off duty, and I'm so tired now.

12th June
It's our Emergency week again this week, and I'm sure we've never been so busy before. We've had 5 emergencies in 2 days and all of them pretty awful cases. One of them is an intracranial haemorrhage and he's had to have burr holes made in his skull to relieve the pressure. He's unconscious half the time. There are drips and suctions as well, and when I came off duty this morning I felt really keyed up and tense after rushing about trying to think of 101 things at once. I'm alone with the new pro this afternoon, so heaven help me! I hope nothing terrible happens. Sister hasn't been too bad at all though – fortunately – and it's her weekend off this weekend so maybe by the time she comes back things will be quieter. The trouble is that several of our patients are on the "<u>downward</u> trend" and look like being permanent.

I think it will be Monday evening 30th June and Tuesday 1st July when I come home again, unless I've changed wards by then. This coming Monday evening I've arranged to go to the theatre with Bish. She's going to get free tickets if she can, and if she can't we'll go in the Gallery.

The exam on Tuesday was <u>horrible</u>. I was most disappointed in it – I managed to waffle along somehow and I did <u>finish</u> alright, but it was such a <u>silly</u> paper! All the first three questions were on more or less the same subject – the blood and arteries, and the last question was an essay "Magic of Medicine". I would have enjoyed that if I'd had more time, but my ideas weren't forthcoming in such a hurry! I prefer to trot out a few <u>facts</u> when I only have ½ hour for a question. <u>Some</u> people <u>liked</u> the paper, though most people thought it was horrible, and everyone was a bit disappointed. I was hoping for something on gastric ulcers and more interesting subjects. They ought to set a paper specially for <u>me</u> I think!! I'm sending the paper for you to see.

Now I must get ready for lunch. I feel slightly more prepared for the afternoon on the ward now. My off duty has calmed me down, and they wouldn't leave me in charge if they didn't think I was capable I suppose!

12th June (later)
I felt so <u>fed up</u> when I came off duty this evening – at 20 to 9 incidentally – and all through supper we were grousing about Sister, in between mouthfuls of chicken and green peas! Oh she has been a b.... today. It's a long time now since that frightful spell just before I went off sick in April, so we've done pretty well on the whole. But all the same one day of her yelling is quite enough for <u>me</u>! I thought 8 o'clock would never come tonight, and then at 8 o'clock of course there was still so much to be done that I visualized being there till 8 tomorrow morning. They're all emergencies who are taking up the time too. I shall be glad when this week is over. Thank goodness Sister will be off this weekend.

I must go and have my bath now. It's after 10.30 and I always like to take my time in the bath! I can never have one in less than 20 minutes – I enjoy it so much!

13th June, Friday
A miracle must have happened because today has been so much better on the ward. Things seem to be organised a bit more, instead of being in that awful muddle of yesterday. Somehow things have straightened themselves out a bit, and, except for that terrible head case who is completely bewildered and uncontrollable, things are bearable. Sister has been in a much better frame of mind, which certainly <u>helps</u>! Maybe she will be off duty for her weekend when I get back.

15th June

Thank you for your letter and for returning the medicine paper. Thank goodness the ward seems to be a bit quieter now. Emergency week ends tomorrow morning at 9 o'clock, and I shall <u>not</u> be sorry! Our head case is a "new man" today. He is talking quite normally, and realises where he is now. He can remember everything that happened up to the time of the accident, but can't remember the van knocking into him, and has no recollection, he says, of spending the last two nights in hospital. Sister will see a difference in him tomorrow when she returns.

I expect I shall be moving from Charlie B before long.

<u>Monday</u>

I've just come off duty and had my tea, and it's a lovely evening. I'm now about to change and go down to Soho to collect Bish. She said she'd get theatre tickets (free ones) so I'm longing to know what we're going to see. Day off tomorrow!

18th June

The tickets Bish managed to get free from Matron's office were for Sadlers Wells! They were 10/- seats – almost in the centre, about 4 rows from the centre of the stalls. They couldn't have been better seats. We could see every expression and every movement. Oh it was <u>simply wonderful</u>. – I do adore ballet. I could have watched it all over again. I was off at 4.30, so I changed and then went down to Soho to collect Bish. We got to Sadlers Wells soon after 6.30 – in plenty of time as it started at 7pm. We went for a little walk round, decided we didn't think much of the neighbourhood so went into the theatre about 6.45pm. It's a beautiful place, and it was thrilling sitting waiting for it to begin. I enjoyed it much more than "Seagulls over Sorrento" and even, I think, than "South Pacific". Of course they're vastly different sorts of things, but there's something so beautiful about ballet that one can't help but love it. We came out about 9.30 and went back to Soho for grub in Bish's room. Langley was there too – she shares a room with Bish – and we had the usual hard boiled eggs (Bish never times them!) followed by sardines and sandwich spread on bread and butter! – followed by apples and biscuits – followed by Nescafé which I had to drink out of a flower vase because they'd run out of cups! Of course we washed it first!!

The coffee was so strong that I couldn't sleep afterwards which made me jolly cross, but still it was all worth it. Good fun!

Yesterday I didn't get up till 10 o'clock, it being my day off. I spent ages in the bath so it was pretty late by the time I boiled my eggs, and breakfasted and dressed. I then found your letter downstairs and promptly began to answer it before lunch.

Immediately after lunch I went down to Soho again, and Bish and I went shopping – for her. Can't think why I went really, cos all I did was help her choose and try on elastic roll-on corsets and bras! She's worried about her "spare tyre", and in the end spent £5 just on "preserving her curves" she said!!! Jolly glad I don't have to put up with those awful corset things. How awful it must be to have tight elastic from above your waist to half way down to your knees! Anyway she was satisfied!

We finished all the jobs about 4pm and we parted company. I came back here for tea and found your parcel waiting for me, Mummy, containing nuts and roses and Sweet Williams and things. It's surprising how flowers pick up even after they've been quite squashed in the post. Thank you so much. They look lovely now.

Between tea and supper I spent my time embroidering my tray cloth and I'm getting on quite well with it now. It's beginning to look quite effective. After supper I did more embroidery and then went to bed early.

Today I've actually made appointments to do my last two crosses. I'm doing my eye cross tomorrow morning and ear cross on Saturday morning, so by the weekend I shan't have to worry about crosses any more. It will be such a relief. I've been worrying about them for ages.

Things have calmed down a bit on the ward, but we're still frightfully busy. The trouble is that we have so many bed patients, and washings in the morning and evening take so long as a result. I get so sick of bathing people!

20th June
The dreadful head case on the ward, who had burr-holes, is up for bed-making twice daily now, and is perfectly in control of his senses.

I think it's wonderful. You remember he retired from work on the Monday, and on Wednesday evening was knocked down by a van. He had an intracranial haemorrhage as a result, and was unconscious for 3 days.

23rd June

There's a notice up today saying that several of us are changing wards next Monday. I'm one of them, so that means my day off will change. I'll go to the office this week to ask where I'm going, and then go to my new ward and ask about off-duty.

I shall be sorry to leave Charlie B really, though it will be a relief to leave the rush! I'll probably go on theatre or somewhere and be just as busy! I've never been as busy and worked as hard before as I did yesterday morning on the ward. There were two of us to cope with everything. Sister was marvellous and helped a lot, but I <u>was</u> relieved when 2 o'clock came and I came off duty. I was thoroughly lazy on my ½ day, and did practically nothing, except for going swimming after supper.

This morning I woke with the hooter, but dozed on until nearly 10. I turned on the wireless at 9.15, and lay in bed listening to Housewives' Choice. Paddy was off this morning and came to my room at 10 o'clock. So after I'd breakfasted I made coffee for her and myself. Blow me if – when I'd just boiled the milk – Mary Barnett didn't come in "all unexpected like"! So I had to get some hot water to make the coffee spin out for 3! She's come off night duty this morning and it's lovely to see her again.

Bish comes back from Soho next Monday, so we'll all be reunited again. It seems ages since we were all <u>together</u>, and yet my 3 months on Charlie B have simply <u>flown</u>. This afternoon I'm going to the Dentist, and then I'm meeting Bish at 6 o'clock to go <u>somewhere</u> with free tickets.

Oh yes – ! I'll have a photograph taken when I get my strings. Then in years to come I'll be able to say "Now when I was a Head Nurse at the Middlesex...!" Oh by the way, they've changed our door labels to "Head Nurse" now instead of plain "Nurse"! I'm coming on!

One of the girls from my set – Isabel Porter – is engaged and is getting married a year next August. A month after me! She and Ian are going to live in Barnsley about 20 minutes from Doncaster. Ian has to go to Kidderminster quite often, and says they could go via Nottingham and come and see Ernest and me when we're married too! Then we could go and see them sometime. They're also very fond of cricket and say they'd like to go to Trent Bridge. I love planning all these things. It will be such fun. Now I'm going to do a little more embroidering.

25th June
On Monday evening Bish and I went to see "Excitement" at the Casino. Jewel and Warriss were in it and were very good – they've always been favourites of mine. But apart from them, and the pretty costumes and one or two bits of clever dancing, I found it rather repulsive. It was a Latin Quarter Revue – rather after the Folies Bergères type of thing, only worse according to Bish's opinion. Nude women by the score (almost) may attract some people, but didn't impress me! And not only that but it was so terribly suggestive in a great many places. Bish agreed with me about it, so it wasn't just me. I think I've got a pretty broad mind by now, but it makes sex look so cheap when it should be so lovely. It just makes me sick to see it made cheap like that. Bish got the free tickets, and we thought it would be funny with Jewel and Warriss. I bet the Office didn't know much about the show when they handed out the tickets!

I went to the office yesterday to ask about my new ward, but Sister said she hadn't completed the list yet and would I go again on Thursday or Friday. It's so annoying because I can't make any plans.

The ward is much quieter now. No drips and no ops today besides one minor one, even though it's op day. Emergency week again next week but I shall be on my new ward. I only hope my next ward is a quiet one for a change. I'll probably go on theatre or somewhere frightful. Mary Barnett is on theatre.

It's Di's 21st birthday tomorrow and she's having a "Beano" in her room in the evening. She's smuggled some drink in too. So it should be good!

27th June

Goodness – it's <u>really warm</u> today! I'm sitting in a deckchair on the roof, and it's really beautiful. With the exception of yesterday this must be the first bit of warm weather we've had this month.

I've now discovered that I'm going onto Whitbread ward on Monday – in the Radium Wing. They're women this time and practically all cancer cases, so goodness knows what it will be like. I don't think it's as hectic as Charlie B though, from all accounts. I'm going there as Head Nurse, so I should think I'll get my strings on Monday.

I went up there this afternoon to discover my off duty. I really don't know what to do – I can't have my off duty changed as soon as I go onto a new ward – I should be unpopular straight away. Next week I have Thursday evening and day off on Friday, and the following week Monday evening and Tuesday. I shall not have to ask for a special day off for my 21st after all as it's on Thursday of that week – so I shall come home on Thursday evening and have day off on Friday.

No don't <u>please</u> put Head Nurse on my letters! I couldn't bear it! I only have my title on the ward. I'm really rather scared of head nursing, but thank goodness on this sort of ward you don't have drips and dressings and things. It's nice to think that at the end of this next ward I go on holiday! And there's less than 3 months till then.

You remember I once said that I wouldn't get married till I have a house? Well now I wouldn't mind if we had a disused barn as long as we could be married! That's perhaps rather an exaggeration because I can't imagine anything like that happening! But we do have such a lovely house to go to now, and some lovely furniture and things to put in it! People are being very kind and generous to us already. I shall be so proud of it! And I shall keep it tidy too! I always tidy up – even if I'm going to be late on duty. I'm getting better!

We had a wonderful feast and party in Di's room last night for her 21st. We gave her a super Ronson lighter with a windguard – it cost us over 50/-, but we pooled our money and she was simply thrilled with it. I felt very tired last night – the sudden change in the weather perhaps? I didn't dress up for the party at first, but Di was so disappointed that I departed ½ way through the evening and made myself into a freak! one bra at the front and another at the back and so on! It caused quite a stir, and Paddy dressed up too. We had wonderful eats, and Di and Paddy and Elizabeth had made some punch in a <u>large</u> bowl, with gin, sherry, port, neat lime juice and lemonade, cider, and cucumber, apple, oranges and lemons and cherries chopped up in it. There was so much of it that we refilled our glasses oodles of times!! We got to bed eventually at 12.30 – I never thought I'd be able to sleep, but I did!

29th June
It's such a glorious day – I have a ½ day morning off and already it's so warm that I'm roasting on the roof in a bathing costume! Last night I was off at 4.30 and spent 2 hours out here till 7.30, and it was so lovely then that I didn't want to go inside. But I had to have supper sometime, and then went to wash my hair and have a bath. As it was, it was 10.30 when I got to bed.

This morning at 6.45 I was sound asleep when suddenly a voice said, "Are you on this morning?" It was Mary Barnett – I'd forgotten to tell her I had ½ day morning and she'd come to wake me as usual! I was so mad! I was sound asleep and it's so rare that I manage to sleep on my morning or day off, with all the banging doors! Oh well! Not to worry!

I did go to sleep again till 8.30ish, and then it looked so heavenly outside that I simply <u>had</u> to get up!

We're hoping to go and look at bedroom suites and carpets and curtains when I come home on Thursday.

I must tell you something that I thought was <u>most clever</u> yesterday – Professor Ascroft, one of <u>the</u> surgeons at the Middlesex and the "special" for Charles Bell, was doing a round of his patients. The telephone rang and I answered it, and it was a former patient asking whether he could safely ride a bicycle so soon after his Hernia op. I told the Staff nurse and she said to the Prof, "A hernia, sir, enquiring whether he can cycle." The Prof turned round and said, "Certainly he can cycle if he has a bicycle"!!! I thought that was wizard! He said it so promptly and so calmly!

1st July

Things have changed a bit because I've been put on Queen Mary Women's Cancer Ward – the one adjoining Whitbread where I was told I was going. So I shall have <u>Friday</u> off each week now instead of Tuesday alternate weeks.

I always hate the first days on new wards. I'm acting as "super" not Head Nurse for a month, but the Head Nurse had an evening off yesterday and day off today. I enjoyed the morning while she was on with me, but I didn't much like being left to cope in the evening. It's a much bigger ward than Whitbread – 22 patients instead of 12, and it took ages to write the report when I don't really know the patients yet. Another girl came up at tea-time – new to the ward like myself – and the two of us had to make whatever headway we could. I thought the evening would never end and that we should never finish. I came off duty after giving the report to the Night Nurse about 8.30. And I was so fed up! I wished I could go home! I woke up about 1.15 this morning and immediately started thinking and worrying about the ward. My mind was just a whirl of thoughts of what I might have forgotten yesterday, and what I had to do today. I kept getting up and having drinks of water and trying to get rid of these silly thoughts, but I couldn't go to sleep again till after 4am! I've never worried about my work so much before. This morning I woke up feeling terribly sick and hot and bothered, but of course when I got on duty it wasn't nearly as bad as I had anticipated! The night nurse congratulated me on my good report of last night! That little word of encouragement pleased me no end I might say! Especially as I hadn't thought it was a very good report with my knowing so little about the patients.

We got on quite well this morning – finished the treatment on time, and now I'm enjoying sunbathing again though I'm so hot I can hardly write! I've got terribly burnt in the last day or two of this heatwave – especially on my shoulders.

I've had to sleep in the nude without even a sheet over me because I couldn't bear any clothes to touch me. I <u>know</u> I should have taken more care.

I simply can't hold a pen any longer! I'll perhaps write a bit more after I go in – unless I spend ½ an hour or so in a cold bath as I did yesterday afternoon.

5th July

Oh how fed up I always feel after a few days at home! I'm longing to be married and not to have to think about catching trains any more! Never mind – a week on Thursday I shall be home for my special birthday! And then it will be just a year to the wedding! These two years have gone so quickly really. PTS seems very remote in 1950 and Grandma Bryan was alive then, and so was Grandpa Peet, and my two months in Paris seem like a dream.

I made an utter pig of myself with those chocolates on the train last night. I was all by myself in that little corner and it was lovely with nobody to disturb me! I ate nearly all the chocolates and read my book. It's lucky I'm only 8½ stones! Until it got dark I just sat and watched the countryside and thought about my time at home. The train was over ½ an hour late arriving in London, so it was nearly 11.45 when I arrived at Foley Street. Another late night!

I've just been on the phone to Eileen and Ivan and arranged to go to Buckhurst Hill tomorrow for my ½ day. I haven't been since the Christening and I feel I have a "duty" to carry out now that I have a Godson! They're all so sweet that I love going there.

The week after my 21st I'm going to <u>try</u> and change my off duty and come home for Mary's wedding. It's so sweet of you to pay my train fare as part of my 21st present.

11th July

It's so maddening that I haven't got my strings yet, but there seems to be some hope! Porter went to the office today to ask about them, and was told that several of us will get them next week. Elizabeth Jones got hers yesterday and she was signed up just before me. They might be Matron's 21st birthday present to me!! I've just been thinking that three years ago, exactly, I was doing Higher Certificate at school, and was about to go to Paris for 2 months!!

This week is going to be pretty hectic. We've got 4 people for Radium insertions, and they'll all have to go up to theatre every day for 5 days. And they're the sort of people who will need a lot of looking after, so I'll be quite busy.

One patient died yesterday morning. I'd bathed her, combed her hair, cleaned her mouth and everything about 8am and she hadn't uttered a sound except an occasional moan. We knew the end wasn't far off, and she died 2 hours later. She looked terribly thin and drawn, and could only speak in a whisper. It's so pitiful isn't it?

Another woman was 58 yesterday. The patients collected 8 shillings for her so I went out in the afternoon and got 6 roses and a big bunch of sweet peas from Shearns on Tottenham Court Road. It's a lovely shop. So her birthday cheered us all up a bit.

Sister went on holiday on Friday for a month. I've heard that she hates the ward, and that there was talk of her not coming back after her holiday. But I expect she will.

I'm having a ½ day morning today. It was lovely to have a lie-in. I didn't wake till after 9.30. Since then I've been thoroughly domesticated – making scrambled eggs and coffee and whatnot, washing up, arranging flowers. And now I'm contemplating going out for a breather. It's terribly windy outside but I can't bear to stay in my room all morning.

15th July

I've decided to come home on the 6.30 train from St. Pancras. It won't be such a rush and it's a much better train. Could you meet me at 8.<u>40</u> at the Midland Station? I'm afraid I haven't left myself much time for writing today. We've got our Gynae exam next Tuesday and we had to give in a written question today. Everyone always leaves these things to the last minute, including <u>me</u>!

No I'm not feeling fed up any more about the ward. I'm getting used to it as I normally do after a day or two. I thought I should never be able to remember everything, but it's surprising how things come to you somehow – when you settle down to the general routine of the ward. When Orme (my Head nurse) goes in three weeks' time I shall be the senior nurse on the <u>two</u> wards, Queen Mary and Whitbread. I can't get used to the idea at all!

Now I must go to tea and then back on duty. Only two of us on tonight and <u>oodles</u> to do!

20th July

This time next year, Ernest and I will have been married for 2 days!! Just to think of it!!

What a wonderful 21st birthday I had at home. 43 cards and lots of lovely presents, beautiful pale pink carnations from Ernest which he gives me every year because they're my favourite and I want to have them in my bouquet when we're married. Paddy has lent me a big glass vase – a sort of royal blue one – and they look simply heavenly in it. Everyone remarks on them when they come into my room. Thank you a million times. Ernest drew a picture of a little nurse holding a key for an extra birthday card. It's super – very clever! By the way, the little nurse is getting her strings tomorrow! After all this time of waiting for them – the very day I go away my name is down on the list to go to the office! Apparently it was down on Friday and Saturday and I wasn't there either day! So now I'll go <u>tomorrow</u> – at <u>last</u>!

It was wonderful to see so many friends on my birthday – the house lends itself to parties doesn't it – although I realise the main party is in September, I did so enjoy it. Pity I came home with a headache! What a lot of hard work went into the buffet preparations. Thank you again from the bottom of my heart.

And now we have to arrange a date for Ernest moving into our little honeymoon home. He starts work in the new parish on the Wednesday following his last Sunday (28th) at St. Margaret's. His ordination is October 1st so I think Monday 29th September will be the best. But it will certainly be hectic getting everything sorted out. We just desperately need to go and look at carpets.

The journey back to London on Saturday morning was frightful. The train was so crowded that I had to sit on my case in the corridor as far as Luton – the first stop. Now I must go and change and go back on duty. Time goes so fast. I'm sitting on the roof again and it's <u>very</u> warm.

23rd July

I had my gynae exam yesterday at 4.30. It was quite a decent paper actually, so we're all <u>hoping</u> we might get through! Now there are no more exams for me till next June, when I take State.

I'm afraid my good news about strings (and your congratulations) was a bit premature! Your estimation of me will have now dropped to NIL! Matron said she felt she couldn't give me my strings yet because my report from Charles Bell Ward was "not all she might have wished for". We had a little natter about it and she said she would get a report for me from Queen Mary this week and if it was good she would give me my strings next week. The Staff nurse has written her report in Sister's absence and she's told me it's good, so <u>maybe</u> I'll have better luck next week. I can't <u>tell</u> you how I felt when Matron said that I couldn't have my strings, especially as the bad remarks were so <u>odd</u>. She said that my work was hastily done sometimes – well how else <u>can</u> work be done when you're so frantically busy? And also she said that I wasn't always punctual in obeying instructions. I simply can't believe <u>that</u>! I always did everything as promptly as I could. Matron nattered on about knowing <u>herself</u> how trying it is to have about 5 people making demands at the same time, and then Sister coming along and asking you to do something else – she said she'd often been in that position herself and she just had to use her discretion and do everything in the way she thought best – as if I <u>didn't</u>! It seems just as well to me that I'm not making nursing a career. I seem to be an utter <u>flop</u> all of a sudden – what with Soho and then this. I thought at the time that I really should have to give up! But now I know that would be silly. People don't give in when things go wrong for them, and I'm jolly well going to finish this job whatever happens.

Please forgive these grumbles! I'm not really as fed up about it as you might imagine, if I get my strings next week everything will be alright. <u>Also</u> I have a sneaking feeling that the bad report might have been Sister Rees being a bit envious about my getting married soon, as she's just had her engagement broken off!

Yesterday was <u>very</u> hot. We were just <u>boiled</u> on the ward. Today started off very hot and sunny but now it looks as though we're in for a storm. I shall be coming home on Friday evening, returning on Saturday on the 8.50pm train. Looking forward to that.

I'm off now for the evening and day off tomorrow. Am just going out with Paddy to the flix or somewhere.

1st August
Joy of joys! – I'm getting my strings tomorrow morning at 10 o'clock. They rang up from the office to the ward to see if I'd be on duty then. So at <u>last</u> I'm going to get them. I wonder what Matron will have to say to me <u>this</u> time?!

Poor Paddy had a bad report from her last ward too, and had to go to Matron the other day. She failed her Medicine exam so that made it worse, and Matron said she was obviously not interested, that she was shirking responsibility and that she (Matron) didn't know why Paddy was there at all! Poor Paddy couldn't understand it because she <u>never</u> tries to shirk responsibility – and she's <u>most</u> conscientious. The trouble is that Matron doesn't give you a chance to stand up for yourself – she just natters on and on and leaves you feeling that you're almost mental!

That happened on Monday and we had the party in the evening for my 21st. Di – who keeps a party going – wasn't there as she had an unexpected day off – so it wasn't as mad as usual. But we had a good time – eating and drinking and laughing and looking at my cards and presents, but we all felt a bit tired I think so the party broke up about 11.30.

Last night Paddy and I went to the "Astoria" on Tottenham Court Road to see "Angels One Five". It was about the war – showing experiences at an RAF station – the way raids were organised and how men were lost. It was a wonderful film and very true to life I should think. We went about 5.30 and got back at 8.45 – we left before the end, but we didn't miss much because it was a silly cowboy thing at the end.

4th August
I have my strings at last!! I went to Matron on Saturday morning and she was very nice. She asked why it was that I had a bad report at Soho, then a good one on the Woolavington wing, then a bad one on Charlie B and now another good one. I told her I hadn't a clue and

that I thought it was most unfair to send in bad reports without my seeing them first. She actually listened to what I had to say. Then she said, "Well, Nurse, I think you will strive to do your best. Forget about the small thing of the past," etc. etc! I thought it was quite decent. So now I'm "strung"!

And they don't "'arf 'urt"! Someone says I'll have a double chin, and someone else says her friend had an abscess under her chin from them. Sounds pretty good!

Nina just got her 'strings'
3rd year at Middlesex Hospital, London
May 1952

Today I started Head nursing on Queen Mary. Staff nurse Orme has gone on holiday, and really I don't think it will be too bad after all. I only hope we get a few more nurses.

I had a very good day off on Friday. In the evening two of us queued for the Prom at the Albert Hall. We queued for about 50 minutes – fortunately it was a lovely evening – and then we sat on the floor of the Gallery for 2½ hours. It was something I'd been determined to do before I left London. It was mostly Beethoven, and though I'm not particularly thrilled with his music I thoroughly enjoyed it.

5th August

I have an afternoon off today and am <u>so</u> glad to get away from the ward. I'm <u>loving</u> head-nursing really, but it's been a bit chaotic today. We've had three new nurses and it's simply wonderful to have a full staff again, but a bit trying while they don't know where to find anything. The whole time this morning I had to be leaving what I was doing and chasing after them to show them this and that. One of them is straight from PTS so of course everything has to be explained to her. I feel so sorry for her – I can just imagine how <u>I</u> felt on my first day. The poor dear took about ¼ hour to clean a sink! However it's cruel to laugh at her. She <u>will</u> be jolly good eventually.

Sister comes back either the end of this week or the beginning of next. I do hope she'll be feeling happy! – and that I shall get on alright with her. I'm sure she'll take a poor view of me after having Orme as Head nurse. But then Orme said Sister never spoke to her at all for about 3 weeks!

Poor Elizabeth is off sick with a boil on her cheek. Her face is terribly swollen. Paddy has had a streaming cold and cough for a month so altogether we're doing well!

We all had an extra hour off duty for Bank Holiday yesterday. I was off from lunch till 5.30. So we made tea in Elizabeth's room – Mary, Paddy, Di, Elizabeth and me. It was wonderful. I thoroughly enjoyed it.

I must have a little snooze now. It's such a funny "heavy" thundery day and the burden of new pros hangs heavy on my shoulders!! It's quite wearing having to explain everything "just so", and having to explain so much and remember so many things. Still I'm <u>loving</u> it.

10th August

What a wonderful day at home, and I so enjoyed Patsy's 21st. I was back here well before 12 o 'clock so had time to unpack my things before lunch.

Several patients had gone home in my absence and we have new ones in their place. The staff situation is noticeably improved since we had the new nurses last week, and for the first time for ages we were off at 8 o'clock.

Our little gang then gathered for cups of tea and my prize chocolates from Patsy's party. I was in bed and asleep very soon after 10 o'clock – I was so tired.

Today I have a morning off – which is now nearly gone. It's cold and rainy again. 6 weeks today I start my holiday. I've been on Queen Mary 6 weeks tomorrow. We're not so busy now thank goodness, and if Sister is in a good humour when she returns on Thursday everything will be alright.

16th August

I've just realised that I shall be taking State just about the time of the Coronation!

The Polio here is quite a headache for the R.M.O. Poor man he looks worried to death. Two more girls have gone off from our ward – or rather Whitbread – but I haven't heard the verdict yet. Another case was confirmed yesterday – one of the new pros on her first ward, having been there a week – and another case today. Yesterday our staff – which had been made up to its full number – was down to the pro and myself.

Sister came back yesterday full of the joys of her holiday and in a very good mood. I think we shall get on quite well together. After our phone call, Priest and I went to the News Theatre together. It was quite good – the Royal Family in Scotland, and Prince Phillip yachting at Cowes etc.

18th August

What a hope – trying to have a lie-in here! At 6.30am doors started banging and these awful new pros yelling to each other across the corridor. Di told one of them what she thought of her last night and the girl was very peeved. So I got up about 8 o'clock – it was a waste of time trying to sleep. I had my eggs (boiled in the kettle!) and bread and marmalade. The milk had gone sour overnight! Eventually I went out shopping and bought two little "crown pottery" brooches for Pat Wood's and Margaret's 21st birthdays, and cards for them. I got back just in time for lunch and since then I've been chatting to Di, who also has a day off, and writing to you. About ½ way through this epistle the thunderstorm stopped and the sun blazed forth, so I went out on the roof for a breather. Of course I'd only been there for about 10 minutes when the sun disappeared!

Now I've had tea and read the newspapers in the library, and listened to the wireless a bit, and now I'm back in my room. I had a very good offer of a ticket to the prom tonight but refused it because it is Beethoven again and I didn't fancy spending all evening listening to him! Sorry, Daddy, but I'm not a Beethoven fan. If it had been Grieg I might have gone! If I had any money I'd adore to go to the ballet – I'm just in the mood for something like that. But I ain't got the money so I can't go! When I've finished this I'm going to do some ironing and then possibly some embroidery and then I might go and watch some television after supper.

I've seen Jones at tea – one of the epaulette nurses from our ward. She arrived on duty this morning to find she was alone! Reed with polio, me with day off, and the two pros off with temperatures. Poor girl! Apparently the night nurses had heard the pros had temps so they washed the patients and made most of the beds. Sister was very decent about it all too, I gather. I'd rather have her than our lazy staff nurse – she grumbles about her feet aching but she never does a thing to help. I get on well with her – I listen to her long tales of boyfriends etc. merely to keep in her good books! But I do not think much of her. She's Guys trained though, so what can you expect?! Of course I'm not biased!

I'm going to do my ironing now. 5 weeks on Sunday my holiday begins! Another thunderstorm just beginning! By the way I've changed my ideas for my bridesmaids' dresses. I want the same design but in floral taffeta now! Ernest has seen some carpets at £28 each, so he thinks he will buy them. The new curate at St. Margaret's has offered us a divan bed that he's getting rid of! We're slowly getting there with our furniture for Wellington Crescent!

Thank you for sending the invitation for me to Sheila Whittle's 21st. She's having it at Daybrook Lodge, "the scene of so many childhood frolics" she says! How well I remember everything there when the Girls High was moved there from the centre of Nottingham during the war. I remember we were told off for playing in the air raid shelters, and Shirley's first day at school when I mothered her so devotedly! I can see her now standing outside B2 on the verandah overlooking the garden, waiting for me to collect her! – a little darling in her enormous black school hat!!

Did I tell you that I might be going on night duty after my holiday? Several of my set are, Paddy and Di are too. Oh – also I've learnt to do the RASPA! Bish and I heard it on the wireless so Bish taught me! It's jolly D, wot?!

On Queen Mary now they've got 8 patients dying. Gant says she was so miserable that she cried in the sluice. They're so busy and she doesn't get on well with Sister. The staff nurse was at lunch with me today, and when I asked about the ward she said, "Oh don't talk about it." So it must be pretty awful. 4 people are having Morphia 4-hourly, and 2 are on continuous oxygen.

At this moment I <u>know</u> what I must do next! I really must go and do my ironing, or some of it anyway.

20th August

I've absolutely no news for you except to say that I shall always remember Queen Mary Ward – sometimes a nightmare and sometimes enjoyable. But most of all I've never had such an adorable Sister as Sister Skeets – and when I leave Q.M. I shall really be sad to leave <u>her</u>! Have you ever heard me say <u>that</u> before?! But really we have got on famously and it makes such a difference. At times when we've been so drastically short of nurses we even had a Red Cross Nurse. All VAD nurses have to do 60 hours in hospital for experience. This one is about 65 I should think and she came onto the ward in her bedroom slippers!!

Yesterday, my dears, I dropped a tin of lead shot all over the ward floor. Sister thought it was a great joke.

24th August

I have another ½ day morning today, and though it's only 10.30 I'm sitting in a bathing costume on the roof in the sunshine. Likewise did I yesterday afternoon for an hour and a half. I didn't go to Communion this morning, but there was, as usual, such a din that I got up about 8.30 and went down to breakfast at 9 o'clock. It really is heavenly relaxing here – the gardeners have made the roof garden so beautiful with flowers and plants and trellis work that it's lovely to be able to enjoy it.

I hope I shall be home for some of the Coronation celebrations, though I suppose it's rather unlikely that I shall be, as we take State about that time. Goodness! – to think that I shall be coming home for good soon after that! You know I'm sure I shall feel a bit homesick too when we're first married, even after 3 years in London. It will seem so odd to be so near home and yet not living there! I suppose everybody feels like that at first.

Holiday 3 weeks on Saturday. Di and Elizabeth are having their party on the 20th – the day our holiday starts, and I have accepted, but Ernest now says he's planned something for us that weekend. He is arranging to come up to London on the Saturday and may be staying a night with Joy and Edgar and family. Paddy will have flown home to Cyprus that day so she won't be there.

Anyway we'll be home on Monday or Tuesday because there'll be so much to plan for <u>my</u> proper 21st party, and getting the new little house ready for Ernest to move in.

26th August

I really must do something about my party invitations. They really ought to be sent out at the end of this month. I'll have to make out another list – I've lost the original one I made.

I'm having a jolly nice day off. It's Mary's 21st today and the others took her breakfast to her in bed, but I didn't get up as it is my day off.

Last night I took my evening dress to bits. I couldn't wear it as it is for Mary's party. So the others have been sticking pins in me and giving me their brilliant suggestions. Don't have a fit – but I've cut the top off completely, at the waist. And I've cut off the top layer of net. I've CUT UP MY MAROON TAFFETA SKIRT, and am making a top to my evening dress out of that!! It really is beginning to look <u>smashing</u>. I was so fed up because all the others of our gang have got new evening dresses and I simply couldn't afford one. So I was determined not to be odd one out, and I consider my dress will look pretty stunning! It's strapless, and the top is gathered at the front, with a wide sash going round and hanging down like a bustle at the back – with black mittens, and pink net stole out of the top layer of the dress. Paddy and Di both have new <u>black</u> dresses, Elizabeth and Bish have yellow, and Mary white. So how do you think pink and maroon will compare?

There are to be 22 of us altogether. We start with a meal – Colin Schwerdt (Queen Mary Houseman) is sitting one side of me, and John Farrell (the houseman from Campbell Thomson) on the other side. Mary is sitting on the other side of Farrell and Mrs. Barnett on the other side of Colin. I feel so excited about it. For Heaven's sake don't mention Colin in Ernest's presence if you talk about this party when I come home. It's only a bit of fun, but I know Ernest wouldn't be very pleased. But I have no conscience about it at all – dash it all I want to enjoy myself as well as the others. I don't come off duty till 8 o'clock, so I'll have to get a move on!

Last night we had a coffee and "weed" gathering until 10ish, and I couldn't sleep afterwards. Serve me right for smoking! At 12.30 I sat up in bed and read magazines. My heart was palpitating and I was in quite a frenzy from not being able to sleep, but reading mags calmed me down. Bish was awake too, she says, but she's used to it because she sleeps terribly badly. I felt quite ill – I thought I would miss the party, and that made it worse!

This morning I woke early but didn't get up till 10 o'clock. Then Mary Priest had one of my two remaining eggs, and I had the other, and we had bread and marmalade and tea in her room. Then Bish appeared and we went shopping and then it was lunchtime. This afternoon I've been in Priest's room all the time, listening to the wireless, and doing my dress. After this letter I <u>must</u> get down to sewing again. Paddy is going to help me or I won't ever get it finished. We're having a taxi at 9.15 from here, unless Colin or Derek Sayers offer to take me.

It was lovely to have a phone call from you the other night, Sorry I wasn't very "newsy", but there wasn't much to tell.

We're closing down for cleaning on the ward. Queen Mary was down from 22 to 14 patients yesterday, and now they've put Whitbread into Queen Mary, while Whitbread is cleaned. Then we're discharging a few more patients, and the rest of us going into Whitbread while Queen Mary is cleaned. Then we're discharging a few more patients. Then all the other Radium Wing wards move down one by one until the whole wing has been done. By then I'll be on holiday though. <u>Must</u> get on with my dress!

29th August

Thank goodness it's only 3 weeks till my holiday. I certainly couldn't stand much more of Queen Mary as it is at present. Isn't it strange how things change so quickly? Only the other day I was saying how much I loved the ward. But since they moved Whitbread patients into Queen Mary I just don't seem to be able to settle down. And the nurses! Well my goodness – I've never seen such an awful lot in my life. The two good ones are off sick, and Super of course went off with Polio several weeks ago. So I'm left with 3 pros who nearly drive me to drink! One of them is fairly reliable, but the other two I wish I could chop their silly heads off! There's nobody senior at all except me – nobody you can really rely on to do the work properly. The Staff Nurse has gone on night duty, and the acting Staff Nurse is off sick, so Sister has had no off duty for two days. Mrs. Jones is at death's door – we didn't expect her to live through the night. So altogether it's HELL – excuse my French (!) but I've never felt so bad-tempered and cross for months. And today I came off ½ an hour late to lunch, and when I got over here the lunch had all been cleared away and I had to wait for ages to get some. Honestly it doesn't pay to help other people, I sometimes think. They just get as much out of you as they possibly can. Oh – !!

I'm so looking forward to coming home on Tuesday. I wish Mummy hadn't got all those engagements. I just shan't see her. But I'm blowed if I'm going to come back on Wednesday evening – I shall insist on having my ½ day on Thursday morning. I've done far too much giving in to other people and changing my off duty for their

199

convenience. Somebody can jolly well suit <u>my</u> convenience for a change! Sorry – sorry – sorry! But that's how I feel!!

I haven't told you about Mary's party! It was <u>wonderful.</u> I came off duty just after 8pm and dashed upstairs to change and was ready in good time. We left at 9.15 – walked through the hospital and down to Oxford Street for a taxi and got to the Grosvenor Hotel (no less!) in very good time.

We started with drinks and crisps and nuts etc. and then when everyone had arrived we went and had a meal. The band was playing all the time. We had it in the restaurant so there were other people dotted about at little tables, who didn't belong to us. We had fresh salmon, then a "fish dish" like at Patsy's 21st, then chicken and all that goes with it, and then ice cream and trifle, then birthday cake and coffee. Then we danced till 1.30am, and got away about 1.45am. It was great fun – the males ordered two taxis and we split up to go back to the hospital. Then we went out into the courtyard for a bit and sat dabbling our hands in the fountain, and then the males took us in through the Medical school and pushed us on trolleys along the underground passage to the Nurses' Home!! Then they departed and we sat and talked for ages in Di's room, and got to bed at 3.30!! It was marvellous – except that we weren't half tired yesterday! Last night I was in bed just after 10.30 and never heard a thing till 6.45 – not even the hooter! Now this afternoon I thought of going out shopping – being "rich" again after pay day. But the weather is so nice that I've come on the roof in my bathing costume to gather up energy for this evening! It will be 9 o'clock when I get home on Tuesday and Ernest will meet me. I've almost forgotten what it's like to come home after all this time.

For goodness sake <u>don't worry</u> about my smoking! I don't smoke much – only on special occasions you know. I quite agree it's a bad habit and I promise I won't cultivate it! Thanks for the invitation list – I'm so glad you had it and I hadn't lost it after all.

Well, chin chin, cheerio for the moment! I'll be seeing you on Tuesday.

31st August

Sorry about last night. Hope you didn't mind me ringing you up to have a grumble! I felt much better after I'd talked to you though, and now that I've had a nice sleep and am off duty this morning, I'm better still. So everything is OK. I just feel ready for a holiday though! I can't see much hope of any improvement in ward conditions before my holiday. Roll on Tuesday evening! I do want you to know that I'm still SANE (on the whole!)

7th September

Thank you for my lovely day at home. It's terribly cold and miserable here – yesterday and today have been quite like winter. I've been perished!

I've got to change wards tomorrow! We are now overstaffed on Queen Mary as the two wards are together during cleaning. And so the two of us who have been there the longest have got to go. I've been told I'll go either to theatre or E.N.T. I expect I'll go back after my holiday to wherever I go tomorrow. So at least I shan't come back from my holiday to fear and trembling – I shall have been "broken in" on my new ward. I shall be sorry to leave Queen Mary though. Sister has been so sweet and I've been really happy there on the whole.

One of the patients gave me 10 shillings yesterday! She came in for an abdominal paracentesis (tapping fluid from the tum!) and Colin Schwerdt did it for her and I helped him. He's simply marvellous – I've never seen anyone do a thing so quickly and well. Anyway later she asked if it was I who had helped the doctor, and when I said "Yes" she pressed a 10/- note into my hand!!

I'm wondering when my day off will be this week. I don't think I'll be able to go to Bridget Boyle's wedding after all, because a new Sister won't be inclined to give me what off duty I want 2 weeks running. And I'm keeping my fingers crossed that I can have my day off and half day tagged on to my holiday. Sister Skeets said I could, so I'll be so fed up if our plans go wrong. Oh ROLL ON MY HOLIDAY. I do want to get away from moans and groans for a bit. Nursing is all very well and interesting and I enjoy it, but I get a bit fed up with only seeing ill people. It's psychologically (!) depressing! When I'm here at the hospital I live in a world of illness, and I sometimes think that everyone must have something wrong with them. I forget about all those people who have never been ill in their life. Well I must be away now. I'll be seeing you soon.

10th September
I've been thinking about my big party and what oodles of preparations there are! At the moment I haven't very much idea of what we're going to do!! If we have that little band we shall be able to dance, but there'll have to be an alternative for people won't there, because we could never have everyone dancing at the same time – there wouldn't be room. And so much is going to depend on the weather. At the moment it doesn't look very promising. Perhaps the sunshine is being specially stored up for us!

That Farnborough tragedy was shocking wasn't it? On Sunday morning we read in the paper that one of those killed was a <u>Mr. Sayers</u> of no fixed address, and we got all hot and bothered because we knew our houseman – Derek Sayers – had gone to the Air Show. But it wasn't him thank goodness.

Thank you for ringing me up last night, Mum – it was a lovely surprise. I'm sorry for the shock you had over Matron's letter. I've felt quite an idiot being in Sick Bay, because the worst came before I came here, I think. But on Saturday I really did feel rotten all day and thought I must just be tired. I struggled through writing the report in the evening then flew to the loo and was terribly sick. The Staff nurse let me go off duty at 20 to 8, and I had a hot bath, hot drink, and took a hot water bottle to bed with me, and was in bed by quarter to 9. I was quite sure I could cure myself, but I didn't! I felt just as bad in the morning, and they kept telling me to go to Sick Bay, but we were so short of staff (being Sunday) that I stuck it till teatime. I'd been off duty and in bed in the afternoon and felt a bit better afterwards – I did have a temperature though, so maybe it's just as well I came here and I have terrible backache too.

Yesterday I was up for most of the day and was lucky enough to get an appointment for a perm – a free one – at Callinans in the afternoon. So I spent the afternoon there and it perked me up having my hair done. This morning Dr. Acheson has just been in to see me, and says I can go back on duty at quarter to one. So now I have to go to the office to find out <u>where</u> I am to go. I've now heard its E.N.T.

Two of us have had fun looking through our charts on Sick Bay this morning! The blood man came on Monday and took some of my blood for a blood count and I'm glad to say that I'm quite normal! I've got 6.100 white blood cells per cubic c.c. of blood, and the normal count is between 5.000 and 10.000. I've got 16 Basophils per. cu.cc. but am a bit upset because I should have 1 Eosinophil per cu.cc. and I haven't got <u>any</u>!! Can't think where it's gone to! I'm most worried! The anti-infection cells (lymphocytes) are very well represented! I've got more than the Staff Nurse on Sick Bay and more than the girl next door to me! So you see my resistance is HIGH! I also read what the R.M.O. thought of me when I came for my Medical before I started nursing, and I'm greatly impressed! He said I was "healthy looking"! Something must have happened since then! And my haemoglobin was 91%, so I shan't be needing a blood transfusion yet!

Well – now that you know all about me and my contents, I must get up and think about doing some work. It's been nice having breakfast in bed for 3 mornings – I could have stayed here longer had I said I still had backache or something!

I might still get a day off this week. If you go back on or before Wednesday they're supposed to give you a day off, so here's hoping it will be Saturday so that I can go to Bridget's wedding. How lovely to be going back on duty knowing that in 10 days' time I shall be on holiday. YIPPEE!

But I'm sorry there's been so much about illness! It sounds as though I'm dying, the way I've moaned about being off sick. I did try <u>not</u> to go off sick!

14th September
I was full of good intentions for getting this letter written to you today – I've come down to the library and simply haven't written a letter at all! I've been watching television for ½ an hour – it's a sort of newsreel of the events of the week, and very interesting.

I was very thrilled to hear about the party arrangements. I'm sure it will all be great fun. I never expected the Slacks to come. I rang them up this afternoon, and Joy said she'd be ringing you to talk about staying for the weekend.

I've had an extremely lazy day off really. It's amazing how one can do nothing quite happily! And appalling how one takes such a delight in pleasing oneself! For instance – yesterday I simply revelled in squeezing three oranges and drinking the orange juice with lots of sugar! And today I've been eating apples one after the other, and even went so far as scrambling all three eggs that you gave me, and eating them! Have you ever heard of anything so disgusting?

Last night Paddy, Mary Priest and I went walking round Piccadilly and Leicester Square and Bond Street – looking at people and shops, and getting quite a "kick" out of it all! We got back about 8.30 and then I spent ages waiting for the phone to be free so that I could ring you up. I was a good girl and went to bed before 10 o'clock. Then this morning I went down to breakfast at 9 o'clock. When I got back to my room there was a note under my door from Bish saying she was off duty and would I go round and see her. I went, and found her and Mary Priest drinking coffee and eating apples, so I joined them and stayed for quite some time chatting. After lunch I did an enormous amount of washing – two cotton frocks, blouses, jumpers, cardigans, and goodness knows what not. I hate packing dirty things, and I didn't think we'd want to be bothered with all my washing at home. Now I've got to do the ironing! I also cleaned (with my special stuff) my grey suede shoes so they're clean too. Thank goodness I shall have the car to dump my things in, as Ernest is coming to fetch me. Then there's a primula plant which is still alive and I want to make it flower again, so I <u>must</u> bring that. I'm so excited about coming home for a <u>month</u> – you'll never imagine how much I'm looking forward to it. And especially as I shall actually be able to go to a Harvest Festival for the first time in three years!

Monday

I have an evening off today and am about to launch on my ironing. I had a present of chocolates today from a Queen Mary patient. I thought it was very sweet of her to remember me. I'm loving every moment of Strathcona – the E.N.T. ward – it's simply lovely up there, and the men are such fun.

I didn't tell you that I went to chapel with the gang last night. I'd really wanted to go to church but couldn't find anyone else who was off. Then after chapel we sat and drank tea in Di's room. Di is going on night duty in October. She's the only one of our gang not going on holiday.

14th September
Ernest has started his holiday, and was saying what a lot there is to think about when handing over to someone else as he's leaving his first curacy. I'm nearly always late going off duty because I'm so anxious to tell the other nurses everything before I go! I'm sure they would manage perfectly well if I didn't, but I just like to be certain for my own satisfaction.

Yes I do love Strathcona, the patients are great and the work is very interesting. It's such a treat to be able to take time over treatment, after racing against time as I had to on Queen Mary and Charlie B.

15th September
I went out a few days ago to buy material for our dining room curtains – so exciting! Ernest has sent me £5. It was 6 shillings and eleven pence a yard, which made it £2-15-4 altogether for 8 yards. I'm quite nervous about whether Ernest will like it, but if not we could use it for a bedroom perhaps.

Oh it's so nice to be on Strathcona as I said. Thank goodness I'm not on the women's side – I had enough with nearly 3 months of females on Queen Mary! And for a change I'm on a fairly slack ward. There's very little to do, and I keep going round thinking I must have forgotten something! It's such a treat after being so hectic on every ward up till now. I expect I shall go back there after my holiday. It's a "special" ward, so it's only a 6 weeks ward instead of the usual 3 months. There is a possibility of our going on night duty after the holiday, and it is lovely and quiet there on night duty apparently.

Anyway the main thing is I have been given my ½ day and day off as I'd wanted it, attached to my holiday, so all is well for next weekend. I have a ½ day tomorrow and day off on Sunday too! I didn't know if I'd have it after being in Sick Bay. I was supposed to be going to Bridget Boyle's wedding tomorrow, but I can't as it's 11am and I'm not off till 2 o'clock. However I'm jolly lucky to be off at the weekend, and then – HOLIDAY! Next time I have a holiday it will be my wedding and forever! No going back to work. Paddy is going home to Cyprus for her holiday.

I've had a perm and my hair is shorter. I know Ernest doesn't like short hair, but it will grow!

The Gynae results are out. I haven't been down to look at them yet. Elizabeth has just been to tell me the list is up.

My day off yesterday was quite uneventful. I had so many jobs to do in preparation for my holiday. Thank goodness I shall have the car to dump things in! I <u>hate</u> <u>packing</u> – it's the worst part of the holiday! I must go to bed early tonight.

19th September
Ernest tells me that Miss Briggs has given us a big fat cheque for a wedding present, so we're going to buy a bed with it! I don't know her, but she must think a lot of Ernest, to be so generous! And Ernest's mother says she will buy the rest of the bedroom furniture! That's <u>very</u> <u>very</u> generous. It will be a terrific expense for her. Ernest and his mum have tried out the new Gas cooker, and his mum and her sister-in-law have been doing a lot of cleaning. I wish I could be there to help! The parish have been very helpful in paying for the decorating, so it's getting very exciting!

I did most of my ironing yesterday so now I must start on the packing! What a loathsome job! But it's HOLIDAY!

I went to the office this morning to get my holiday pass, and was told I'm definitely going on night duty when I return from holiday. I have to come back on Sunday 19th October for day duty on Monday morning, and night duty on Monday night. Sister Smith said that as I had done only 4 weeks on the Woolavington wing I shall probably go back there on night duty. It looks as though I'll be on night duty for Christmas for the 3rd year running. Paddy and Bish and Di will all be on night duty with me, but I don't know about Mary or Elizabeth.

I had a sweet letter from little Mrs. Wilkinson yesterday. She says she's convinced I have "one of the best" for my future husband. She says, "He's GRAND and a very good preacher too. I shall miss him very much when he goes to West Bridgford – especially his <u>smile</u> – he ALWAYS has a smile for <u>everyone</u>."

I'm furious because they haven't brought my trunk up yet, and I must have it this afternoon unless I'm to be up till midnight tonight. I <u>must</u> get some sleep tonight, as Ernest is picking me up tomorrow to go and stay with Joy and Edgar for the weekend. I come off duty at 2pm and need to have everything ready to load up the car when Ernest arrives. It's possible that they will send me to late lunch at 12.45 and not go back to the ward. Fingers crossed!

CAN'T WAIT!!

19th October
Oh dear! I didn't want to leave you all! Thank goodness these are the last 8 months! I'm afraid the excitement of being married is taking precedence to everything now! Now that Ernest has moved into our lovely little house with his mother it all seems much nearer! I hope Mrs. Sheeran can find all the things she needs after I've put them all away in my own special places. I wonder if she could sleep in her new surroundings in our lovely "honeymoon home"! It's pouring with rain today, so quite gloomy.

My train was on time – I intended to do some embroidery and some reading, but I lapsed into a state of semi-consciousness dreaming about the future and the lovely time I'd had on holiday. Before I knew it we were in London. I got a porter and a taxi and was at York House before 9pm. I had to wait ages for Sister to appear and give me the keys to my room, but eventually she came, and I unpacked a few things and had something to eat, and got to bed just after 11pm.

This morning I woke early but didn't get up till 9.45! Then I had a bath and something to eat, and spent the rest of the morning trying to make up my diary. I came up to Foley Street at 1 o'clock for lunch, and saw Mary Priest so now I'm in her room writing this.

We've had a long chat and cups of tea. Paddy is coming back late tonight from Cyprus, and Bish will be back sometime today.

I'm sharing a room with Bish again at present – there aren't any spare single rooms until November. But once we've settled in this room I don't suppose we'll want to move to single rooms. It's rather a nice room anyway with a bathroom attached. As I arrived first I've got the bed I want!

I've still lots to do before tomorrow, so I don't think I shall go to church after all, especially as it's pouring with rain. I'm going to have tea here at Foley St. and then go back to York House. I'm not looking forward to working again!! But I still think it's the right thing to finish my training even though Ernest is having to be patient and wait. We are happier than we ever dreamed of and I'm sure our marriage will be wonderful. My happiness and peace of mind are indescribable.

Now I must go down for tea with Priest and then go and post this. When I next write it will probably be in the "peace" of Night Duty!

20th October

What a rum life this is! I'm not on Night Duty after all! – yet anyway! All those who came back yesterday, expecting to be on Night Duty, are on Day Duty pro/tem. I've gone back to ENT but am on the women's side, worse luck! Women always look so miserable in bed! So we're all completely confused – I think the office must be going crazy!

I haven't seen Paddy yet, but as far as I know she came back late last night. And I haven't seen Bish at all during the day, to see what sort of a day she's had. Elizabeth Jones has come back feeling very miserable – she's been in bed with tonsillitis for 10 days. Mary will be back tonight, as she was expecting to be on Day Duty, and Di is on Night Duty.

I'm off duty this evening, and I've been writing up the diary of my 21st party and of my holiday. Do you know I'm very pleased with myself because I've remembered what I did on every single day of the 4 weeks! I started on the first week which was easy, and then worked back from the end!

After I'd written to you yesterday, and had tea, I came back to York House to my room. Everywhere was so deadly and quiet and horrible – I felt as if I was in a padded cell or something! And there was absolutely nobody to talk to and I was so lonely and miserable! In the end, as you know, I telephoned you about 8.45 but you were both out for supper. Shirley answered and greeted me with, "You would ring up in the middle of a play!" So that cheered me up no end!!

However when I went back to my room Bish was back, so things livened up. She was a scream telling me all about her stay in the 5 star hotel in Bournemouth, and how she was waited on hand and foot. And of <u>course</u> I told her all about the house and how wonderful it is. We unpacked our things and talked for ages after we got to bed. It was frightful, I might say, having to get up at 6.30 this morning after my holiday! And we had to go up to Foley St. for our meals.

Oh well, it's nearly 8 o'clock now, and I shall have to wend my way back to Foley Street for supper. It is a bit of a fag really, but still it's nice to be still on Day Duty. If only I knew for how long!

21st October
I'm off this morning and we're just off to do lots of "jobs". Mary and Bish are off too. Paddy's plane was 24 hours late last night. Must fly as I'm keeping the others waiting, but just wanted to finish the letter.

23rd October
It's almost a week since I came back! This is such a different life here in London – an entirely different sort of world and existence.

Goodness only knows when I shall be going on night duty. It seems it won't be for another week or two yet. Elizabeth Jones and Christine Jones and Barbara Evans have been warned for Nov. 3rd. So it looks as though we're going to have to wait till after that.

There's a lady on Berners Ward at the moment who has been here for 9 months now. She's had an op. which entails the removal of everything round her throat, except for her tongue. She can't speak <u>of course</u>, so she has to write everything down. Her husband is an extremely nice man, and it struck me the other day that it must be simply frightful for him never to be able to hear his wife's voice. At one time he must have been thrilled to hear her speak to him, and now he knows it will never be possible again.

I'm having a quiet day off. I've decided not to go to see my Godson. I got up late this morning – Bish was very considerate and didn't have the light on at 6.30. She got dressed in the bathroom. I had some breakfast here in my room, and then I had a general re-arranging of flowers and so on, and did some washing. I went up to Foley St. for lunch, and now I'm going out to shop window gaze.

I've got to get a train ticket for Bish, and do something for Langley as well.

This evening Bish and I are going to the theatre. It's only 3/6 in the "Gods", so it won't be too expensive. Then I'm going to bed early! The theatre starts at 5.30, so we shall be out by 8 or soon after, and Bish is going home for her day off afterwards. I think we shall go to "London laughs".

25th October

I was so pleased to find letters for me when I came down to York House off duty at 2pm.

Ernest has entertained his first visitors to 7, Wellington Crescent – George Cowley and his wife stayed one night on their way to the Alamein Reunion. He prepared a meal from what we had in the cupboard, and gave them a bed for the night, then prepared breakfast! Clever man! I'm proud of him!

We couldn't get in to the Adelphi Theatre on Thursday night for "London laughs" after all. I was disappointed to miss Jimmy Edwards, but instead Bish and I went to the Tivoli cinema exactly opposite the Adelphi in the Strand, and saw Merle Oberon and Richard Todd in "24 Hours in a Woman's Life". It was a very good film, with lots of Mediterranean scenery, and views of Monte Carlo. Bish loved it especially because she's been to Monte Carlo. The story was good too, of a loving woman, widowed in a car accident, who was staying with friends on a houseboat on the Mediterranean sea. They took her to see the Casino while she was there and she watched a young man lose his last franc gambling. And so the story went on – showing how he was grateful for her help and vowed never to gamble again. They went away together and were blissfully happy spending an afternoon in the country. Then she left him to go back to Paris alone, and instead she found him later gambling again in the Casino. It was just the sort of story that appealed to me. There was another film with it about Alaska, which was most interesting. Bish left before the end of the Alaska film to catch her train home, but I stayed to the end, and then came back to York House and had something to eat in my room.

Do you know I've got a half day today. I went up to Foley St. for tea after lazing about this afternoon, reading magazines. Then this evening I went for a <u>long</u> walk through Regents Park for an hour and a half, and landed up on Bakers Street, and had to find my way back past Madame Tussauds. I wished I could get a bus eventually, but I hadn't taken any money with me except for the theatre. It was lovely and fresh in Regents Park. Tomorrow I'm off at 4.30 for another day off on Monday! Then I have to wait for ages for the next one – till a week on Thursday. But at this stage of the proceedings I seem to be doing precious little work!

Well it's nearly supper time again. Tonight we have an extra hour in bed with the time change. I expect I shall go to church with Bish tomorrow night.

28th October
I had an evening off on Sunday and Bish and I went to Evensong at St. Martin in the Fields. I was imagining Ernest preaching his first sermon at St. Giles – very scary in the new church. In the hymn before the sermon at St. Martins I imagined how Ernest would be preparing to go up into the pulpit, and I felt a nervous feeling inside me! I was perfectly confident that his sermon would be good but I know what an ordeal it is for him.

Then I had a good day off yesterday. I woke early – when Bish got up at 6.30 – and couldn't go to sleep again, so I sat up in bed drawing and listening to the wireless. Eventually I got up about 9.45 and made myself some breakfast. Then I had a "domestic morning"! – arranging flowers, and washing and so on. I love pretending I'm doing housework in our house! Then I went up to Foley St. for lunch, and left York House about 2.30 to go to Starkes in Buckhurst Hill, to see my Godson. I arrived about 3.15pm and thoroughly enjoyed myself. Eileen and I had lots to talk about of course! They've had their house painted a very arty colour outside – pink tinted walls with French grey and yellowy cream woodwork. It looks very attractive. They've also altered the inside and now have a dining room and lounge instead of just one sitting room. It all looks charming. I told them all about our house and about my 21st and so on.

My Godson is a <u>terror</u>! He's 16 months and positively into everything!! Eileen polished the floor yesterday morning and then he tipped a flower vase over, and the water went all over the floor. He throws his food all over the new carpet, and pulls his parents to bits! He tugged at Ivan's ear so hard the other day that it bled! I don't think Eileen ate a thing at tea-time, trying to keep Jonathan still! She said, "It's fun, Nina, but doesn't this put you off?!!" We just hooted with laughter at the thought of a 16-month-old son torturing two grown people like that! They're quite at his mercy! I stayed with them till just after 10pm.

I've been talking to Bish about exchanging stamps. Her uncle has been a stamp collector for some time and has a pretty good idea of values. She's going to ask him if he'd look at my collections and give me an idea as to how to exchange them properly.

I can't decide when to come home again. My day off is Monday every week on Berners, with ½ day Sunday one week and evening Sunday the following week.

Well now I must be going up to Foley Street again for supper. And tonight I must go to bed early, as I was late getting back last night, and <u>then</u> had a sudden nose bleed. I thought I'd have to have my tonsils out the other day too – I suppose it's only natural, being on ENT!!

Did I tell you I've been nominated with about 5 others for the new council they're setting up here? I don't know when we hear if we're elected. I'll tell them a thing or two!

30th October
Thank you for speaking to the Bishop about marrying Ernest and me. I hope the Archdeacon won't be upset. I think Ernest favoured having him! They're such good friends. I've a feeling he put it in his diary when Ernest mentioned it!

By the way, since I came back from holiday they've instituted a stupid new idea! Nurses can't be called from their rooms for the phone. If they are expecting a call they must be waiting in the hall for it, otherwise a message will have to be taken. It is quite crazy, and we're all <u>livid</u>! Surely the purpose of telephones is for contacting people in a hurry when you can't send a message by letter.

Incidentally they now lock the nurses' home door at 10.45pm <u>and</u> the one into the home from the underground passage. So now we can't get in through the hospital up till midnight. We have to be in by 10.45. Really! – We're being treated like school children, and yet on the ward we're expected to undertake such a lot of responsibility. We're all fuming, and Bish and Mary and Paddy are all determined now to leave after 3 years.

The new council is a hospital council, consisting of representatives of each year of nurses. So far two have been nominated for 1st year, one for 2nd, and 3 for 3rd year. We have to put all our grumbles and grievances to Matron and the Board. So I hope I don't get elected. I don't know any more than that.

Oh how time flies – having been out to cash my cheque this afternoon and send a telegram for a patient, and to Cooks about trains etc. there's no time at all. And now I must go up to Foley Street for tea and back on duty. There's <u>nothing</u> to do on the ward though – yesterday I read magazines from about 6pm onwards!

5th November
Thank you for another brief spell at home. I had a good journey back yesterday. It seemed strange to be eating breakfast at home and on the ward at 1.30pm!

Do you remember that poor little man on the station platform saying goodbye to his rather fat girlfriend – she was weeping on his shoulder? Well he was in the same compartment as me. He looked so miserable, poor soul, and took out his writing pad and wrote a letter almost as soon as he'd sat down. I suppose he was writing to the girl and telling her how lonely he was.

I also felt desperately lonely when I got back, and very homesick. But I soon settle down again once I'm on the ward. Sorry – no time for more.

7th November
I was thinking only this morning – if I go on night duty after Christmas, as now seems to be the idea, it will be April when I finish, and then there will be only just over a month till I leave. That gave me quite a shock!

I had a most awful dream last night about the wedding! Everything went wrong! The wedding had to be brought forward quite suddenly, and nothing was ready! The dog turned up in some sort of red garment with white spots! Mummy darling was being particularly aggravating (which you rarely are!). For instance you insisted that I wore my nurse's cap on top of my veil! I was livid! I called you all the names under the sun! Then the wedding started, and then I woke up and it was 6.45!!

We had good fun on Wednesday. We went down to Piccadilly after duty and saw quite a lot of lorry loads of students – yelling and throwing fireworks – rather dangerous though. I wish we had gone to Trafalgar Square because apparently they had lots of fireworks there. We had one or two thrown at us, which went off "right under our tails" as it were. And we saw lots of folks dressed up and having fun. Well – next year Ernest and I will have our own firework night and have lots of fun!

I dropped my watch this morning on the ward and it has stopped. That's the first time it has stopped since you gave it to me in the 6th form at school! I must take it to be mended because I'm lost without it.

I've had some wedding cake from Bridget Boyle (now Henderson!) who was married in September. You remember we worked together on nights on the Private wing, and made good friends because we were both getting married. I was so disappointed that I couldn't go to her wedding. So I've written to her to see if I can go and see her on my day off. She sent me a postcard from her honeymoon. It would be fun to see her and Ian again.

8th November
Bish and Mary have gone to the News Theatre tonight, after duty, to see the State opening of Parliament, but I preferred to stay here. So I've had my bath and am now snug in bed writing this.

I'm a bit worried because Ernest is so miserable that I'm back here nursing. I feel it's all my fault because I'm putting my career before him. But I couldn't stop nursing. I really must go on to the end, having got this far. And no! I haven't found life in London too attractive to leave, even though I have an interesting time. But I know that after 18th July 1953 another sun will shine in my world!

11th November

I'm so sorry that you have had a temperature of 100 and tummy pains, my darling Mummy. I can hardly believe you actually stayed in bed for two days, knowing you! I do hope you will soon be back to normal. I'm sure you really missed the Armistice service on Sunday, with lunch at the college afterwards.

I've just heard that I'm changing wards next Monday. I'm possibly going to theatre. Night duty on 29th December so I'll have Christmas on Day duty.

I've been out with Paddy, Christmas shopping this morning. On Sunday we went to St. Martin in the Fields to Evensong, and stayed afterwards to hear Mozart's Requiem – a recital by orchestra and choir in the church. It was very good.

Must fly up to Foley St. for lunch now, and back on duty.

13th November

I don't know yet when my day off will be on theatre, but I want to come home the week after next if I can. I'll let you know as soon as possible. I shall be on theatre for Christmas, and, as far as I know, theatre closes on Christmas Day. Maybe I shall have the day off and come home, or maybe we shall have to go on the wards for the day. I go on Night duty on Monday 29th December, so I shall be on nights for New Year's Eve.

One of the children on Berners ward said to me the other day, "Do you wish you were me, Nurse? My mummy is going to give me a chicken when I go home." So I said: "I've already got a chicken myself because we keep hens." To which she asked: "Is it a real live chicken?" So I replied: Oh yes – very much a real one!" She then wanted to know if I had to feed it! – So sweet!

I was very touched this morning. I went to say goodbye to one of the patients before I went off duty as she was going home. And she said in a whisper, taking hold of my hand, "Do you know, Nurse, you're the sweetest girl I've ever known!" I was so thrilled. I always am when people say things that that, because one never knows how people think of you.

I loved Hilda Young's remark about "all the other Sheerans who will be coming along"! I <u>long</u> to have children of my own. I used to envy one of our patients so much, who is having a baby at the end of the month and who has now gone down to the Maternity ward. She talked so much about "Jane Elizabeth", wondering what she would be like, and so on. It must be thrilling for a husband and wife seeing, or waiting to see their very own baby.

15th November
We've all had our ½ days stopped this weekend. I should be off at 2pm tomorrow, and can't be till 4.30. Isn't it annoying? The staff situation is frightful.

<u>Sunday</u>
It's now 5 o'clock and I've just come to York House off duty. Having had our ½ days cancelled I have a long evening instead. And that has been considerably shortened, as I'm doing my Stores cross this week, and have had to do all the filling in of forms so that the patients don't starve! I also had to order equipment for the kitchen. So I've had a lovely time ordering new flower vases etc. because we never have enough. I haven't had time for any tea, and I'm afraid I have only 20 minutes or so before I must post this. I'll write again tomorrow as I have a day off.

I'm going to sit by the fire and knit this evening, and then go to chapel when the others come off at 8.45. It will be a change. I haven't been to chapel since before my holiday. The Bishop of Berlin is preaching at St. Martin in the Fields tomorrow for a recorded service to overseas visitors, so I might go.

The Remembrance Service was lovely last Sunday at St. Martins. The sermon was very simple and very good. "How can we possibly hope to achieve peace in the world without first seeing that there is peace in our own homes. There are far too many people – i.e. married couples, neighbours etc. – who can't get on with one another, simply because they don't try." That was the theme.

17th November

Here I am, sitting alone in the sitting room at York House, I've been told that I have another week on Berners after all. They are so short staffed that they can't send a Head nurse to replace me, so with great delight I'm staying on Berners till next Monday, and then go onto theatre. That means I shall have just over a month on theatre before Night duty. Do you know – I'm a bit terrified about working on theatre. I'm sure I shall never remember everything. And laying up all those trolleys for the ops – I'm sure to leave off something vital and be yelled at! Still – it won't be any worse than for others I suppose.

Something terribly funny – Paddy is working down at Soho on Night duty, and they've got a private patient called NINA BRYAN – just like me!! She's about 40 apparently, and is the wife of a publican! How about that?! I never thought there <u>could</u> be another person with my name, it's so unusual.

Today is the 17th November, and tomorrow it will be exactly 8 months till the wedding! With a bit of luck in <u>7</u> months' time I shall have left London behind, and be excitedly looking forward to being married!

19th November

We are having frightful weather. We had a bit of fog a few days ago and we've had two attempts at snow, but it didn't settle. Nevertheless it is perishing cold, and working on the ward with short sleeves is a joke, even with central heating.

On my day off last week, Paddy, and Anne Key and I went, with free tickets from Matron's office, to see a comedy thriller called "Meet Mr. Callaghan". It was wonderful. I don't usually like thrillers but this really was exciting.

Goodness! It's 12 o'clock already. I must go and get ready and go up to Foley Street for lunch. How time flies.

I want to decide on when I'm coming home again, but I can't before Monday when I go on theatres. Sister Thomas wouldn't appreciate me going to ask about off duty before I've even started there. Just think! I'll have 5 sisters to cope with instead of one!!

But for now I must <u>hurry</u> – I'm on duty alone for the rest of the day with 6 ops to cope with.

23rd November

I've been trying to do a bit of investigation into days off on theatre and apparently most days off are Saturday, Sunday or Monday as weekends are quiet with no operations.

Bish's uncle is in The Middlesex and his wife has come up to see him. She was taking Bish out to tea and asked me to go as well. I hesitated at first, but the idea was so tempting that I couldn't resist! We went to the Bryanston café in Marble Arch Lyons and had a lovely tea. Mrs. Church has a car, so we went in style. By the time I got back it was so near post time that I didn't attempt to rush through a letter. Now I have the evening ahead of me so I can think about writing properly.

Today I have finished on E.N.T. and I was so sorry to leave Berners that I considered going to the office to ask if I could stay on a bit longer. But there was no point really. I wouldn't have gained anything by it, and anyway going on to theatre will be another step towards the wedding!

Do you remember me telling you about the girl in Block with me last April, who left half way through Block to marry a man who was going to Australia? June Smith was her name, and she was in the set above me. She's having a baby in February!

I'm sitting by the fire in the Sitting room here at York House and sort of half listening to the wireless. Isn't it terrible about the Doctor and his wife who have been attacked in Kenya? They've just said that there was a rehearsal of the Coronation procession today.

By the way I've completely changed my mind about my wedding dress. I want to have an evening dress underneath, and a sort of jacket on top, so that I can wear the dress afterwards. Economy you know!

Bish has just returned from seeing her uncle, so I had a bit of an interlude. And I've been playing the piano while she has been lying on the couch reading "The Cruel Sea". I've been delving into the cupboard too, to see what I could find! There are some interesting charts.

9.30pm

Time has gone speeding on and now I'm in bed. Bish is in bed too, and we've just feasted on bread and butter and cheese and two boiled eggs each, and Horlicks. Bish is undressed, but I'm still dressed, cuddling a hot water bottle and keeping warm under the bedspread. I wish I hadn't the fag of getting into my pyjamas! Mary and Paddy have just been in – annoyed because we'd said we would join them for coffee when we came off duty, and we didn't! Paddy is on nights off from Soho.

Bish and I have been listening to the hymn-singing half hour. The hymns were lovely. The chaplain said as an introduction to "Come Down O Love Divine" that God wants us to be His agents, to spread His love through our lives. I like to think that Ernest and I could be His agents when we are married and always try to spread His love through our lives.

I've just realised that I came back from my 2 months in Paris 3 years today! And how homesick I was in Paris. They wouldn't let me speak any English and I was longing to come home. But the Middlesex demanded at least two months abroad to qualify for applying for training here. So it was worth it!

Well Bish is now yawning – still reading "The Cruel Sea" and I'm feeling sleepy too. So I'll say Goodnight, and finish this letter tomorrow in my off-duty, hoping to be able to tell you when I'm coming home.

Monday

Oh – oh – oh! I'm having a half day today, and my goodness I need it! Theatre is wonderful really, except that I haven't a clue what I'm supposed to be doing half the time, and everything I'm asked to do seems to be a matter of life and death. I was asked to boil up <u>one needle</u> as quickly as I could, and I felt that it was quite an emergency! I almost thought the hospital would fall down if I didn't do it quickly! Two other girls came up new with me today, so at least there are three of us being clueless together!

This morning I was in theatre with Mr. Patey, who was doing just investigations to do with the liver. The Bile duct had got blocked and they were trying to discover how. He is known to be slow, and we were there from 8.30am till I went to lunch at 11.15!! And he hadn't finished then! The anaesthetist kept "eying me" to get things, and I hadn't the vaguest idea what they were! So I just dashed out of theatre and asked somebody else!

Tomorrow I'm off in the morning and then I'm Instrument nurse for Mr. Hudson in the afternoon.

After I came back from lunch today I was <u>alone</u> with Sister for a Hernia – it nearly killed me! And then I was with a Staff Nurse for another op, and quite enjoyed it. And then there was a flood in the sterilizing room, so Cockle and I spent the time till 2 o'clock mopping up!

I've got my Stores Cross today. I did Stores on Berners last week, so I'm feeling quite pleased with myself. My off duty is not so good I'm afraid, and I positively can't do anything about it. I did nearly die on the spot when Sister told me my day off would be <u>Sunday</u> every week. Day off Sunday, ½ day <u>afternoon</u> on Monday, so that means coming back on Sunday night. Isn't it crazy?!

What a wonderful concert you went to – I wish I'd been there with you. I adore all those composers, though I can't call to mind <u>all</u> the music. The Bach Chorales must have been super. I was pleased to hear that the gramophone has been taken to be repaired.

I have asked one of the nurses who has a ½ day morning on Monday after her Day off on Sunday if she would mind changing with me one week, and she says she will – any weekend except this coming one. So now I have to approach Sister Thomas and ask <u>her</u> if it's alright.

26th November

I'm going to be able to come home the weekend after next – can't wait! By then I will have been on theatre nearly a fortnight and will be more used to it.

Before I went into theatre I was determined not to worry any more! I thought I really was no longer sensitive to the trials and tribulations one meets! Consequently on Sunday night and Monday morning before my first day I didn't bother at all! But on Monday night, after my first day, I hardly slept a wink for hours. I kept hearing Sister saying "Go and boil that up quickly, Nurse", "Go and do this" and "Go and do that" until I nearly went mad. And yesterday I couldn't eat any breakfast and hardly any lunch. So to make up for it was asleep by 9.30 last night, and have been more courageous today!

No I'm not the first of our gang to go on theatres – Mary was on Stafford Bourne (Head ops) and Elizabeth was on theatre at Soho. I'm on Main Theatres which is nicer because you have a chance to see general cases as there are 6 theatres on the unit and you move around them. The funniest thing is tying up the surgeons' gowns, and washing their vests! You have to wash all the vests in the evenings.

We've had two terrific chest ops today in Theatre 1 where I am at present. I had five trolleys to lay up, and several times I had to go and re-boil instruments that Mr. Belcher dropped. The sterilizing room is so hot, and in theatre I had to stand so long in one position that I thought my back would break. And wearing a mask from 7.30 to 12 made me so thirsty. I was glad to go to lunch at 12, even though it meant I missed the second op because I had to do clearing up from 12.45 to 1.30 when I actually went off.

My first time of instrument nurse yesterday nearly killed me – I was so frightened! But today I knew a bit more what to expect. Tomorrow will be terrible – I'm instrumenting in the morning and table nurse in the afternoon. I shall need the evening to recuperate! On the ward you can be more or less relaxed, but all through an operation you're "tensed up", waiting to be told to do things for Sister, and at the end of the op you just sort of FLOP like a jelly!!

This evening I go back to sluicing – we all do cleaning in the evenings. Sinks of <u>blood</u>! (watered down!). For the last two nights there's been a baby in the sluice cupboard too, but he's disappeared today.

When I came off duty at 1.30 today I went to see the patients on Berners ward again, and Mrs. Perch gave me a pair of nylons, for which I am very thankful!

Yesterday I watched Varicose veins being cut – the man only had a local anaesthetic, and he was laughing and joking all the time. When

I'm going scranny boiling up instruments and setting trolleys I think to myself "what an idiotic person you are, Nina! There's a wonderful man waiting eagerly for you, and give you everything you want to make you happy, and you don't leave this and go to him!" But one day I'll be triumphant when my 3 years are over and hopefully I will become a State Registered nurse! By the way, apparently we collect £30–£40 superannuation when we leave here after 3 years.

27th November

I had a wonderful time being table nurse yesterday for the first time. Christine Jones, one of my set, was doing my rota when she was on theatre, and she says it's the best of the lot because you have all the <u>important</u> surgeons to watch!

You really are tense all the time, because you have to follow Sister's movements all the time, and be on the alert to do whatever she says. This morning in my hurry to find something which I hadn't the vaguest idea where it was, I knocked over the jug of forceps onto the floor! Clatter, clatter, bang crash!! They were only extra ones but I nearly collapsed on the spot! That was in the middle of a removal of breast. Old Fergusson just zoom zoom zoomed and it was in the bucket! And it's nothing to find a bit of stomach or something when you're sluicing! I wouldn't let anyone play around with <u>my</u> inside like they do!

This afternoon was plastic repairs. Mr. Mowlam chopped off half a nose, and repaired it with cheek flesh. It was wonderful. We did 5 ops in 2½ hours. I was just running round in circles and my head ached <u>so</u> <u>much</u> afterwards. But I do enjoy it so much, though a great deal depends on which Sister you're with.

28th November

I'm so sorry you're all "in the wars" with colds. And poor Daddy bumping into the toilet door and cutting your eye! And poor sister Shirley having toothache ever since you went to the dentist. So you're going to kill another hen too for lunch when I go home. Boo hoo!! Only joking! They're so delicious but I get upset at the thought of killing them.

– Sorry I had to go out Christmas shopping then, and time absolutely flies when I'm off duty.

30th November

I've just come in from an hour in the "fresh" air with Bish. I have my day off and she has had an afternoon. So we promenaded round Regents Park and thoroughly enjoyed it. But it is _so_ <u>cold</u> outside.

I went to see Bridget and Ian the newly-weds yesterday evening and thoroughly enjoyed myself. They are completely crazy but very much in love. I missed my tea here and went straight to Palewell Park, which took nearly an hour on the bus. We had supper when I arrived, and then had a marvellous evening, just the three of us. They have a flat consisting of sitting room, bedroom and kitchen, and they share the bathroom with another flat. It's just as I expected Bridget's home to be – very untidy, but quite homely and comfortable. They're particularly proud of an old chair upon which, they say, William of Orange once sat!! As I sat there I realised how <u>very very</u> lucky Ernest and I are to have such an exquisite little home. Ours is very different – so much more orderly and pleasing to the eye! It's so spick and span and beautiful. Oh what a lucky girl I am.

Bridget is a delightful hostess – she makes you feel at home immediately. I must learn the art! Bridget said how she had a good old weep the day before the wedding, and what a strain the ceremony was.

I got back about 11pm, and Bish was out at a dance and got back about midnight. This morning I got up just after 8, and spent the morning here in the drawing room, knitting. I was listening to the "people's service" from a theological college. The Principal of the college was talking about parsons and their work. He said that when he's deciding whether a man will make a good parson, he goes on 3 points:

1. whether he's a good worker
2. whether he can "mix in" with everybody else
3. whether he can stand the pace, for a parson is never off duty, he says.

It was terrifically interesting and I really enjoyed listening.

I went up to Foley St. for lunch and then Anne Key and Bridget Luck asked me to their room for a cup of tea. There I stayed till about 2.15. When I got back to York House Bish was off duty, so we went off for a walk. And now I must settle down to knitting Mummy's jumper again. I shall be going to chapel after supper. Now I must fly to the post or I shall miss it.

2nd December
I'm sad that I can't be home for Christmas – unless I get Christmas Day off when theatre is closed. Then the weekend after Christmas I go on Night duty, so I'm sure to get nights off at the beginning of the New Year. I've bought some streamers for our new little home because I want it to look festive even if I can't be there!

There's great excitement here. Elizabeth Jones is getting officially engaged to Brian Luck (Bridget Luck's brother) today. She's been keeping it very quiet but she told me. She's very excited about it. Brian is coming up to London this morning and they're going to buy the ring together and then going to Brian's home for tonight and tomorrow. How I remember the day Ernest and I were engaged. Ernest was sick before he met me at the station, and we were both literally trembling with excitement when we met. It was so strange to see the announcement in the paper too! I could hardly believe it was true. Elizabeth is thinking of leaving after the 3 years if they can find a flat or a house. She's the 4th out of our set of 40 now to be engaged.

I heard on the wireless that it had been horrid weather in the Midlands. It's a bit better here today, but I feel as if I'm getting a cold. I think it is being so hot on theatre and then going out in the cold. Isn't it a nuisance? I hope it wears off before I come home.

4th December
My cold has <u>gone</u>! I went to bed early on Tuesday night after a hot bath and hot drink and codeine etc. and I'm glad to say it has done the trick.

I shall be coming on the 5.32 train on Saturday getting in to Loughborough at 8.19. Ernest will meet me. Sorry about this skwiggle but I must dash up to Foley Street for supper and post this en route.

9th December
Another lovely break at home! Thank you! I'm so glad I decided to come back on an earlier train because we ran into fog at St. Albans

and were held up, so I didn't get back to York House till the time the later train would have got me there. But on that train with a hold-up I would have been late on duty.

There was panic on theatre when I got there. The girl who changed her off duty with me also got stuck in the fog and didn't get back till 10 o'clock yesterday morning, instead of being on duty at 7.30. And believe it or not Sister Thomas had <u>forgotten</u> that she'd said we could change our ½ days, and she swore I'd never asked her! She's getting a bit aged to be a Sister I think – all the other Sisters complain about her.

Anyway the other girl wasn't allowed to go off till 4.30 in the afternoon, instead of 2pm for her ½ day, so I was sort of extra in the afternoon. They put me in Theatre 1 at first, and I was thrilled because they were doing a circumcision, and then of course they found they didn't need me there after all, and I was packed off to the sluice before the op. started. And I didn't manage to see the ENT ops. either.

But there was an emergency mastoid at 4.30, for which I both tabled and instrumented, and it lasted all evening till 8 o'clock. Nobody was annoyed with me thank goodness. It was poor Cockle who had the worst of it when she came back at 10 o'clock.

There is now some hope that I can be home for Christmas. I've heard today that if I wish to have my day off on Christmas Day I can. So what do you think? Should I ask for evening Christmas Eve, day off Christmas Day and ½ day Boxing Day? I wonder if travelling might be difficult?

I must now get ready for lunch and go back on duty. I think it's warmer here since the fog lifted. I'm going away next weekend to Welwyn Garden City, to stay with the Fletchers.

11th December

I have an evening off today. At least I came off at 5.30, but it was nearly 6 when I got down to York House, because I did my little good deed for the day en route. I more or less collided with a dear old lady who was trying to find the toilet! So I marched off with her to the nearest, and waited, and then guided her back to the front hall. Then she wanted a taxi so a taxi was duly found, and she was very pleased. I was very thrilled because she said very sweetly, "Oh, Nurse, you are a joy." Wasn't that nice?

So I'm feeling very pleased with myself. Having been complimented by an Honorary too! This afternoon I was table nurse (as usual on Thursday afternoon) for Mr. Mowlam's plastic ops. I always enjoy them because he's so marvellous. I was doing something at some stage, and he said, "How nice it is to have someone who anticipates one's needs. It's a very rare thing you know." I was quite taken aback – actually to have done something <u>right</u> for once!! I just sort of said, "Thank you, Sir," very awkwardly, and he said, "Well you see it doesn't <u>save</u> time, but it ensures that the work is done promptly because no time is <u>wasted.</u>" I was simply <u>thrilled</u>! And I wished old sister Thomas had been there! As it was, not a soul heard but <u>me</u>! – as far as I know. Pity!! Forgive me but it was so unusual for me to be complimented that I <u>have</u> to blow my own trumpet. I've told everybody about it now, and the Staff nurse said, "Oh well I must say <u>I</u> don't have any work to do now"!

Bang go all my plans for Christmas. I have no difficulty in deciding what I shall do – my mind has been made up <u>for</u> me. Sister Thomas has informed me today that I shall be going on night duty on theatre a week on Monday – December 22nd. That means I'll be on for Christmas. I shall have 5 nights on, then 2 off – coming home on Saturday morning 27th, and returning on Monday afternoon in time for night duty <u>elsewhere</u> on Monday night. So there we are! That's quite definite and correct with no alterations to come. I don't know when the next nights off will be.

I've bought a lovely skirt for Christmas with some money Ernest gave me. Actually it's not the one I wanted and it's 2/6 more, but I do like it. It's maroon with an almost invisible green and an almost invisible navy stripe, and it's pleated all round. It's jolly nice.

I wonder how Shirley is getting on in the Wrens?! I haven't heard anything from her yet. I'm glad you had a good afternoon in London with her, Daddy, and that she found two other girls on the Reading train. Fancy my little sister being a Wren! – Now I must go and have some supper!

15th December

I've just been remembering how I was penniless one night duty and needed desperately to have enough money to buy two stamps! I searched my handbag and found a purse which I hadn't opened for ages. And in it was sixpence! If ever I've thanked God for looking after me it was then! That sixpence was like £6,000 to me then. Ernest said he was broke the other day and needed £15 to pay for a gramophone. Then Canon Wilkinson gave him some money just at the right moment. I think he was penniless because he'd given me the money for my Christmas present skirt. Oh dear. Do you think we could have some of your records, Daddy?

Poor Ernest is also afraid that Mr. Mowlam has fallen for me!! But he needn't worry because he's about 50!! But the other nurses tease me about him now! That's what I get for showing off!

Do you know – I simply loathed a Staff nurse on theatre for the first two weeks or so. She seemed to loathe _me_ and I couldn't understand why she was always so beastly to me. I used always to complain about her to everybody and talk about her in a not very nice way behind her back. Then one day another Staff nurse said, "Yes but I think you must excuse her because she is so nervous by nature, and can't help getting worked up. She's only horrid when she's worried." That made me think, and I realised what a beast I was. It wasn't _she_ who was to blame really – I'd been too ready to condemn her, and hadn't tried to see _why_ she was like that. So I made a point of talking to her and getting to know her instead of avoiding her and keeping out of her way whenever I could. And now we are good friends and it has made me feel so happy. It seems even _more_ wonderful to be friendly with _her_ than the ones who are easy to get on with!

I was so pleased to hear from Shirley last Friday. She seems very happy in the "Theseus Division" HMS Dauntless. She says she's made friends with several of the girls, and is already talking about her "gang" – just as I do. How lucky that she has 14 days holiday for Christmas.

Well now I must go for tea and I haven't even changed yet. I did want to be sure to get this letter finished as Bish wants to go out tonight. I've had a ½ day, and have been writing in my uniform all afternoon!

17th December

What a joke! Cockle – another girl on theatre – and I are going out to Lyons for supper to celebrate "our success on theatre!!" We're both quite confident that we are the greatest idiots on theatre! We are going about 6.30 so we should be back by 9, so I can telephone you.

Cockle is 2 sets above me and we have become very friendly through working together on theatre. I was cleaning the sterilizing room last night and she came to help me. At 7 o'clock, after the Sister had gone to supper, we went into the kitchen to eat some sandwiches and cakes left from the surgeons' tea. Before we went, Cockle turned on the tap to fill one of the boilers, and she said, "Remind me to turn the tap off because I shall never remember!" The next thing we knew was Hobart coming into the kitchen and saying, "Which one of you two thought it would be a good idea to have a swimming pool here?" We flew back to the sterilizing room and the place was <u>flooded</u>! We got mops and brushes and cloths and started to clear it! You can perhaps imagine the chaos! We both got soaked, and it took us ages to do it because we were doubled up with laughter!

But really it is <u>marvellous</u> on theatre. Nothing seems to worry me very much now that I've settled down better, and I do enjoy it so much. This morning Mr. Holmes-Sellors let me listen with the stethoscope actually <u>on the heart</u>. It was an amazing experience.

Cockle came into the nurses' room the other day with a very <u>long</u> face, and I was <u>singing</u> at the top of my voice! She said, "Good old Bryan – always full of the joys of Spring!" Such is my reputation! But no wonder – I'm so happy about being married next July – 7 months tomorrow!!

It's so cold here. We've had a lot of snow in the last two or three days, but it's all melted now and messy. I've been thinking – when it begins to get warmer again, and the sun returns to England, and the little flowers come out of their cold hide-outs, and everything comes to life again – THEN…! How lovely to be married in summer!

Well now duty calls and I must be away to tea and back to work.

19th December

This morning we were told that a cross-action towel clip was missing after yesterday's ops. So we had to go through seven laundry bags and the whole of the dirty dressing bin to look for it and still didn't find it. It was simply frightful – the bin especially.

Please will you forgive me now if I leave the letter and rush out shopping? It's my last opportunity before the weekend. I'm longing for next weekend, to be home again.

21st December
I've asked about night duty and I'm not going on Woola (the private Woolavington Wing) after all. I'm going on Campbell Thomson cubicles where Bish was on her last night duty. She says it's lovely and there's not very much to do. It's a bit lonely apparently as you're the only one, but you have a room to sit in with light and gas fire, instead of the dim religious light over the desk on the wards! It's <u>Brains</u> this time, so I shall be neurotic before long! But I'm looking forward to it. My nights off will be Tuesday to Saturday. In January – 6th to 10th and 20th to 24th. I don't see how I can possibly come home both times though, as including next weekend it would cost me £5 all but 2/- for train fares.

I've had 8 Christmas cards so far, and Ernest's calendar presides over all!

I had a dream about the wedding last night, but it was miserable. Mrs. Sheeran and Mummy were crying their eyes out, and Auntie Gracie was trying to soothe them! It was awful!

Christmas Day will be awful.

I shall go to church in the morning but otherwise I shall have to sleep all day! How awful missing it all! I've never slept through Christmas Day before!

Last night Bish and I went to "Kreme Crackers" – the medical students' concert. Mr. Kremer is the brain specialist at the Middlesex. It was wonderful. They're <u>very</u> clever you know at "taking people off", and some of their imitations of honoraries were marvellous. They did a skit on Sister Clarke (the Home Sister) introducing Square Dancing. One of the students, David Patey, apparently goes square dancing, and has taught his father, Mr. Patey, who is one of the surgeons I table for. They said that he's gone so mad on it that he's even started making SQUARE INCISIONS now!!

I thought that was a scream and very clever. It didn't finish till 11.15 so we had a late night.

It's my day off today and I was feeling ready for it. I've been doing Christmas cards and parcels, and trying to finish Mummy's jumper which is driving me frantic trying to finish it for Christmas! Sorry, Mummy! I posted all the cards yesterday. I wonder how you're getting on with yours?

I'm going to be <u>alone</u> on theatre tomorrow from midnight to 7.30am, night duty.

24th December

I was hoping for just a quarter of an hour, at least, last night in which I could write – but NO!! I had a feeling in my bones that we would have an emergency during the night <u>sometime</u>, and we did! Everything was so quiet when I went on duty, and I got well ahead with the work before midnight. Sister was back from her nights off, and she said, "Well tonight you're going to rest, Nurse! You'll be the first nurse to have done so while I've been here!" But I didn't break the record! At 11 o'clock we had a little gathering of housemen and anaesthetists for whom I made coffee – just when I'd cleared ours away of course! And they informed us that an appendicectomy was on the way, and what time would we like it?! We told them 1am, which gave me plenty of time to lay the trolleys and get theatre ready. Mr. Ranger was very quick, and it was all over by 2 o'clock. I couldn't go to lunch at 1am because of the op. So one of the nurses on E.N.T. brought some over for me, and Sister told me to leave the mess in theatre and get on with my meal. We sat till 2.30 chatting and hoping for a bit of quiet.

But no! At 2.30 we had a telephone call to say that there was to be an Obstruction at 3am. That, I suppose, was our penance for leaving theatre in a mess! Between us we cleared up, and I laid the trolleys. This woman patient was 29 and positive T.B. which meant that everything had to be carbolised afterwards. That op made me in an absolute sweat – we were running round in circles. It finished at 4.30am.

I helped to clear up, and then Sister said she'd do the rest while I made the tea. I'd had to have coffee ready for the men after the op as it was. (Incidentally those men ought to be shot! They left the surgeon's room in chaos – they'd just thrown their boots and gowns and masks and caps on the <u>floor</u>. I don't know what they think we are!!)

At 5 o'clock we had tea and did the masks at the same time, and then at 6 we started on boiling up the sterilizers and instruments, washing theatre, sluicing, and boiling the gloves, and finished about 7.45am.

And now I feel so tired that I could go to sleep standing up! But it is going to be great fun with Sister – she's a great sport and full of fun and frolic. She's 40ish and is terribly energetic. She's so kind – when I said I wished I could catch an earlier train on Saturday, she said she'd see that I got off early to catch the <u>8.</u>15am! So you can you possibly meet me at 10.57? I hope it won't be too early for you.

Well here I am rambling on and I haven't said, "HAPPY CHRISTMAS" to you. All the very best of good wishes!

By the way another of our set – Barbara Evans – has just got engaged to someone she met only 4 months ago. That sounds a bit hasty to me, but she's that sort of person. The glamour of it, sort of thing. Cheeribye for the moment.

Enjoy your chicken and I'll be there to enjoy the turkey!

1953 – The last few months of my single life! And the lead up to SRN exams

(Taken from 1953 DIARY)

1st January

On night duty again for the New Year. Watched 1952 go out and 1953 be born – standing with the headphones of Bed one in Queen Mary ward. "Your thoughts go out to your loved ones, whether they be near or far," they said. And my thoughts were with my very beloved husband to be, so many miles away from me. "My husband to be in 53!!" Somehow the beginning of the New Year made it all seem so much nearer.

We had a busy night on Queen Mary. Off duty about 8.15am, supper, letter from Mum.

Wrote to Mummy, then went to bed about 11.15. Bish came in from nights off at 4 o'clock, and woke me – worse luck. Letter from Ernest headed, "Report for the end of the year 1952". I rang him about 7.15. It was full charge – no cheap rates for Jan. 1st, so I had only enough change for 3 minutes and he was very <u>disappointed.</u> On duty again at 8 o'clock.

Managed to get things organised better tonight, so by midnight most of the night's work was done.

2nd January

Got breakfasts in reasonable time to the ward, and was ready by 8 o'clock. Went up to theatre to get my crosses signed up, but Sister Thomas was too busy. Supper, wrote to Ernest, ironing, then bed. My letter took till 12 o'clock – Bish was asleep by then. So it was about 12.30 when I got to bed after my bath, had a wonderful sleep, and hardly heard the bell at 7 o'clock. Fairly easy night, <u>again on Queen Mary.</u>

3rd January – 2am (letters)

I've got things a bit more organised these last two nights on Queen Mary, so that although we're quite busy I have a little time for writing my thank you letters and so on. I think this will be my last night on Queen Mary. Strugnell goes on nights off tomorrow from Campbell Thomson so I might go there. All this chopping and changing!

Off duty at 8.15am, then supper. I didn't get to bed till 12.30 today so I wasn't at all ready to get up at 7 o'clock! I really <u>shall</u> go to bed early on Tuesday I think when I come home.

There's absolutely no news for you at all – night duty is so uneventful here. All I can say is that these women nearly drive me to drink!! My only consolation is that my pro is <u>very</u> nice, and most sensible and hard-working, so that makes life a little more bearable. The first night I was here the pro was new too (another one) and at 2.30am she informed me that she was going to rest till 4 o'clock! I was far too busy to rest myself so it didn't really bother me, and I let her go. But the <u>cheek</u> of it, my dears! She said, "You see I've just come back from nights off," so I said, "Oh really? So have I!" And that was that. I think she had rather a guilty conscience when <u>I</u> didn't get any rest. Thank goodness she was only here one night. I would have pushed her down the sluice I think, otherwise!

We had an <u>awful</u> meal tonight at midnight. Horrible fried fish and carrots and insipid looking sauce. I've quite gone off my food except breakfast and supper. I never can eat at midnight. I hope I shall be able to put on a bit of the weight I've lost, on Campbell T.

I'll tell Ernest not to meet me on Tuesday. I shall come on the 10.15 from St. Pancras getting into Loughborough at 12.23pm so I hope that will be OK for Pa. I'm looking forward to <u>4</u> nights! I must go and get on with my cleaning now.

Sunday 4th January
Yesterday Paddy had a Day off – she's gone on theatre now. So she came down to York House at 9.30am and she and Bish and I went out for coffee. We went to a lovely little café off New Bond Street where we've been before – called "Susan's" – Bish was feeling wealthy and treated us both to beakers of chocolate. It was super. From there we walked to Selfridges to get some carpet binding stuff for Bish, and from there to the Czech Restaurant in the Edgeware Rd where Paddy left her ring in the cloakroom when she was out with Tony for supper on Friday evening. <u>She found it fortunately</u>.

233

Monday 5th January
I'm on Campbell Thomson now, as expected. I didn't know there could be such a blissful ward – women but charming. And absolutely no work! I had an hour's "sleep" last night but felt so awful afterwards that I decided not to do it again. It's quite wonderful to be on an easy ward for a change, though Sister Jones told me she thought it was "a waste of a strings nurse"! No compliment to me particularly of course.

6th January (diary)
Paddy is in Princess Alice Staff ward with pneumonia – a consolidated left lower lobe. She is having bad luck. Finished early and was off duty at 8.10 after reports. Supper, then packed and changed and caught the 10.15am train from St. Pancras to Loughborough. Kept falling asleep on the train, I was so tired. Daddy met me at 12.30 at Loughborough station with our beautiful doggie – Jill. It was miserable weather, rainy and dull and cold. I always take rain home with me! Grandma Peet was there, while Uncle Bob is in hospital. Lunch almost immediately and then Mummy washed up and I dried. Mum had to go to her club in the afternoon and Daddy was out parish visiting, so I stayed to look after Grandma. Ernest rang up about 2.30 and was bitterly disappointed that I'd said he shouldn't come over, but I was so tired I went to bed as soon as Mummy and Daddy came home, at 7 o'clock.

Wednesday 7th January
Woke about 8am after quite a good sleep. Grandma woke me once with her perambulations! Mum brought my breakfast to me in bed – lots of porridge, fried egg and bacon, and toast and marmalade. Sheer luxury! She insisted that I spent the morning in bed.

Friday 9th January
Ernest came over for lunch. In the afternoon Mum went into town to have her hair done and Daddy took her. They left at 2.30 – Ernest and I washed up, made the fires, fed the hens, bottled the goat's milk, and had the rest of the time to ourselves! – apart from being interrupted by Jock, the gardener, who came for a cup of tea! Then we went to the Post Office to post a letter to Shirley, and collected a letter from her about all her recent activities in the WRNS. When they were in London she and her friend, Sally, got lost in the

Underground, and went backwards and forwards twice between Baker St. and somewhere else before they went the right way! Not used to London like me! After supper we played Rummy, all four of us and Grandma watched. Ernest left at 11pm.

Saturday 10th January
Got up at 9.30, washed up, and then we all went in the car to the South Notts. HUNT, which met in Sutton Bonington. We followed it to Stanmore, stage by stage, and then it got so horrid and drizzly that we went home. Lunch about 1.30 and Ernest came at 2.30. We had a short time together before Ernest and Mummy and I went to the station for my 3.53 train. But it was 40 minutes late owing to fog, so Mum went to do some shopping while Ernest stayed with me. The train got later and later and was an hour and a quarter late getting in to London – arrived at 7.30. I nearly had kittens! I jumped into a taxi at St. Pancras, and changed and managed to get on duty for 8pm! Not such a quiet night as usual, as I had to help a girl on Nash ward with a man who was dying.

Sunday 11th January
So tired by morning. Meant to go to bed early but had several jobs to do, and got to bed eventually at 11.15. Went straight to sleep. On duty at 8pm and had a lovely quiet night. Coffee with the other nurses and the houseman at 10.30 in the kitchen – at least I had Ovaltine and Horlicks mixed! – and consequently went to sleep between 2 and 3am.

Monday 12th January
Decided to go to bed early, and finally snuggled down at 10am. But it was no use – I didn't go to sleep till nearly 12! On duty as usual at 8 and another quiet night. Had visitors again for coffee at 11pm – our houseman, the nurse on Casualty, the houseman acting Casualty officer for the night, and a physiotherapist. It was good fun! I'm sure Campbell T. is the ward to be on! Obviously others think the same!

13th January (letters)
Here I am again the spiv of Campbell T! It's simply wonderful and we have such fun. The only time I'm really busy is between 6.45 and 7.30am, coping with breakfasts. But that's rather fun if you start in good time. The rest of the time I do what I like – knitting, writing letters etc. I've at last finished all my Christmas thank you letters.

At 10.30 every evening the head nurses from Campbell T. male and female wards and myself have coffee in the kitchen. And every night we have different visitors to coffee with us. Furnass, our houseman, always comes, and tonight the nurse from Casualty and tonight's Casualty officer came too. We sat there drinking coffee and chatting till about 11!

We have super tea-times too! We spend ¾ hr to an hour over boiled eggs and toast. What bliss to think it will be like this till April, all being well!

Apart from this I've done <u>nothing</u>, absolutely nothing, that is apart from doing absolutely nothing of course!!

Yesterday morning I was determined to go to bed early, and was actually in bed by 10am. This morning we have a lecture at 10.15 till 11 – on the respiration system I think. It takes the form of questions round the class – as sort of revision.

On Wednesday morning I go to the dentist at 10.30. I haven't been since the summer. I'm glad I had all those fillings at Fenton's before I came here. It wasn't very nice at the time, but it was worth it because I haven't had to have anything done since I started nursing.

On Friday I have another lecture at 10.15. Bish will be back from nights off then, so we shall go together.

Mary came back from nights off feeling lousy, and went on duty last night thinking she had flu. The houseman had a look at her and told her she had measles!! But she seems better now.

Did I ever tell you that one of our set – Langley – had been thrown out? She was on Maternity and was test weighing a baby one morning when somebody called her. She left the baby on the scales while she went to see this person, and forgot all about it, and went off duty not giving the baby another thought. Meanwhile the baby fell off the scales and fractured its collar bone. Langley was told she could come back in 6 months, but she said she wasn't going to at first. Now she <u>is</u> coming back in May to finish her training. You may not have heard me speak of her much – she was the girl who shared a room with Bish in the summer. GREAT NEWS! They've found my pyjama top at the laundry and returned it! I'm so pleased.

I <u>have</u> read all the newspapers about the Earl of Dalkeith's wedding. His bride looked like a fairy princess. I also read about the difficulty in cutting the wedding cake. Your paper must have missed the point – the thing was that the slice was already cut and marked with white ribbon for them, and then the Earl moved round to suit the photographer and consequently got in the wrong spot! So instead of just slipping the knife through the cut slice they tried to cut the other part. The cake was made 2 months ago, and a layer of icing has been added every day since then! No wonder it was hard!

16th January

I went to the dentist on Wednesday and nothing needed to be done. They just said, "Come back in 6 months." Then I suddenly realised "avec beaucoup de plaisir" that I shall not be here in 6 months!

We now have a man on the women's side of Campbell T. – a charming old man of 74, who is the father of Miss Beck's Houseman. He doesn't sleep awfully well so needs a bit of attention. He's a pet, and I feel I want to mother him! So that made me a little busier than usual, but a fairly slack night even so.

Also I suddenly got an urge to write my two case histories for finals, so I set to and got them <u>both</u> finished! It has taken me most of the night but it is a relief to have them done.

Sister Eplett, who was Sister on E.N.T. when I was there, is now Night Sister on this wing. This is her second night on. It's lovely having a Sister I know and like – we get on very well together, and I hope she may give me a good report when the time comes!

Last night – her first night – didn't start very favourably from our point of view. She came at 11.30 to do the midnight checking round and caught us unawares. We'd had a crowd of visitors in the kitchen for coffee, and the Head nurses from the male and female wards were still in the kitchen chatting. As it happened – fortunately – I felt rather uneasy about leaving Cubicles for long as I had a post-op patient, and it's difficult to hear bells from the kitchen. So I went back to Cubicles just after 11pm and was there when Sister came round. She came to me and was furious about the other nurses – the trouble was the pros go to lunch from 11 to 12 and there was nobody on the wards. I thank my lucky stars that I'd come back to my department, or I can see we'd all have been down to Matron's office.

Also last night the telephone rang on Cubicles about 9.45 and I flew to answer it as I thought it might be you or Ernest. A man's voice said, "Is that Nurse Bryan?" And then when I said it <u>was,</u> he said "Will you go down to Matron's office immediately.... (long pause) .... for serious breach of conduct." After that last bit I began to think there was something fishy, and asked who was speaking. The voice said, "Brigadier Hardy-Roberts" and the phone crashed down. I <u>knew</u> then that it was the houseman playing the fool so I flew downstairs to the ward as fast as I could, and there he was hiding in a corner! So I gave him "what for"! We do have some fun up here!

I went to the revision lecture on Tuesday morning and my goodness it <u>was</u> a waste of time. I could have spent the time more profitably learning alone in my room. As it was I nearly went to sleep half way through and didn't get to bed till 12 o'clock. There's another one tomorrow morning but I'm going to wash my hair instead of going to it. Apparently Finals exams are the week beginning 23rd February.

Bish came back from nights off and had really enjoyed them. Yesterday morning we both went and did a bit of shopping, and I met Anne Dickenson from the High School in Woolworths! She was in my form and is now Mrs. Large and works near me in London!

We had Communion on the ward yesterday morning – 2 of the patients took part in one room. I had to prepare the altar for them etc. We have portable altars, and put the flowers on them ourselves. It was rather nice preparing it.

18th January
Exactly 3½ years yesterday since Ernest told me he didn't love Olive and asked me as a friend what I thought he should do! I never thought that would ever happen – I was sure they were going to get married!

Secretly I think we both fell in love with each other when he came back from the war. He looked so handsome in his uniform and he must have seen a big change in me from 8 years to 14! I had grown up!

I had a letter from WRN Shirley today, saying she'd been in sick bay with tonsillitis and post-vaccination symptoms. She was hoping to go to Wimbledon today – I wonder if she enjoyed it as much as I enjoyed my day in bed asleep!

Yesterday and this morning it was much warmer here – almost springlike. But this evening it's colder again.

Well here I am on my 9th night. Only one more night to go before nights off. When the bell goes at 7 o'clock in the evenings I immediately count how many nights before I'm off, but once I'm on the ward I thoroughly enjoy it. In fact I find that the night goes so quickly that I don't have a chance to do all that I want to. Once 4am and tea time comes, that's the end of knitting and writing letters!

Must break off for a minute or two – it's 2 minutes to midnight and I must go and give Mrs. Williams her 12 o'clock dose of penicillin. Poor dear is supposed to have it strictly 3-hourly, but I give her a double dose at midnight so that I don't have to wake her at 3am.

Well that was an extremely long minute! It's now 3am and quite a lot has happened since I got up to give the penicillin. And the minute I sat down to continue then a bell rang – a Beep wanted and another dear switched her light on and got out of bed to stroll around the corner to the toilet. We're having fun and games tonight!

I gave Mrs. Williams her penicillin and her sedative which I'd saved till midnight for her. Then I was relieved by a nurse from downstairs while I went to lunch.

There, at that juncture I heard such a banging and a clattering downstairs that I simply had to go and see what it was all about. It was two nurses (one of my set) out in the kitchen <u>two</u> floors down. So I told them politely that I hoped they didn't think me rude, but could they make a little less noise, and I closed the door on them. Fat lot of good it did incidentally – the "racket" is just as bad now, but I'm not going down again. On my way back I popped in to look at one of the patients and she wanted a drink of milk. So I promptly boiled enough for <u>two</u> cups, and made some Horlicks for myself at the same time! I drink coffee till 3 o'clock and then it's safe to drink more somnifying liquids! (If that is a word?)

Well to go back to where I left off – we had soup, ham salad, pears and cream and biscuits for lunch, and then Mary read jokes from "Punch" to me while I knitted. At 1am I returned to find a light on in Mrs. Ellis's room. I went in to her and she said she'd wakened from a nightmare ¾ hour ago, screaming at the top of her voice, and had turned on the light! I went back to the bunk to the pro who had been relieving me and asked if everything was alright. "Oh yes! Not a sound from anybody," she said, so I asked her if she'd done a round at all because Mrs. Ellis had had her light on since just after 12. She was rather shattered I think.

I gave Mrs. Ellis her Seconal and made her comfortable and left the light on at her request, and then went down 10 minutes later to relieve the nurse on Nash for her meal. I had already called in there on my way back from lunch to say I would be taking over, so she wasn't kept waiting by my being late.

At 2am I came back here and the other pro said Mrs. Ellis was asleep. So I went along and turned out her light. The minute it went out she screamed and asked me to put it on again. So I stayed with her for a while and tried to shake her out of her nightmare. She wouldn't tell me what it was about but assured me that she'd be alright. So then I departed and crept in to my little old man of 74's room and to my delight he was fast asleep. He hasn't been sleeping on Persedon so I got the houseman to write him up for something else. And Tuinal seems to be much more effective. Sister told me not to worry last night because old men don't need so much sleep, but I didn't like to see him lying awake for most of the night.

So then – I went downstairs and acquired the Poison Cupboard keys and gave myself a draught of Codeine, feeling a bit "Hors du combat", and then ate three cream biscuits to take away the taste. The biscuits, by the way, we have obtained by foul means or fair from the store cupboard. They're best Paris assortment – pre-war I should think! We eat a layer each night, and nobody has noticed! They should finish the last layer while I'm on nights off, so maybe I shall miss the row!

Then – as I came back upstairs to Cubicles I heard this awful yelling "Oh help! help!" again, so I flew as fast as I could noiselessly, to Mrs. Ellis, and found that she'd been dreaming again. So this time I was very firm and made sure she was wide awake. She says she's had these nightmares periodically ever since she was a child.

Then I sat down to pick up the threads of your letter from midnight, and was interrupted by the bell, and then I sat down again and wrote a line or two and was forced to go and stop that awful banging, and on my way back looked in again at Mrs. Ellis and she decided she would have some hot milk after all. So there we are – up to date!

One of the patients, Mrs. Holliday, has made an adorable little blue and grey felt bear for me. Sister says he ought to be called "Gooffy", but I object, and I've called him PLINK PLANK PLONK, or Treble P!!

I've just heard night Sister's bustle upstairs, so I'll just remove my ring and be ready to whip off my cardigan. She comes about 3 usually to collect the Bed Returns (a 24 hourly record of the bed state on each ward.) But this Sister is about ¾ hour late for everything.

I made out a list of wedding presents the other night, and there's no end to them! I keep thinking of more things to add to the list. I'm just waiting for Ernest to censor it this week, and then I'll send you a copy in case (ha – blooming ha) anyone asks what we'd like! If such a thing should happen perhaps you'd get them to put a tick by what they choose.

I was reading the inset of the St. Giles January Magazine the other night, and was particularly struck by the Bishop of Lichfield's New Year letter. It's quite uncanny that he should have written in that strain only a few weeks before he died. "Another New Year arrives and we all look forward and wonder. What is going to happen to the world, to our country, to our loved ones, to ourselves? … The Christian who is quite sure that God is in control of events may be anxious – but will certainly not be afraid." And then later – still more uncanny, he quotes, "I go to prepare a place for you – I will come again, and receive you unto myself." If you've still got the other copy left, do read it again if you haven't already done so. It's as though the old Bish knew he was going to die.

Well, now Sister has come and gone, having been in to see Mrs. Ellis, and Mr. Shanks, and having beamed on me with her rather artificial, unconvincing, affected smile! It's now 5 to 4 and very

241

nearly tea-time again. Another night nearly over and very little to show for it. Once again I'll have to say cheeribye. I'm afraid this is a rather odd sort of letter, but as nothing ever happens at any time other than between 8 and 8, I've had to "concoct" an epistle, on practically nothing!! I hope you haven't been frantically bored! I've almost finished knitting your yellow jumper, Mum, and will post it to you within the next day or two.

19th January (diary)
Off duty in very good time. Bish and I donned our coats over our uniform and caught a bus to Selfridges. Bish collected her polyphotos which are very good, and I bought "Doctor in the House" with Uncle Stan and Aunty Betty's Christmas Book token. Bish then looked for and bought some new curtain material for her room at home. In bed by about 11.30 and on duty again at 8 o'clock for my 10th and last night before nights off.

20th January
The day for which I've been waiting for 10 whole nights! Came off duty late, packed, had a bath etc. after supper, then eventually settled into bed about 11.15. Dozed off for a little while and got up about 1.30. Ernest arrived early and I wasn't ready! Went down at 2.10 and we set off straight away in the direction of Guildford. Ernest thought of going to Hindhead, and we found a good little hotel for Tuesday night. Had tea there, and then sat in the lounge before and after supper. After supper we watched television too, and went up to bed about 10.30. I was feeling utterly worn out, not having slept for 28 hours.

Wednesday 21st January
Up at 8.45 and went into breakfast just after 9am. Then packed our cases again and went for a walk round Hindhead. Explored the Devil's Punchbowl, and then walked through Golden Valley. I finished Mummy's jumper – alias Christmas present! Left Hindhead after lunch, and after perusing the map for some time made for Bognor where we arrived about tea-time. We pottered around for ages in the car trying to decide which hotel to choose! The one we did choose was perfect in every way. Went out to the Green lounge café for tea and then back to the hotel to unpack and for supper at

6.30. Coffee in the lounge afterwards, and a heavenly quiet evening with no one to bother us. We were the only guests there!

Thursday 22nd January

Went for a long walk along the front and round the shops in the morning, with coffee at a little café. Back for lunch, and in the afternoon we went to see Alan Ladd and James Mason in "Botany Bay". It is a seagoing film about the transport of prisoners from England to Botany Bay in Australia. It was a real treat as Ernest and I haven't been to the cinema for ages. Dinner at 6.30 at the hotel, and then we had the lounge to ourselves all evening and nobody bothered us – it was like having a home of our own.

Friday 23rd January

The meals are excellent here and everything "top-hole". Went for another long walk but it was much colder this morning. Had coffee in the Green Lounge café again with a lovely fire to warm our frozen hands and feet. Back for lunch and we meant very seriously to go in the car to look round Pagham church in the afternoon. Mrs Yorke, the manageress of the hotel, said it was well worth a visit. But the fire in the lounge was so inviting and it was so cold outside that we stayed put on the sofa all afternoon. Popped out to post some cards to friends and family about 4.30 and then had tea by the lounge fire. Supper at 6.30, and then after coffee went for a brisk walk along the front. Made out a list of wedding guests after that, and already the numbers have come to 140, and we must have forgotten somebody.

Saturday 24th January

How time flies when one doesn't want it to! Our 4 days together almost over. Went for a long walk along the beach by the sea and the front after breakfast, then had coffee in a little milk bar. Tried to start the car when we got back, but the battery was flat. So we walked round to a garage and the man came and towed us a few yards with his van, till we started. Then we went for a ride over to Pagham and saw the lovely church and village. Lunch at 1pm and set off back to London at 2pm. The Yorke family (proprietor and family) of the St. Andrews hotel are very friendly and said they hoped we would go and see them again sometime. We got more and more miserable as we got nearer and nearer to London. Ernest says the very name "London" haunts him as the place that takes me away from him. We were looking forward so much to these nights off, and then they go in a flash. But the memory will live forever, and we are 4 days nearer to our great day! Got back to London about 4.45 and Ernest left me at 5.15 after a cup of tea at the Devonian café outside the hospital. I felt so sorry for him having a 5 hour journey ahead of him, especially after driving 63 miles already from Bognor. The more I see him the more heavenly it all is and the happier we are together, but I <u>must</u> <u>get</u> my <u>SRN</u>!

I went up to the sitting room and read the paper, then to my room and unpacked, and got into bed for an hour. Went straight to sleep! Don't know how I dragged my weary bones on duty at 8 o'clock, and all night I had the dickens of a job to keep awake. Off duty in good time. Went up to theatre and got my theatre crosses signed up. Was in bed by 10.15 – I was so tired – and went straight to sleep. On duty at 8 after a wonderful sleep, feeling fine. Still only 6 patients, so life was very cushy.

25th January (letters)
A very happy birthday, Daddy! May your new year and those ahead be joyful and prosperous.

26th January, 12.30am
So sorry – I intended to finish and post this yesterday, but was so tired last night that I simply couldn't write any more!

Ernest and I had a wonderful time away. It was nothing short of heaven. I was in a complete daze when I had to leave him and come back to work. But I do enjoy it, and when the work is easy like this you can really get to know your patients, and give them the attention they need, and do all those little "extras" which normally you don't have time for. Also you have time to take a pride in the ward and keep everything clean and tidy. It's grand.

Ernest wanted to go to Hindhead for part of our time together because he was stationed in Godalming during the war, so he knew the surrounding country. The hotel was quite expensive – £3-2-6 from teatime Tuesday till after lunch on Wednesday, but it was very cosy and we had tea by the log fire. I managed to finish your jumper, Mummy, and I'm very pleased with it. I've washed it now because it got quite dirty in the making!

Back to my patients – four of them have departed since I went on nights off and I have two new ones, and two empty rooms – 6 patients altogether. So I have even less to do, and Sister gets very worried that I might be bored! But I'm far from bored!

Bish is on nights off. Mary and I are doing our classroom crosses on Wednesday morning, so think of us about 10am. We have trolleys to lay up and a bed to make. Having got my theatre crosses, and done my two case histories, there are now only about 2 left to do. I must get them done, and my crosspaper handed in by February 13th.

Ernest and I made a list of guests for our wedding and discussed the venue for the reception. Although we agree that obviously it would be lovely in our garden, whatever would we do if it rained? The Rectory is lovely but not really big enough for 140.

Mummy darling – yes! I do feel refreshed after my little holiday <u>and</u> I've got ROSY CHEEKS for the first time for months and months, so that will make you happy. I wonder how long they will last?! We had our pay day (£8-2-6) today! So Bish and I went to cash our cheques. Bish got more curtain material and I got my watch back from the Menders at long last, having left it there in November! I also bought some fawn wool to make a pullover for Ernest.

We had a large party in the kitchen last night – a farewell for Brian Furnass, our houseman, who is leaving to go in the army. So there were about 20 of us, students and nurses, making and cooking pancakes! They were jolly wizard!

2nd February

Sorry I haven't written, but things have been a bit haywire because I've been moved down to Campbell T. Female ward instead of Cubicles for 3 nights, replacing Head Nurse Stansby who is usually here. She's on nights off. There are 16 night nurses short in the hospital at the moment, mainly due to the flu epidemic and consequently they've had only pros for reliefs. They could hardly send a pro here to the female ward, but it's easier for a pro to take over on Cubicles. But she's not allowed to give out drugs or give injections, so I have to do all that for her.

I do miss my Cubicles women, and of course the easy life there! The first night here was rather trying – I had two post brain-op cases and

I was a bit scared as I've never had any immediate post brain op ones before. But they're doing fine now, so there's nothing to worry about and I'm enjoying it immensely. My patients up on Cubicles said they're going to write to the Brigadier because their nurse has been taken away! So I go up and see them every night and have a little chat.

My pay is already catered for! £3.6.0 for train fares, 30/- for repairing my watch, 10/- for church restoration – that's £6 approximately. Then I must leave myself £1 for "living", and the other 24/- I spent on wool for Ernest's cardigan, which I suppose will be an Easter present. My May pay will all have to go for taking State, and then registering later on, so I just have 3 months' pay for wedding things like trousseau – that's £24 approximately, and out of that £8 or more will go on train fares. It really is incredible. The only "frippery" was the wool for Ernest's pullover, but Ernest <u>must</u> have a pullover, and I <u>must</u> have something to do other than write letters and read during the night. Oh dear what a boring letter – I'm sorry!

72519

THE GENERAL NURSING COUNCIL FOR ENGLAND
AND WALES
23, PORTLAND PLACE, LONDON, W.1

DATE	RECEIVED FROM	£	s.	d.
23 MAR '53	MISS NINA A. BRYAN	4	4	0

FEE FOR ~~PRELIMINARY~~ FINAL EXAMINATION

This Receipt is an acknowledgement of the fee only.
If the application is found to be in order, a card
of admission to the examination will be issued.

M. Henry SRN
Registrar.

Paddy is in Princess Alice ward again. She's better from the pneumonia but this is for investigations. They're trying to discover what is wrong with her, and she's had x-rays and goodness knows what. She's worried about the T.B. in her family still, especially as her father may have to go into hospital again with T.B. She's quite cheerful though – Bish and I went to see her tonight on our way on duty.

Fancy only just about 4½ months now till I leave. I have heard that I should take my written papers for State on June 3rd, and the Practical exam will be sometime during the week beginning 14th June. As I am at the beginning of the alphabet it's quite probable that I shall get mine over at the beginning of the week. So I shall be able to leave about the 17th or 18th June which will give me a month before the wedding.

I'm still on female ward, and David Ford and Hutch came up at 1am, so I cooked eggs for them and toast etc! Quite enjoyed the ward now that I'm used to it and the patients.

Saturday 7th February (diary)
Back to York House at 6.30 after nights off, and Hurrah, back on Cubicles. I had a very quiet night and finished at 7.30am so helped the day nurse to make beds till 8 o'clock.

8th February
Supper – washed some "smalls" and had a bath, and was in bed just before 10.30. Woke again at 11.20 – must have been some stupid so-and-so making a noise in the corridor. Woke again at 4 o'clock, sitting up in bed and staring at Bish's bed and wondering why on earth she wasn't in it! She's on nights off of course! Up at 7.15. Good job I set the alarm because I went to sleep again after the bell.

9th February (letters)
It was nice to talk to you last night and to hear about Uncle Bob.

Six of us have to go to Matron's office tomorrow morning. I think I told you on the phone that Sister Few thought I should be coming off night duty on March 1st instead of the beginning of April. Well now I've heard that all 6 who are to go to the office in the morning are going to Great Ormond Street for 2 months. So that means I shall be there from the beginning of March to the beginning of May. Of course I don't know quite how true all this might be, but it sounds reasonable, and I <u>was</u> told before night duty that I was on the list for G.O.S.

If I do go there it will mean living in Foley Street and going backwards and forwards by bus every day. We have special outdoor uniform for the travelling to and fro. Di Willis is there at the moment. I believe it is very interesting – you don't have the same amount of responsibility obviously. The G.O.S. nurses who are training there do the head nursing and we have to go down a peg or two, but that won't matter. I'm quite looking forward to it, and it's certainly a thousand times better than the wretched time people have on our children's ward here, with such an awful Sister.

So it looks as though my next nights off will be the last. What a shame! It's so nice having nearly a week at home at a time!

Bridget Boyle rang me up last night to say that she can't come into London tomorrow morning (that is this morning!) for coffee after all. She has her 8-year-old nephew staying with them and he's developed flu. So he can't go to school and she can't leave him. She wants me to go there instead, as soon as I can, for coffee, and she says she'll give me something to eat, so I needn't bother about supper.

That was before I knew about going to the office in the morning. I thought it meant during the night. So it's a bit of a bind because I shan't get away till well after 9 o'clock. But still it will be fun.

We've discovered tonight an article in the "Nursing Times" about a rise in pay. We have reckoned that we should get about £9-5-0 a month instead of £8-0-0 when it comes into force, and there'll be about £10 back pay to come if we get it this month, and more if we have to wait. So one month we're going to get about £20. I say! I didn't really think it could be possible! It sounds too good to be true!

I'm relieving on Nash ward – the men's skin ward – at the moment, while Lane has gone to lunch. I loathe it! I'm so thankful I haven't had to do any training here. It makes me itch just sitting here in Sister's bunk!

I have only 5 patients on Cubicles tonight. They're all very early Disseminated Sclerosis, and are up and about, so there's absolutely nothing to worry about. No wonder they're whisking me away to G.O.S. I tell you, my dears – I simply wasn't born to a lazy life. I always have to work for my living. And as far as I can see it must be for love, cos there certainly hasn't been much money!

I was telling Sister about Auntie Rene yesterday morning in reports, and saying how strange it was that Uncle Bob should have the same thing. We'd been discussing the possibilities of D.S. being familial, because we have one patient whose husband has it too, and have seen other instances. I mentioned that Uncle Bob's seemed to start with sleeping sickness in the desert during the war, and she immediately said, "Oh that isn't D.S. it's Encephalitis." Somebody else to whom I was talking said the same thing. The symptoms are very much the same, so I wonder if they've made a mis-diagnosis? I shall be interested to hear the outcome.

It's a bit miserable with no Mary and no Bish. Mary will be back tonight though.

Apparently they had snow here yesterday afternoon while I was asleep. And when I came on duty last night it was pouring with rain. Have you had any snow?

Well, my dears, there isn't anything more to tell you. Oh yes – we had a most interesting coffee hour tonight. We had Chris Kurwan, one of the medical students from this floor, up here for coffee. And he was telling us how he swallowed his false teeth just before Christmas, and had to be whipped up to theatre! I'd often wondered just who it was, because I was on theatre at the time and heard a lot about it. He told us tonight that he'd been talking to a friend in his room till 4 o'clock one morning, and just before 5am he woke up with a start, and discovered he had all the symptoms of a Coronary Thrombosis, about which he had been reading the previous day. When he sat up in bed he found he could hardly breathe, so he rushed into his friend and yelled, "Mike! I'm having a Coronary." His bleary-eyed friend looked at him in amazement, and then called in another chap and said, "Look here, old man, Kurly's having a Coronary." This 3rd medic however wasn't quite so daft, and noticed the gap in the top set of teeth! Thereupon he was taken off to Charlie B. ward and then up to theatre. They had great fun in theatre too, just when they thought they'd got the teeth, the blessed things slipped further down! But they got them in the end!

The following morning (or later that morning) old Chris was just coming into his own again – physically but not mentally it appears! And he jumped out of bed and went and rang his parents up, and blurted down the phone, "Ha! Ha! I've swallowed my teeth!" and then slammed down the receiver and went back to bed! And he says that Sister Rees (my friend of old) delivered him the biggest telling off he'd ever had in his life!

Well now it's time to go back to Cubicles. Lane has just come back from her lunch hour, so I must settle down to some work.

Really, the room where I've been sitting is more or less like the one on Cubicles, and yet <u>what</u> a difference. No fire on, hard chairs, and doors <u>and</u> <u>windows</u> open!! It's frightful!! I take two armchairs into my room, and turn on the fire, and even put a vase of flowers on the desk to inspire me! It's worth being on night duty then! Oh well – cheeribye for the minute!

11th February
Thank you for your letter which I received last night before I came on duty. It was lovely to find it when I came down to breakfast. Fancy you having 2 inches of snow! We had a sprinkling the day before yesterday, but that's all.

On Monday I went to the office as you know, and I was quite right. I come off night duty on 1st March and go on day duty on some ward or other at 4.30pm. Then I go to Great Ormond Street hospital on 2nd March for 2 months. Sister Bird said she didn't know whether I'd have to do another 3 weeks' night duty after G.O.S. and before my final Block. What a crazy idea that would be.

After I'd been to the office on Monday am, I changed quickly and went off to Palewell Park to see Bridget. I'd told her I'd be there about 9.30am, but with going to the office first it was of course 10.30 by the time I arrived. And, my dears, I expected to find a mess, but there was complete chaos! She had her nephew in bed with flu and Ian off work with a bad cold too. They hadn't had breakfast even by 10.30. So I helped Bridget cook sausages and so on, and then ate breakfast with them. Then we talked and I left just after 12. It was after 1pm when I got back to York House and nearly 1.45 by the time I got to bed. My mind was buzzing with thoughts, having been talking all morning, so it was nearly 3pm when I got to sleep. Felt jolly tired when I had to get up at 7. Very quiet on Cubicles as usual, but 2 new patients – one an ex-Guy's Sister, so I have to mind my P's and Q's!

12th February
I've heard from Ernest that we've been given a canteen of cutlery – great! We are so lucky.

Went to bed in good time to make up for yesterday and went to sleep quite quickly. I'd had an uncanny feeling and was quite convinced before I went to bed that Bish was due back and that I would be wakened up. Then I decided I'd made a mistake, but blow me! At 11.30 her key in the lock woke me, and I heard the door open and I shot up in bed wondering who it could be. It was Bish, come up to London to meet her sister! When she saw me sitting up she said, "Oh good! So glad you're not asleep!" And she put the light on and started telling me about everything. Was I mad?! She even arranged her blinking flowers, and then asked me to look at them to see if I approved. Finally I told her to buzz off, so she did! She looked at my new coat which Daddy told me to buy, and thought it was wonderful. And the first thing Bridget said when she saw me was, "What a lovely coat you've got on." She tried it on and decided she looked too fat in it!

Tonight I've done my cupping and leeching and blistering, and my medicated baths crosses. So that's all now – never any more crosses to do!!! What a wonderful thought!

Mrs. Ellis is beginning to get on my nerves. She came back on Monday after 3 days at home, and she said everything went right when she was home. So she's got no excuse for nightmares now. She did however fall over at home and hurt her foot, but it's not nearly as bad as she makes out, I'm sure. And she says she can't sleep for worrying about whether she'll fall over again. Last night she didn't sleep all night.

At 3am I went in to her for the umpteenth time and said, "Look here – there's no danger of you falling down any stairs between now and 6.45 so for goodness sake go to sleep." But she didn't. I just give up!

Tonight she woke up about 3am and her foot was hurting and she was cold. So I gave her some codeine and an extra blanket, and said how thrilled I was that she'd slept and hadn't been dreaming. At that

251

she put on a little act, as much as to say "who says I haven't been dreaming?" So I turned out the light and went out. I wasn't going to have any more dramatising! Lo and behold! At 4am I heard wailing coming from her room – the sort by which you can tell her nightmares. So I thought that I'd try another technique and leave her to get over it herself. After 5 minutes the wailing stopped! So now I imagine she's going neurotic too, and she revels in having attention. From now on she's not going to have more than her share from me!

I had to go and see Night Sister on Monday night about nights off. She's going to give me 2 between my next 4 nights off and the end of night duty.

I actually did some revision towards dawn. Started reading my medicine book about pyrexia etc. Off duty at 8.30.

Friday 13th February (diary)
Unlucky? Well no letters and a – of a pain in my tum. Went to bed at 10 with 2 Anadins and a hot water bottle but still couldn't get to sleep till 2pm. Bish and I decided not to go to the revision lecture at 10. Late down to breakfast. Tummy a bit improved – but I took 1 oz of APC when I got on duty and had a glorious feeling of well-being all night! Repeated the dose later!

Saturday 14th February (letters)
Isn't it cold? Ernest says you've had snow, but it hasn't settled. We've had quite heavy snow too, but it has all gone to nothing thank goodness. It seems to be terrible further north. I'm wondering what the sea is like – for tonight is the spring tide isn't it? And the gale here is terrific.

I've got a full house here on Cubicles so am frightfully busy. One patient decided she was too hungry to go to sleep, so I cooked a poached egg on toast for her.

We've had quite a gathering of medics for coffee at 11 too. We have a new houseman now – a married man named Peter Ball. He's very nice and very keen. But we all miss Brian Furnass who left to go in the army for his 2 years. You remember we had pancakes for his farewell party. Stansby, the nurse from the female ward, is going on holiday the week after next, and is having pancakes to celebrate her leaving! But that party is to be next Thursday so Maxfield and I will miss it.

Great news! – the accountants are trying to give us our back pay <u>this</u> month! So Bish has bought some new maroon suede court shoes to celebrate! Paddy and Mary are both on the look-out for new costumes to wear at our wedding too.

Paddy has had 2 teeth out on Princess Alice ward, and they found, in the culture they took from the teeth, the very bug that has been causing her P.V.Os. So now they've got to the "ROOT" of the trouble, ha ha, as Mary so aptly said, maybe she'll be better.

I've given my cross paper in on time, and complete. I've had my case histories back, but am a bit disappointed in them. Apparently I didn't put in enough detail of nursing care. Still – I've done them both, that's the main thing. I felt so good after I did some revision during the night. Happy Valentine's day tomorrow! Maxfield and I are both looking forward to nights off!

23rd February
This is only a short letter as I <u>must</u> spend my time working now. I'm getting more and more worried about Hospital Finals. The more I study the more I realise how much more I still have to do! There's just masses of it.

The exam is on Tuesday afternoon – Practical from 4.45 – 5.30pm and orals at 6 o'clock and 6.10pm. It will mean getting up about 3.30 or 3.45, so that I'm properly awake. At least I shall have an hour and a half afterwards to recuperate before coming on duty. What a relief there will be then. I shall feel like jumping over the moon. Really, from the way I talk about exams anyone would think they're a major event in my life! It's just me.

My patients are all very quiet here at the moment. I found the place in a bit of a mess when I returned from my nights off. One's Relief never seems to bother very much with keeping things tidy and clean. There isn't the same incentive I suppose.

Bish is in Sickbay. I'm going to see her tomorrow morning. I hope she will be better for the exams. She's my partner in the Practical! I must also ask Home Sister to find me a room at Foley St. for next

Sunday. I'm so looking forward to living up there again after so long – 6 months almost.

The snowdrops and winter jasmine look lovely on my dressing table. I thank you so much for giving them to me to bring back – a reminder of home! But I forgot the eggs, and I do love them for a snack now and then. Must fly now and study.

By the way I'm so pleased we've managed to discuss properly about the reception. What a good idea to have it in the dining room at the School of Agriculture – the Prin. is wonderful to have offered, with their catering staff doing the food. How amazing!

26th February
Here I am – all my cares over at last! Oh it's simply wonderful, for although Finals don't matter as far as results go for me, I've never felt so awful before an exam _ever_! How I stopped myself being sick before I went into the Practical room I just don't know, and Bish and I were shivering from head to foot (thankfully Bish came out of Sickbay in time). Of course when we got in, Sisters Brown and Smith were both _extremely_ nice and encouraging, and both so calm and sweet that I didn't worry at all. I immediately felt calm _myself_, and even quite enjoyed laying up the trolleys for them. I felt I did what Sister Brown wanted, but perhaps not so well for Sister Smith. Then the Medicine Oral was lovely – I actually knew what I was asked, and what I didn't _know_ I could make up, and everything went smoothly. But Sister Grahame was _beastly_ in the Surgery and Gynae oral – she asked me about a type of case I'd never nursed, and I had to just _guess_ the answers so I hummed and hawed a bit! Then she asked me the _names_ of vaginal pessaries and I could only remember _one_! If you forget _names_ there's absolutely nothing you can do because you can't make them up! But she just sat there and said nothing till eventually she asked, "You _have_ done your Gynaecology lectures haven't you, Nurse?" I said, "Oh _yes._"

I'd taken ages getting clean cap and strings made up, and dress and apron and shoes all ready. Bish was OK again but on nights off, so we worked together, until she went to lunch at 12. I continued working till 12.45 and then slept (believe it or not!) till 2.45! Up at 3.30, and Sister Jarry brought us a pot of tea and cakes at 3.45 to sustain us! Even though I made a mess of the surgery and gynae, the

254

rest was quite nice and it was such a relief when it was all over. I felt I could jump over the moon, even after so little sleep. I went on duty at 8 – and no studying to do!

Yesterday it was lovely coming off duty and having nights off. I was quite determined all night that I would go to bed straight away, but when I came off duty it didn't happen quite like that. Bish was off for the day till 8pm, so she and I went window shopping all morning! I went to be fitted for my Great Ormond Street outdoor uniform, a super navy blue mac, and a navy blue velours hat, rather like our old school ones. I heard at the same time that there were tickets for the Matinée of "Call me Madam". So Bridget Luck and I went – to the Coliseum – it was simply wonderful, much better than "South Pacific" I thought. It finished at 5.10, by which time I felt jolly tired. Bish was in bed then, but not asleep, so I talked to her till the bell went, and I went to bed when she got up to go on duty.

I got up at 8.30, having slept solidly from 7.30pm to 7.30am! Bish came off duty just after I'd got up and we went to get our backpay. So I went out and spent mine straight away! – ON MY WEDDING DRESS! I went into lots of shops on Regent Street and so forth, and I tried on one or two dresses, but didn't really like any of them. I had almost given up by 12 o'clock, and decided to go back to Foley St. for lunch. I called at Peter Robinson's on the way back, at Oxford Circus, and THERE IT WAS!! The very thing – the most elegant of creations and made for me!! It was new in that very morning and I was the first person to try it on. It cost me 13½ guineas. I also bought some Dolcis white sandals to go with it, for 29/6. Back I went then to Foley St. for lunch, and then spent a quiet afternoon with Anne Key in the York House drawing room, listening to music. Anne and I made toast by the fire, and had tea in the drawing room. I rang Ernest and told him about the wedding dress, and he told me that the telephone wires had been put in our little house, so there's just the telephone to come! I had supper at the same time as the night staff had breakfast. Then I had a mannequin parade by myself in my wedding dress! I went to bed about 10.30pm.

Next morning, February 27th, I had breakfast while the night staff had supper!! Then Bish and I spent the morning buying things for her, and had cups of chocolate in "Susan's" off New Bond St. again.

Then Bish went to bed, and I went for another little shopping expedition after lunch and then back to York House drawing room for the afternoon. Again Anne Key and I had toast and tea together by the fire! Very cosy!

Then I had to go back on duty at 8pm on Campbell Thomson <u>female</u> ward. I was rather upset not to be able to spend my last two nights on Cubicles. But I went up to see the patients and had a good grouse! There was nothing to do on female – even less than on Cubicles.

Ernest has told me that our telephone number at Wellington Crescent is 88989! Lots of 8's of course for our lucky number 18, and the only two numbers that aren't 8, add up to 18!

Saturday 28th February

Today I had to do my packing because tomorrow I'm moving back to Foley St. I got to bed about 11.45 and slept solidly all day. I didn't even hear the bell at 6.45! I was on Campbell T. female ward again – very easy but I do miss my little room with the gas fire! So now – ALL CHANGE!

2nd March

Thank you so much for another letter, received when I got back this evening from Great Ormond Street. I was glad to note that you'd remembered to send it to Foley St. without being told!!

I came off night duty yesterday morning (Sunday) and went to bed about 11.30, and slept for about 1½ hours. I woke at quarter to 2 and didn't go to sleep again. I got up at 3pm and dressed quietly (as Bish was still asleep of course) and went up to Foley St. for tea. Then at 4.30 I went with the others going to G.O.S. to the office, and discovered that I was going on Campbell T. for the evening. That was simply wonderful because I knew the ward and there was nothing to do! I had been expected to help out for the evening on some very busy ward.

Then I came off duty at 8 o'clock, had supper in Foley St. and went to Home Sister to discover where my room was. It is next door but one to Paddy which is marvellous. It's on the 2nd floor, overlooking Foley St. This time I have orange curtains and cream furniture, so it's a colour scheme I haven't had before! And it's very cheery.

I went down to York House and brought up a load of belongings from my room there, and arranged it in my Foley St. room, and then went down to York House again for the night. I had a little discussion with myself as to whether I should sleep at Foley St. or not, and decided it would be quieter at York House. We didn't have to be at G.O.S. till 9 this morning, so I didn't want to be wakened by the Foley St. hooter at 6.30 when at Y.H. I could sleep till 7.30.

I was up with the alarm at 7.30 having wakened after 9 hours' sleep at 7.20, and I went and had breakfast with the night duty folks having supper. Then I set off at 8.30 with the others going to G.O.S. to be there for 9am.

We had talks all morning, and were shown around the hospital. A break for tea and cake at 10am and then lunch at 12.30. Apparently we are allowed to spend some days in the Mothercraft department and the baby clinics, and have lectures on Mothercraft, so it's all very useful for my last two months!

The Sister Tutor said that they are anxious first and foremost for us to learn to handle a <u>normal</u> child, and then having learnt that, to adapt the knowledge to nursing <u>sick</u> ones.

At 2 o'clock we were taken to our respective wards. Mine is DRESDEN ward, a surgical one specializing in genito-urinary conditions (bladder and reproductive organs – mainly congenital abnormalities). I was shown round the ward, and then given a 2½ year old to feed, wash and make her bed. Of course it took me ages to do everything.

It's a super hospital and I must say that they have many ideas which could well be introduced at the Middlesex. For instance – all rubbish bins at G.O.S. are washed and sterilised after emptying. Nothing like that ever happens here. And everywhere <u>looks</u> so much cleaner and tidier than at the Middlesex. Maybe to outsiders our hospital looks clean and tidy, but I have been very much impressed by Great Ormond Street's methods.

We came off duty at 4.30, had tea, and then walked back. It takes about ¼ hour or 20 minutes to walk. I shall be at G.O.S. for 2 months.

I collected the remaining things from my room at York House, and have been arranging them in my room this evening. It's a heavenly thought that I can go to bed now, having had my supper. Oh yes! I like my night duty, but it's nice to be the right way round!

Sister Kaye, incidentally, on Dresden ward, is having her "spring week" this week, but I'm told she's very nice. Tomorrow I start work at 8am, and we have every evening off.

Yes my wedding dress certainly is a dream frock. I couldn't have <u>dreamt</u> of anything more lovely. And as for when I'm going to bring it home for you both to see – well the sooner the better, because then I shan't be able to try it on to show people! And everyone wants to see it!

I don't yet know when my day off is to be, but I <u>expect</u> it will be either Saturday or Sunday, with 4.30 evening before, and on again at 11am on either Sunday or Monday morning. I suppose I shall be told definitely tomorrow, and if I can choose I shall say Saturday because it's easier getting back.

4th March

It's lovely to have a change by being at G.O.S. The children are from the age of 6 months to 12 years. My day consists mainly of potting, washing and feeding.

Just thought I'd drop you a little line before I wash my hair. I've just had supper at 8 o'clock and I'm having a little series of early nights because I still feel frightfully tired after night duty.

I like your idea of having an "At home" on 17th July – my birthday and the day before the wedding – as long as you could cope with eats. But as you say you need only have "a cup of tea and a bun"! You don't need to prepare anything elaborate. I'm so glad you've got the spring-cleaning all mapped out! I shall be doing the same thing next year!

I'm enjoying G.O.S. very much. I got a <u>bit</u> bored yesterday and was quite convinced that I'd be bored stiff by the end of 2 months. It seems to be an endless round of potting, washing, making beds and feeding, and then starting all over again! But today I've had a super time. I was allowed to spend most of my time in theatre as we had 2 op. cases, and it was most interesting. It was interesting watching the G.O.S. nurses doing the work! I kept seeing things that should be done, and wanting to do them myself! It was so odd.

Then this afternoon I was allowed to bath a 6-month-old baby. I have fed and washed the 18 months baby several times, but never the small one. And she's such a darling – actually they didn't know whether she's a he or a she, poor soul. She has characteristics of both sexes.

The nurses are all charming too – I like them all immensely. I think they are full of respect for the Middlesex too!

When I got back from G.O.S. I had to go to Matron's office. There were notes on the board for Rickards and 6 others. I don't know yet who the others are. Of course I knew this might happen to me even before the exam, because I hadn't done enough revision. Poor old Rickards went in first, and was in for about 20 minutes, and came out crying her eyes out. So I wondered what would happen to me. Apparently Rickards argued with Matron though, and that's fatal. I mostly let Matron talk, but put in a few words here and there. It was obvious that I hadn't worked, and she said she was disappointed in my poor results, after I'd come top in PTS and doing well in a lot of my other exams. So I was perfectly honest, and said that, as I am getting married in July, my mind has been concentrating more on our new house and the preparations for the wedding, than my work! I said I was really sorry, but assured her that I will work hard for State, because I don't want to leave the hospital after doing the 3 years, without my State Registration. In actual fact the results will probably arrive on my honeymoon! The trouble was also that I knew finals didn't matter to me, but now I've taken it I feel happier about State. The pass mark for finals is 60%, but for State it's only 33 1/3%. My finals mark was 59% which after all isn't a disgraceful mark. I was in and out of Matron's office in about 5 minutes! I think she'd run out of things to say, but she was really nice. I've spent the rest of the evening consoling Rickards! Well now I must stop as it's post time.

16th March

Thank you once again for a lovely day off. Ernest no doubt told you that the train was on time and that we had lots of time to spare before it came. The journey was good even though it took nearly 3 hours.

Most of the folks got out at Leicester and I was left with one lady in my compartment. I felt sad to be going back, but she was much more miserable, poor soul. She'd been for a day trip to Derby to see her 17-year-old daughter, who has been in a Salvation Army Home (for girls needing care and protection) since she was 14, and she has to be there for another year. She is the only child, and her mother seemed a very sweet woman. She (the mother) can only afford to go to Derby once every month, and she's longing to have her daughter home again. What's more, her husband travelled to Derby overnight in a lorry, leaving about 11pm on Saturday. He told his wife that he would meet her at Derby Station, but she hadn't seen him at all and didn't know what had happened to him. She hoped he might be at St. Pancras, but he wasn't there either, so she had to set off on another journey home to Gravesend alone, wondering whether he'd be at home when she arrived. I gave her a biscuit and a chocolate to help her on the way. The poor dear – I did feel sorry for her. One meets all sorts of people on train journeys. This was a contrast to my companions last time I came back to London – they were just married, and off on their honeymoon.

19th March

I was rather cheered today by a compliment! A girl came up to the ward to x-ray our 10 days old baby John, and wanted an assistant to undress the baby and hold him for her. He has a drainage tube in and is very poorly, and I've never been allowed to touch him yet. So when the radiographer asked me to help her I told her she'd better fetch Sister instead. The message came back from Sister that she thought I was sensible enough to cope! I don't suppose she realised that I would hear what she'd said, but I was thrilled!

Last night Paddy got tickets to admit 4 to the Palace Theatre to see Anna Neagle in "The Glorious Days". We had (FREE) £1-10 seats, my dears, and it was wonderful. It's quite the most super theatre I've visited yet in London. It's at Cambridge Circus, on the corner of Charing Cross Rd and Shaftesbury Avenue.

I'm now hoping you will tell me that it is convenient for me to come home next week.

I've had so many late nights recently – now that our "gang" is complete, except for Bish, we have cocoa parties and "chin wags" most evenings and before we know it's 11 o'clock. I can't stand going to bed after 11 and getting up at 6.30 for very long! So tonight I must be early.

24th March
The Guard of Honour of nurses at the wedding appeals to _me_ alright, but I'm not sure that the gang would appreciate it. And we might be had up for wearing uniform outside the ¼ mile radius.

We haven't had any cocoa sessions for the past few nights for one reason or another. Paddy is very flighty now, and goes out quite a lot with medicos. And now after nearly 3 years <u>Mary</u> has found a boyfriend – a medical student who is apparently much fancied around here!

She's absolutely full of Paul Massey! Paddy has a wider selection! Di isn't the type for that sort of thing, though she likes to think that one day she will get married! And Elizabeth and I are quite "solemn and secluded" through being on the verge of marriage!

Nevertheless my heart does a little flutter sometimes! At the moment my fancy is taken by Mr. Conelly, the Registrar on our ward! I've been in theatre once or twice when he was operating and was quite impressed! However – that's just a side-line which doesn't really exist very much! I've just been rather flattered by the charming way in which he greets me on the ward!

Isn't it dreadful – I've just heard the news about Queen Mary. Paddy came in to tell me. Now we're anxiously awaiting the 9 o'clock news.

I'm so devastated because our little baby boy of 10 days died at the weekend while I was on my day off. And today little Gary French died after his op – having been in theatre for 3 hours this morning. He was 18 months and very adorable. The other day when I was feeding him I was trying to imagine what he would be like when he was older, and now I can hardly believe that his little life has ended.

These children are angels when they are in pain – they're far better than adults! It makes you want to cry sometimes.

Did I tell you that our dear Matron has a seat in the abbey for the Coronation? My dears she is representing all the matrons in London! How about that?!

I've learnt so much at G.O.S. about handling children now, and I have met a lot of new types of complaints. I have discovered that I didn't know the first thing about dealing with young kiddies, but now I'm much more confident. I've decided that the most important thing is to let them have no doubt in their minds as to who is the boss!! I seem to achieve much more satisfactory results when I impress upon them that they have to do what I want, and no nonsense!! The only danger with these children is that one tends to have favourites, which I know is a terrible thing. Some of them make me so cross that I want to spank them, and others are so adorable that I could hug them all day long. It's so touching when they put their arms around you and kiss you.

30th March

I had a good journey back on Saturday – the train was on time and I caught a bus straight away. I was back at the Nurses' Home just after 11. Then I had some cheese and Ryvita and made myself some cocoa with milk I fetched from the kitchen, and eventually – after arranging my flowers and unpacking, I got into bed just after midnight.

On Sunday morning I didn't wake till 9 o'clock. So I missed Communion. I got up more or less immediately, and had a boiled egg, toast, and cocoa – all made on the hot plate near my room. I was on duty at 12 o'clock, and we had a hectic day. The Head Nurse and Staff Nurse spent the entire afternoon and early part of the evening with the two small babies, so I was left to cope with the children in the ward – endless pottings, and their teas at 3 o'clock, then washings and bed-making, and eventually suppers and medicines, and tucking them up. I was just whizzing around in circles but at least when there's only one person you do know where you are! You don't have to keep asking the other folks what they're going to do or have done!

I went straight back to Foley St. at 7.45, and went to chapel at 8.45. It was rather nice – we all had little palm crosses given to us afterwards.

Then I scrambled the 2nd egg and had it with toast and cocoa! It was delicious! I shan't need any more eggs, Mum, because I shall be up for breakfast next Sunday after I've been to communion.

This morning I went to Mr. MacNab's clinic from 10-12.30, and it was quite interesting. We go to one Outpatient's clinic every week.

It was so sad to hear about the death of Queen Mary, and I had thought of going to the Lying in State tonight, but I thought I'd have so long to wait and it would have been awful by myself. I wouldn't have minded if I could talk to somebody.

I'm sending you the receipt from the General Nursing Council for my State. Many, many thanks for helping me out once again.

If I come home again on 12th April I can see Shirley, and by then she will have probably been with Margaret to get her bridesmaid's dress, so I can see that too. Or maybe if she goes on Saturday morning I could go with her.

G.O.S. is still flourishing. I do adore the children now that I know them individually. And I was thrilled because when I went on duty on Sunday morning at 12, two of them came running up to me and gave me a hug!

9th April
Easter now over, and I have had a fairly ordinary day at G.O.S. – four small operations. A new Head Nurse by the name of Howgego appeared too, and seems to be just the sort of girl I like! She's full of vitality and fun!

In the evening I caught a tube train to Buckhurst Hill – or supposedly to Buckhurst Hill! That was at 6 o'clock from Tottenham Court Rd. I never got any further than Stratford Tunnel. You may have read in the papers today about the crash in Stratford tunnel. The train in front of us crashed and we were held up behind it. The train that crashed must have been the one I saw going out of Tottenham Court Rd Station and I just missed it – thank goodness!

Our train kept stopping in tunnels all the way from Tottenham Court Rd. and we wondered what was the cause. Then finally in Stratford tunnel it came to a standstill and all the lights went out. That was 5 to 7. About 7 o'clock a railwayman came through and said, "Open up all the windows, you'll be here a little while yet." But he wouldn't say any more. The "little while" lengthened into 2 hours – during which time, the atmosphere got pretty grim – even more than necessary because so many folks were smoking one cigarette after another. I never thought I would suffer from claustrophobia (I can't find that word in the dictionary!) but goodness there were times last night when I realised how possible it <u>was</u>. The trouble was that nobody, of the railwaymen who passed through the carriages from time to time, would give us any indication as to what had happened, or when we might get out.

It was a horrible feeling – being closed in on all sides. If we'd been in the open it would have been different, but down there the outlook was pretty hopeless. There was just nothing one could do but sit in the dark and hope there was a way out! It was amazing though. Nobody seemed troubled, and several men were cracking jokes. I chatted to the folks around me and that helped to pass the time away, though I felt a bit lonely and sick when we were first told we'd be there some time, and then again when railwaymen came through looking so worried.

In the end, at 9 o'clock, people from the coach behind us started moving back to the end of the train, so we all followed suit, and had to walk along the sleepers back in the direction of Mile End. We came out through an air shaft, and I got a bus back to London. It was heavenly when we first got out into the fresh air.

All I can say is thank goodness I wasn't just a minute or two earlier at Tottenham Court Rd., or I would have caught the train that crashed. I kept thinking of Ernest being buried in a trench during the war, and I've never been able to visualise so clearly just how he must have felt when he heard voices saying they couldn't get him out. To me – with all the space on the train – it would have been <u>dreadful</u>. How much worse it must have been for him in a confined space in a trench with two other men who had been killed. That thought helped me no end while I was waiting. And then as I walked back along the sleepers I thought of the <u>100 mile</u> trudge he and 6 others had to do along the sleepers in Norway, to get to safety.

We wouldn't have known what had happened if we hadn't heard it on the 10 o'clock news when we got back to Foley St. I tried to phone you because I'd said I was going to Buckhurst Hill and thought you might be a bit worried if you heard the news. By the time I rang Ernest he'd heard the news and was almost hysterical. "Thank goodness you're all in one piece," were his first words. Eileen and Ivan were relieved when I rang because they'd been waiting for me for supper, and Jonathan stayed up to see me.

Must now go to the post with this, and of course I'm longing to see you for my next day off.

12th April
We've just been given the schedule for our 2 weeks in Block MAY 18th – 30th.

I'm nearly going scranny with all the work now for the State exam.

There's so much to revise, and this time I really am being serious about it all. In those 2 weeks in Block, I have:

- 12 lectures on surgery by Dr. Handley. Extra tutorials on surgery by sisters afterwards because they say the doctors leave out such a lot of important facts!
- 4 lectures on Bacteriology by Prof. Selbie plus a demonstration on bacteriology.
- 5 theatre lectures by Sister Barlow, in Woolavington theatre (in the Private Wing).
- 2 lectures on Chest surgery and 2 on Orthopaedics by Mr. Newman. We also go to the Fracture clinic to watch blood being taken from blood donors.
- 6 Materia Medica lectures by Sister Webb-Johnson and a few nursing lectures.
- Revision of all our PTS subjects, and 6 lectures on elementary psychology.

So you see the time will be pretty full! We shall have about an hour each day for study and I think I could do with a whole day! How I shall ever get through it all I don't know! But this time it is absolutely VITAL!

It's now 6.15 and I came off duty at 5.30. I've been out to buy some Dreft, and tried unsuccessfully to find some file paper. I'm free for the rest of the evening but have so much work to do that really I'm not very free at all!

On Saturday, when you went to "Iolanthe", I was working till 8.15, having had the afternoon off. I got my pay and we've got 3/6 tickets for the Albert Hall on Monday evening at 7.30. Sir Adrian Boult and Eileen Joyce are performing in a Beethoven-Tchaikovsky programme. I'm not very fond of either, but the other three want to go.

On Tuesday night we drank tea in Bish's room and had a good laugh and listened to the Budget. Isn't it awful. Then there's the news about General MacArthur and the Coronation Stone.

Last night I had to do some work so just had a quick cup of tea in Di Willis's room and departed. They all love the nighties Stella Caunt has made for my trousseau!

13th April

Mummy darling I hope you're not too lonely without Daddy and Shirley. But no doubt you will cope! You must have a day in London with me before I leave.

Sister was awfully nice about changing my day off. She gave it to me without any fuss at all. I asked if I could still have my ½ day on Sunday morning.

We've been terribly slack on the ward today – much too slack in fact. I hate that feeling of knowing you ought to be doing something and yet not knowing what you <u>can</u> do. We've had rather an amusing time too with a little boy of about 4 who speaks nothing but Hebrew or something. It must be horrible for the poor little soul.

The daffodils and primroses look <u>wonderful</u> in my room. Everybody admires them. Well now I'm going to bed – it's 10 o'clock and I feel sleepy!

16th April

I had quite an interesting day today. I went to Mr. Brown's clinic in Outpatients this morning, so was only on the ward from 8-9.30 and then 2-4.30pm. Tomorrow I have a lecture in the afternoon so that will be another "spivvy" day. And this is Sister's weekend off so we shall have fun and games, even though she's very nice always. I wonder where I shall go after G.O.S. I think probably the eye ward. I shall break my heart, I think, when I have to leave these kiddies. They're so absolutely adorable, and I've become so attached to them.

I had an early night last night – in bed by 10 past 10. Tonight I hope to be even earlier.

20th April

I was hoping to get a letter in the post for you today, and just as I was about to begin I remembered I'd promised to ring Mrs. Tomlinson about the square dancing classes. Whereupon I took myself to the telephone complete with 3 pennies and got through to them. But she had some quite worrying news about her daughter Jo. She developed a cough before Christmas and when it didn't improve the doctor said she must have an x-ray and they discovered a patch of TB in one lung. Her mother nursed her at home for a week or two and then she went into Brompton hospital. Now she's at Frimlay convalescent home for a few weeks. Sometime in July they hope to go to Nottingham and will try to see you. I said I hoped it might coincide with the wedding!

Well so much for that! When you receive this letter it will be your wedding anniversary – the 23rd one! Many, many congratulations to you both, you dear wonderful darlings. I have been thinking how excited you must have been this time 23 years ago. Now that the same thing is happening to me I can imagine how you must have felt! What a lovely time to get married – the beginning of spring just when everything is waking up. It's lovely to know that you've always been happy too. Several girls here have parents who are divorced, and I just can't imagine how awful it must be not having a real home to go to.

We've had a SUPER warm day today – though of course I couldn't be out in the sun till 5 o'clock. But oh how wonderful this extra hour of daylight is – the evenings seem so much longer and everything is much more cheerful!

I'm pleased to hear you've ordered the invitations, especially that Mr. Millward will print the Service Sheets as a present! Of course we hoped he might, didn't we?!

Mrs. Tomlinson asked if I'd seen anything of Tony Carter (whom I met there at a dancing class and who is a medical student here). I said I'd seen him once or twice, and lo and behold after I'd finished talking to her I saw him in the hall on my way down to supper. He's more or less engaged, I think, to Diana Wood who was at the High school with me. She's a Staff Nurse here.

I've just washed my hair and now I'm going to bed – it's about 10.15. I <u>have</u> been having some early nights for a change. On Friday I developed an enormous boil on the end of my nose, so I thought a bit of sleep was indicated. And it did the trick – the boil has gone!! I was asleep at 9.15 the other night.

Ernest should have come to London this weekend, but his vicar is now not returning from his holiday till Saturday. So Ernest can't come after all. I'm jolly disappointed, but he's coming for my day off from my new ward whenever it may be.

24th April

I'm getting worse and worse at my correspondence. There's only 10 minutes till the post goes! I've been busy this evening discovering where I'm moving to on Monday, and when my off duty will be. I'm going to 1st floor Woolavington wing – the private wing – where I worked for a month with Bridget Boyle on my 2nd night duty. My day off next week is Saturday, with a half day before it on Friday, and the following week I have ½ day Tuesday and day off on Wednesday.

I'm so furious because Ernest was hoping to come up for my day off this week as you know, and then when he said he wouldn't be able to after all, I changed my day off with a girl who wants to go to a wedding tomorrow! Hence I had Wednesday instead this week. And <u>now</u>, if you please, Ernest's vicar has said that he <u>could</u> come this weekend, and of course I've <u>had</u> my day off! I could swear – but I don't, as you know! Ernest is terribly fed up. So we decided that he should come for my day off <u>next</u> week, as long as it was Wed, Thurs, or Friday. And as luck would have it you see it's Saturday, and Ernest has a Diocesan Conference at Mansfield that day. The following week he's all booked up, so everything in the garden is b---- awful!!!

I hope I get some wedding presents on Woola!! I'll tell them <u>all</u> I'm getting married, I think! By the way you can add another pair of sheets to the list, which Mary is giving us.

Yes the "Teddy Bear" was really good – there were 2 child actors in it who were <u>very</u> good. The whole thing was very well staged. On Wednesday evening Bish and Paddy and I went to a Newsreel at 8 o'clock after they came off duty.

Must fly or I'll miss the post!

27th April
Oh – how hectic it is on Woola after G.O.S! I was so glad to come off duty at 1.30!! I hated leaving G.O.S. last night – I could have wept. I've <u>never</u> felt so sad at leaving a ward before. And Sister was so sweet. She said she really would miss me, and that she hoped I would go back and see them sometime when I'm free. One of the things I shall miss most is being able to take a child (who is well enough) out of the cot and hold them and dance around to the music that plays continuously. Just to see them smile and look happy. They're all so adorable.

Now this morning at 7.30 I went on 1st floor Woolavington wing, where I was on night duty 18 months ago, as I think I said in my last letter. I have three women patients for whom I am completely responsible, and I'm really quite busy. The routine is so entirely different too – I've been in quite a turmoil this morning trying to get everything done. Being there on night duty has helped as far as knowing where things are kept, but everything else is new.

The patients are nice, but when they pay for being in hospital they're so fussy! It doesn't help one to get the work finished on time when they keep ringing their bells to have the windows opened, or the telephone brought in, or their pen filled! But that's just Woola!

I said in my last letter that I might come home this week I think. But I've managed to change my day off to Wednesday, so Ernest is coming up tomorrow. I have a ½ day tomorrow – off at 2, so it will be rather nice. But I'll come home definitely next week – arriving about tea-time on Tuesday for Wednesday day off. It will mean returning about 8 on Wednesday as per the last few times I've been home. Those would be the days you have W-l and clubs and things,

Mum, but it can't be helped. I <u>must</u> come home, otherwise it will be over a month.

I went to see Ivan and Eileen again on Saturday. I rang them up on Friday and they asked me to stay over Saturday night, as I didn't have to be on duty till 12 on Sunday. So I got there about 7 on Saturday and left about 10.30 yesterday morning. It was great fun. Eileen and Ivan have given me my belated 21st birthday present of a set of pink dressing table mats.

3rd May

I'm so sorry it's so long since I wrote to you, my dears. I feel very dreadful about it and hope you will forgive me.

Ernest and I had a wonderful time together, even though it hardly stopped raining the whole of the time. He arrived at 25 to 2 on Thursday afternoon and I didn't come off duty till 20 past 2 as it happened (instead of 2) so... in spite of all my plans he had to wait a whole hour for me by the time I had changed. We arranged to stay at a hotel in London the following night. We thought it would be as well to book the day before. Then we spent an hour trying to find our way out of London. We had gone away from our usual route when we went to this hotel, so we had quite a lot of trouble getting back to it a different way.

However we plodded on in the pouring rain, and decided we wouldn't go far as it was such awful weather.

Eventually we saw this lovely old place at Newland's Corner – a very picturesque spot 3 miles from Guildford, and where, strangely enough, our set went from PTS for our picnic. Unfortunately we weren't able to appreciate the countryside in the rain.

We had dinner quite soon after we arrived at the hotel, then coffee in the lounge. But we got tired of jabbering females in the lounge after awhile, so we went out for a walk in the rain!! It was too much sitting there and having to make polite conversation!

On Friday morning we had breakfast at 9 o'clock and then we went into Guildford and looked round the shops, and had a coffee, and arrived back at Newlands Corner in time for 1 o'clock lunch. In the afternoon we drove over to Seale on the spur of the moment, to see the Ginevers. They had their school in session, as I only remembered when we were on the way – but Peter was still at home and entertained us for about an hour. Auntie Violet was at a Mother's Union meeting in Farnham and wouldn't be back till 5.30, so we couldn't stay to see her. But Uncle Edwin finished teaching at 3.45, and he and Peter made some tea in record time, and we had a good old chat over cups of tea and so on.

Maureen came in from school about 4.30 so we saw her too. It was all very happy. We set off back to London soon after 5 and arrived at 7, and felt that the hotel dining room was far too super and that we would rather go out somewhere else for supper. So we went to Lyons Brasserie and it was marvellous with the band playing to us. Incidentally the meal was pretty expensive anyway.

I suppose it was the Night Porter who called us on Saturday morning at 6.15 – with tea and bread and butter for breakfast! Anyway I was on duty early, before anyone else, and Ernest went straight back to Nottingham.

And now it's such a lovely day (after all that rain!) that I've been sitting in the sun on the roof for the first time this year.

I had an appointment last week to see Matron to tell her I am leaving after my State exams. She was very nice, and I've fixed my leaving date for 18th June (Thursday). I can hardly believe the three years are <u>over</u> and in just over 2 months we shall be married!

Thank you for sending one of the wedding invitations for me to see. They are even more super than I was expecting they'd be.

I've just had tea and am on duty in 5 minutes, so must fly!! And then later I have clean strings and cap to make up tonight, and do my laundry to be collected tomorrow.

Thank goodness Matron didn't know I was leaving before I went to Great Ormond Street. She would never have allowed me the luxury! And it was something I loved so much and wouldn't have wanted to miss.

6th May
I'm so sorry my letters have been so few and far between just recently, but I'm afraid they might have to be the same from now

until I leave. 4 weeks tomorrow we have our State written papers, and there's a fantastic amount to be learnt before then – and do you realise that 3 years ago tomorrow you brought me to London to <u>start</u> my training?! On Saturday we shall be <u>4th year nurses</u> – V.I.P!! There's so much to tell you, but in my last letter it was time to go back on duty and I couldn't write any more.

First and foremost it's simply <u>heavenly</u> weather and such a pity to be stuck in London! I wish I were in our garden, sitting on the terrace, mowing the lawn etc. I'm regretting that I didn't bring back any summer clothes, but I'll bring them back next week. Do you realise it is almost 4 weeks since I came home?

I'm going out this morning to match the material for the tops of the bridesmaids' dresses. I've also been trying to choose a head-dress for myself, but simply can't decide on one. I really would like you to send me some of my savings. I shall get £30 in August which can go with my savings, so what do you think? It depresses me to see Isobel and Stannard getting nearly all the things they need, and they're not getting married till <u>after</u> me! I dreamt the other night that it was closing time for the shops on the day before the wedding and I hadn't got any of my trousseau! I had another dream too – strangely enough the same night as Daddy had <u>his</u> dream about the wedding! There was ½ an hour to go before the wedding and I was in Aspley near the church watching everyone filing into the wedding. But I still had to go all the way back home to get ready and then back to Aspley. I knew the bus was hopeless – an hour there and an hour back – so I had to drive myself in the car, and of course I couldn't get the car going! So I went back to church to <u>you</u> and said I couldn't possibly do it in time, and the wedding would have to be postponed to another day! But Daddy said, "Oh no! You can't disappoint all these people!" So <u>he</u> drove me back home and somehow we were only ¼ hour late for the wedding! The number of dreams I have about the wedding!! – and in every single one something goes wrong! and nearly always it's that I'm late!

I was most interested to hear about the water cuts, and it has provided me with a good point of conversation with my Woola patients! They're all so intelligent and I find it's more effort keeping the conversation going than doing their treatment! Are there any books on the "art of conversation"??? If there are I'd like to read them! They're all in single rooms as I've told you, so I wish my mental capacity had more magnitude!! Some people are much easier to talk to than others aren't they? But with those who have nothing forthcoming, when one subject is worn out it gets rather difficult. There's a sudden lull while I go through the letters of the alphabet to find another idea! It's safe enough to begin at W with the weather, but you can't talk about the weather every time you go in!

I've had some super presents from them. One of my patients goes home today, and yesterday when I went to say goodbye to her she gave me £1. Another is going to knit me a bed jacket and wants to know my size in stockings, and has already treated me to two morning coffees and one afternoon tea in my off duty. She is a Bacteriologist – Dr. Watson, aged about 50. She is the aunt of one of our Honoraries. Then Mrs. Packham goes home today and is not a particularly important person, and Mrs. Peltz runs a Jewish shop on Oxford Street, with her husband, and she is definitely not very interesting! I don't have any difficulty talking to her – she never stops talking to <u>me</u> about her son who is training to be a doctor in Dublin. We've also had the Honourable Lady Whittaker, and Dame Katherine Courtnay. I brought Dame C. back from theatre and had the time of my life slapping her face to bring her round!! Who would have believed I'd ever have the opportunity to slap the face of a DAME?!

For the past 10 days I've been waking up deaf in my right ear. So yesterday I went to the R.M.O and he's given me some drops to put in for 3 days, after which he will syringe it for me. I said, "Is that too <u>little</u> or too <u>much</u> washing?!" And he said if you make a lot of wax you get this sort of trouble, so we must be a waxy family because Shirley had the same trouble didn't she?

Oh – we've also had on Woola the brother-in-law of the man who produced "The Teddy Bear" – the play Paddy and I went to see. He was dishing out free tickets!

How sweet of you, Mummy darling, to bottle rhubarb for our new house as well as yourself. You think of everything. While Ernest was here in London, his mother stripped the wallpaper off the hall walls, my dears, and stained the upstairs floors! Also Mrs. Flewitt said she

273

thinks we'd best like a cheque for a present. She's also given us a bedroom chair, a spade, and a watering can!! And Hilda Young has given us a bathmat.

Paddy, Mary, Bish and I went to the flix last night. It's the first time we've all been together for ages. Now I'm going shopping and then doing some STUDY.

10th May

Thank you so much for your newsy letter received on Friday. I just don't believe it, my darling Mama, that you think you won't be able to order me about for much longer!! I should be very sad if the day came when that happened! I really mean that. The way you talk anyone would think that from 18th July onwards I become cut off from the Bryan family. Don't you realise, my dear sweet Mummy, that I still go on being your daughter even if I'm married and have another name! I'm so thrilled because we shall be able to do things together – you, Daddy, Ernest and me – which we haven't been able to do while I've been in London. It will be such fun. And you can order me about as much as you please! I shall love it!!

I'm so glad I was put on Woola for my last few weeks here. I <u>am</u> enjoying it. I once thought this last year would be terrible. I had visions of Children's Nursing on Bernhard Baron with that awful Sister, and a terrifying time on theatre, gruelling hospital finals and then State! But things never are so bad are they? I was <u>blessed</u> with Great Ormond Street and had a lovely time there. I enjoyed theatre so much that I wished I could go back there! And the exams weren't too bad either. Sister Smith on Woola is very nice when you get to know her, and the work is marvellous.

The visitors who come to visit the Woola patients bring flowers from their gardens, and recently several have brought lilac which was freshly picked. It makes me realise that our lilac must be in bloom too, and the garden is looking lovely I expect. I wonder if any of the plants in the "Coronation Border" are in flower yet? I miss all this in London.

Mr. Vaughan Hudson – our Senior Surgeon – went to Buckingham Palace last Monday when his daughter was presented. Mr. Vaughan

H. said the Queen looked very tired, and Philip looked as if he was ready to bite off their heads!! But he was quite impressed with it all.

Sorry this letter is so untidy but I'm hurrying because I must do some work.

I dreamt last night that Ernest was told he had to marry the girl who lived in the end cottage on Aspley Lane instead of me! He didn't seem to mind at all – just took it as a matter of course. But I hated the dream – it was awful! I had my ears syringed yesterday morning and now they're perfectly alright again. Sister Clarke, the Home sister, did them so I expected it to be done very much à la Middlesex Hospital PTS standards. But, my dears, she soaked me to the skin. Literally – even my vest was sopping wet. And we're taught to direct the flow onto the cheek first so that the patient is prepared, but she bunged the nozzle in my ear and the water went wooshing (good word!) in so fast that I really thought it would come out the other side! However it certainly had its desired effect! I noted the polite conversation throughout the process too – when was I going to be married and was it a white wedding and so on!

Well that's all for now. The train gets in about 5.30 on Friday, but I'll check up.

12th May
Our 2nd engagement anniversary and Ernest has sent me a lovely card and some exquisite pale pink carnations. I'm so thrilled. I also had a screamingly funny letter from him saying he'd been to the church Jumble Sale and found a coffee service, two copper jugs, a cut glass decanter, a biscuit barrel, a cake stand, a gadget to cut mint, a pan scrubber, and last but not least a CARRYCOT FOR RODERICK!! All for 7/6!!!

I spent all my off duty yesterday shopping for patients, and this morning I've been doing ironing for Dr. Watson, so what time is there left for study? I did some work on Sunday though, and found it came back quite easily. And I enjoyed doing it too, knowing it needn't be rushed. I must do some work now. On Friday the train gets in at 6.6pm. (3.20 from Marylebone).

18th May

It was so lovely to be home again but oh how the time flies! But this time I shan't have 4 or 5 weeks to wait – we have been given Whit Monday off, so I shall be home at tea-time on Saturday till Monday night.

I had a good journey back on Saturday evening, and arranged all my flowers before I went to bed. They look wonderful and the maid is overwhelmed! She said to me today, "What a lot of flowers you have in your room. Where <u>did</u> you get them?" You see my carnations are still exquisite too.

I said farewell to my patients on Woola last night and had yet another promise of a wedding present. One sweet old lady who has a special day and night nurse asked what I would like, and I said cutlery! I thought she would perhaps give us some teaspoons. But, my dears, she said, "Have you got a <u>canteen</u>?" I didn't like to say <u>yes</u> in case we haven't <u>got</u> the other yet! Dr. Watson gave me a box of assorted cream cakes! They are so rich that I've had to share them with the rest of the gang!

The first day in Block has been splendid, and I really feel in the spirit for working hard. I'm determined to get through this time. We had a "clinical" on the ward this morning – one of the registrars gave us a very enlightening talk on his particular patients. It was meant to be <u>revision</u>, but I <u>learnt</u> lots and lots that I didn't know before. The revision lectures have been very helpful too.

We have been off since 5.30 and I've been over to Queen Mary ward to see Mrs. Naylor. She's been moved from the side ward into the ward. She's such a sweet soul, but oh dear what a <u>sight</u>. This cancer of the skin is a dreadful thing. Her face is so disfigured and all her hair is falling out. She has to wear gloves to prevent her rubbing the skin, and it really doesn't look the sort of thing to improve at all, even with palliative treatment. She says her husband goes to see her every weekend, but apart from him she has no visitors. It must be a miserable existence for her. I must go and see her again and take her some flowers. She can't read because her eyes are affected, and of course with gloves on she can't do anything with her hands. So I imagine she just lies there with her sorrows. She sometimes listens to the wireless, but can't always be bothered, she says. And she obviously doesn't like mixing with the other patients as far as I can gather, and presumably they don't attempt to be very friendly with her. Although she's such a very sweet person her outward appearance is rather repulsive.

It's getting on for 9 o'clock now and post time, and at 9.15 Mary, Paddy, Bish and I are going to have coffee. Then I shall go to bed early for a change. Sitting down all day has made us all terribly sleepy! I do hope you won't mind if I don't write again before I come home on Saturday. I do feel that I must work though, as you can understand.

27th May
The beginning of the "last lap"! 3 weeks tomorrow the Middlesex will be a thing of the past! That seems so strange!

Work didn't go down very well yesterday after I'd had such a lovely time at home. Today I'm more in the spirit of study, but nevertheless I'll be thankful when there's no need for any more stress with exams looming. Block finishes on Saturday at lunchtime, and we go back on the wards on Sunday morning. I am going to <u>Ground</u> floor Woola – not 1st floor where I was before Block. Apparently they have enough nurses on 1st floor now, and are short on Ground floor. It won't make much difference except that I should have loved to have gone back with the nurses with whom I worked before, and especially to have joined in their CORONATION DAY party. I hope someone on Ground floor has a television! But no doubt something will be organised.

Mary couldn't go home after all at the weekend. Her sister came home from the WRAF for Whitsun with German measles. Mary didn't want to catch it just before State. So Paddy's plans were messed up too, as she was going home with Mary. The two of them spent the weekend here at the Nurses' Home.

The train on Monday evening was <u>packed</u>, and while Ernest and I were keeping our eyes skinned for an empty seat, Isobel Porter came up to me and said she'd got a seat in the 1st class compartment. She'd come from Derby on that train. She decided it was no fun standing in the 3rd class all the way. So we both paid a bit extra, and it was worth it to travel in comfort. In the same compartment was a

Methodist Minister – Mr. Haines – who had come over for the Cliff College Festival. Isobel's father is a local preacher and she met this man at Cliff College on Monday through her father. It was interesting hearing all about his family and so on. We got a taxi in London – Isobel is even more extravagant than I am! I said I was going by bus, but she didn't want to be bothered!

The lupins look lovely, but my goodness they do drink a lot of water! I have to refill the vase twice a day!

Last night we went swimming for the first time this year. It was super and I really could swim from one side to the other. We were in for about 20 minutes, and then had a warm shower afterwards. I think I'll go again tonight.

I had a postcard yesterday from Dr. Watson – my patient on Woola who knitted the bed jacket for me. She's home in Kent and seems to be making good progress. Also you know I told you that Mrs. Samuel – another old Woola patient – had promised to send me a wedding present of linen? Well she's sent a most beautiful tablecloth – <u>tea</u>cloth embroidered in Madeira. I'm so thrilled with it. It came actually from Selfridges, so you see she remembered!

Well now I must get down to some more work. Cheeribye for now and God bless you.

30th May

I've been thinking about you so much since dear Miss Monk's sudden collapse. I've nursed several people after attacks like she had. That man on Woola who used to call me Sally Ann Howes (my first time on Woola) had a cerebral haemorrhage and was paralysed down one side. He was unconscious at first – they usually are – but he got better, and when he went home he was able to walk with help. These folks do get better with good nursing, unless they have weak hearts which won't stand the strain. I don't know if Miss Monk is worse or better, but I shouldn't give up hope. It would be a long business for her and those looking after her, but it would be worth it.

What a shame you had such a trying time and such a shock when it happened. You couldn't have anticipated such accidents happening, you poor dears. I know what a heart-aching job it is even when these folks are in hospital, but in your own lounge it is ten times worse.

And it isn't always the way that everything comes at once. You certainly had your share of troubles last week.

I'm spending the weekend with Eileen and Ivan. They gave me a half day yesterday and day off today from Woola. Eileen and Ivan insisted that I stayed the night, and I'm now going to stay to lunch and SWOT here. They're both such fun, and my Godson is a darling – he seems to remember me now and follows me around all over the place! I'm thrilled because he used to be so shy.

Block finished yesterday quite happily after a HECTIC time! We were told to be in the Lecture room by 10.30 for a test, and at 10.45 we were still waiting and no tutors had turned up. We couldn't study because we'd been told to clear away all our books, so it was an utter waste of time. We all got so furious that I plucked up courage and went to find one of the Sister Tutors. I found Sister Grahame and said, "What time is this thing supposed to start?" She was a bit dumbfounded I think! But she came and looked through the lecture room door and said, "When you're all sitting down in straight lines, two desks apart, then we are ready!" So while she stood at the back of the room watching I marched up to the front of the class and passed on the instructions! Then I went back to her and told her we were ready! It just made my blood boil having to wait, when we could have been doing other things!

The exam is on Thursday. The Medicine paper from 10am to 11.30 and Surgery and Gynae from 2-4.30. Keep your fingers crossed for me. Failing Hospital Finals has rather un-nerved me.

I must get down to some more work now. 2 weeks on Thursday I'll be home for good! Just think – ! Not long now and if only I can pass State I shall feel so triumphant that I managed to finish my training and not give in part way through.

On Friday morning we had an hour of "Practical Team Work". We are all divided into groups of 8 in Block, and we had to select three representatives from each group to <u>perform</u> while the others watched. One of the Sister Tutors was the patient, and for each set of three representatives she staged an "emergency" with which they had to cope. I am in Group 1, and our crew chose Paddy, Evans and <u>me</u> to represent them. As we were Group 1 we sort of broke the ice and were all terrified. But it was <u>great</u> <u>fun</u> and we all enjoyed it. We had a Rigor to deal with, and I was jolly pleased with myself because I was the only one who thought of turning off the Blood Transfusion! Blowing my trumpet again you see!

I must stop now as lunch is ready and then I must work.

8th June

On Monday I started on Ground Floor Woola and there was absolutely nothing to do. So it was rather boring. But it did give me time to do some study in odd moments. I had an evening off and Paddy was off too and feeling so fed up that she cried her eyes out (almost!). So she and Bish and I decided we'd go to the Medical School Dance to cheer ourselves up! So that was another late night. It was 1am.

Mary had a Coronation Seat in her father's club off Whitehall. Paddy stayed out <u>all</u> <u>night</u> after the dance! – with 5 medical students. She didn't have any sleep of course, but saw the procession perfectly, so it was well worth it. I managed to see quite a lot of the day on television on the ward – really exciting.

Wednesday we got a bit worried about State of course, and then came Thursday <u>and</u> <u>State</u>! Two questions I'd learnt up specially the day before the exam!! How lucky!

The party was super at Barnett's after the exam, and yes my dress was admired. There were about a dozen of us altogether and Mr. and Mrs. Barnett. There were 6 of us and 6 students. We all met in the front hall of the hospital at 7pm, and then had to wait <u>ages</u> for a No. 3 bus to Upper Norwood. In the end one came – after we'd waited an hour! It was pretty full so the others got on and I was left with 3 men! They didn't know the way at all, and I'd only been there twice before, but we all arrived safely about 9.15.

We had delicious eats and then played "Demon Patience" all evening – all of us round one table. A taxi came for us at 12.30am for which we all paid our share, and we got back to London about 1.15am. The taxi left us outside Joey Lyons on the Strand – the only one that stays open after midnight. We had coffee there and sang silly songs! I'm sure the other folks must have thought we were drunk but we weren't! Just elated to have the written exam over. We arrived back at the Nurses' Home at 2.15am!

I had to wash my hair before I went to bed because I was due to have my free Perm next morning at Callinans, and they'd asked me to wash it the night before. So at 2.30am I was washing and drying my hair!

10th June

I've suddenly got a day off to come home – I didn't think I would be home again till the 18th! I don't come off duty till 2.30pm so can't catch a train till 3.20. I think I shall be due for a day off next week as I'm staying till Thursday officially. So the idea is that I count Thursday as my day off and leave on Wednesday night. My Practical exam is at 9.30 on Thursday morning but at least I can walk out of that to <u>freedom</u>!!

There seems to be so much to do before I leave. I want to go to the dentist and the chiropodist and I'm having my hair set on Monday morning.

The Gang are all very excited about their wedding invitations and are deciding what they're going to wear!

14th June

Only three more days! If only there wasn't the worry of this beastly Practical it would all be so thrilling. Nevertheless I'm very excited now, and there's so much to do. I have all my packing to begin tomorrow. I'm having my hair set in my off duty tomorrow and then on Thursday there are several bits of shopping I must do. All this as well as trying to do some work for the exam. I think we shall have our "Gang festivities" on Tuesday evening after all. Mary has a "firm party" – of all doctors and nurses from the floor on which she works – on Wednesday, and Di has swimming practice.

I wish this miserable weather would look a bit more like summer! It's so depressing.

Mrs. Lustig – one of my patients – gave me the material yesterday for the stiff petticoat for my wedding dress, so that's lovely! I must be off to lunch now. I <u>did</u> enjoy my day with you!

17th June

Just a wee note to let you know that I've <u>almost</u> left! This is my afternoon off and Ernest is coming up to London tomorrow, arriving about lunchtime. We want to do a bit of shopping in London and then start on our way home. We'll be spending the night wherever we find a suitable hotel en route, so will be back home for lunch on Friday.

It doesn't seem a bit as if I'm leaving – isn't it strange?! The work has to go on just the same on the day before you're leaving as on any other day. I haven't <u>started</u> my packing yet!

Paddy and Mary and Di and lots of others have now had their exams. The Hammersmith hospital ones seem to have been OK – Paddy went to Hammersmith but Mary and Bish went to Paddington and were very fed up. I'm going to Paddington for 9.30 tomorrow, so I'm wondering what on earth it will be like. But still – this time tomorrow it will be over. I can't really realise that I've got to the stage of taking State! I can't think that <u>I</u> am clever enough to take <u>final</u> exams to <u>qualify</u>! Think of me 9.30-10.30 tomorrow morning!

We had our little celebration last night. I got some cheap sherry – cooking sherry I think – and chocolate biscuits and strawberries and we enjoyed it all. We all dressed up and looked really silly but it was hilarious.

I've been moved for my last day to 4th floor Woolavington Wing to relieve as they're so short-staffed. It was a bit maddening just the last day. However they're nice folks so why worry?

My love to you all, and the <u>last</u> <u>letter</u> <u>from</u> <u>Foley</u> <u>Street</u>!!! It seems unreal!

Well – the results come out on 28th July, so <u>you</u> will have to open the envelope and tell me the news on our honeymoon! Ernest doesn't want me to work after we're married, but I do need my SRN just in case. AND I SHALL GET IT, YOU SEE!! (and I <u>did</u>!)

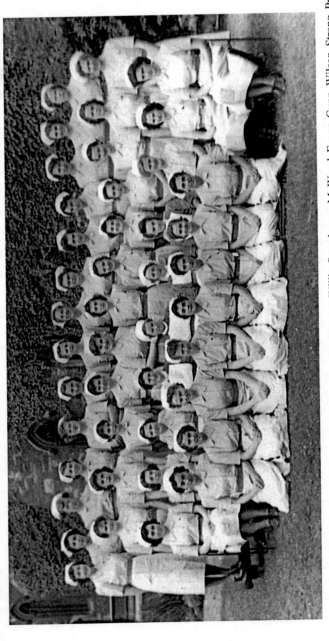

Back from left: Niblett, Simpson, Bishop, Marles, Langley, De Carteret, Willis, Saunderson, M. Wood, Evans, Gunn, Wilson, Strong, Priest
Second row standing: O'Conner, Porter, Bell, Luck, Burley, Yates, Logan, Fletcher, S. C. Jones, Haworth, Bryan, Thompson
Sitting: Powell, Strugnell, Willmott, Sister Byron, Sister Slater, Sister Burgess, Sister Jackson, Wright, Bryeant, Gee
Front: Stannard, E. P. Jones, Mackie, Ellerby, Sebire, Woolveridge, Sellicks, Key

283

Postscript

So now Middlesex Hospital THANK YOU for my 3 years training which made it possible for me to become a STATE REGISTERED NURSE, and move on to a completely new and exciting life, beginning with my wonderful marriage to the Reverend Ernest Sheeran in St. Margaret's Church Aspley Nottingham.

From St. Giles' Parish church where Ernest did his second curacy – this report in the church magazine:

"A beautiful service took place in Aspley Church on July 18th, when Rev. E.W. Sheeran was married to Miss Nina Bryan. The Bishop wore his robes as D.D. of Nottingham University, and he made the service impressive and full of meaning. He was assisted by the Rector of St. Giles. The music and flowers added to the scene in this fine modern church, when the former vicar gave his daughter away, and the bridegroom was attended by the present vicar, Rev. T. Richardson as Best Man. A large contingent came over from this parish, and the whole Fellowship seemed to be having a morning out, armed with confetti. It was a happy ceremony altogether, and was continued at the College of Agriculture at Sutton Bonington, the bride's home village. All their friends wish them every happiness, and Mrs. Sheeran has already made many friends and received a warm welcome. There is much to do and think of, when beginning home life, and we must not expect her to join all the church organisations at once.

They left by car for the Island of Arran, and will be there for about 3 weeks. Arran is a bit of the Highlands dropped in the sea! We hope the car will survive the crossing and bring them safely back."

From the Young People's Fellowship early in July:
"A Splice of life"

We are very pleased to announce that the curate, Rev. E. Sheeran, is to be married on Sat. July 18th. Needless to say, Fellowship arrangements for this momentous occasion are proceeding very much to plan!

18th July 1953
Ernest and Nina Sheeran
on their Wedding Day
at St Margaret's Church, Aspley, Nottingham

And after the ceremony:

"AND SO IT CAME TO PASS."

All the many members who attended the wedding of Mr. Sheeran and Miss Nina Bryan will agree that it must have been one of the most beautiful weddings that they have ever attended. The Bishop of Southwell officiated, assisted by the Rector, and the wedding went through without a hitch – in spite of threats of "prankery" by Fellowship members!! The beauty of the bride was equalled by the surprising "composure" of the groom!!

From the father of the bride,
formerly the first vicar of St. Margaret's:

"One of my greatest joys is that the church family has remained faithful and still forms the core of the continuing life of St. Margaret's. That joy is further heightened by the remembrance that the first St. Margaret's boy, Ernest Sheeran, was eventually ordained, in 1950, to become curate to his friend, Tom Richardson. And when on 18th July, 1953, he was married by the Bishop, to our daughter Nina, in the beloved church, with his first vicar giving her to him and his second acting as the Best Man, surrounded by hundreds of our Aspley friends it seemed that our part in the family life of St. Margaret's had been completed in true story-book fashion."

The icing on the cake was a letter received on our honeymoon addressed to – Mrs. E.W. Sheeran S.R.N.!

We soon had a baby boy, Bruce, who is now 55 and has two lovely daughters, aged 22 and 20. We also had a little girl, Julia, three years later, and she is now 52 with two handsome sons aged 29 and 26. Who knows? Maybe soon I shall be a Great Grandmother! They are all the joy of my life, having lost my dear Ernest, after two major strokes, in 1999.

The first Vicar of Aspley (Rev. T.W. Bryan) with his eldest daughter Nina and son-in-law, Ernest Sheeran, at the baptism of Bruce Sheeran on 5th August, 1954

Ernest and Nina Sheeran
with Bruce 3½ and Julia 5 months, 1957

I continued nursing when Bruce and Julia were 12 and 9 years old, and spent 25 years working (surprise, surprise!) on the Operating theatres first at the General Hospital, Nottingham, and then, when it was pulled down, at the big University Hospital. Theatres became my "second home", and I loved every minute working at the "hub of the hospital universe"! I received my 25 years long service award when I was 60! This was a £75 voucher which I spent on winter boots for long service feet!!

I had tremendous job satisfaction on theatres, which was complimented by a very busy life as a vicar's wife for 30 years in what Ernest called "a combined ministry". He became a Canon of Southwell during our time there in Edwalton.

I had to retire at 60 to look after Ernest who had a major stroke in 1991 and another in 1993. He became very disabled after the second one, but I am so proud and thankful that I was able to give him true one-to-one Middlesex Hospital standard nursing which, according to our G.P. gave him several more years. His brain was "ace" to the end, and we managed to actually enjoy those eight years in a very different but very close relationship. His sparkling eyes and beautiful smile captivated all who knew him, as his only method of communication when he could no longer project his voice.

During the 8 years of his disablement we spent holidays about 3 times a year at the Netley Waterside Winged Fellowship Home for the Disabled, with Ernest being wonderfully cared for by trained nurses, while I was with him but resting. He actually died in that place, which we both came to love, 2 minutes through the gardens to Southampton Water, and with a lovely view of the water from our very large room.

On the morning he died, at 5am, I went to him and we had our usual Good Morning Kiss, with him holding my arm with his only active hand – most of the rest of his body being paralysed. He looked into my eyes then with as much love as when we first discovered what we meant to each other when I was 18. So it was a perfect end to a wonderfully happy life together, and I was with him when he closed his eyes and left this earth 5 minutes later.

A Nurse's Prayer

(by Alwyn M. Law)

Lord, give me grace, on this and every day,
To do my work the best, not simplest way;
And to remember that in all I do,
The very smallest task, is seen by you.

Grant to me courage, Lord, when things go wrong,
To stop and think, and not rush blindly on.
And though the task I'm set, may not seem fair,
May I remember, that Thou too, art there.

Give me a humble heart, that I may know,
That things worth while, are not just things that show.
For though efficiency and skill mean much,
The greater gift of all, is Human Touch.

Fill me with love, that I may realise,
The suffering and the pain that round me lies,
And grant each day, that I may seek to share,
The burdens of the people, in my care.

Lord, give me strength, to help me play my part;
To make my work the essence of my heart;
And show me patience, and true kindness Lord,
That I may spread Thy radiance through my ward.

So, when at night, I come back to my rest,
I pray that I may feel I've done my best.
And, Lord, at times I know I forget Thee,
But please forgive, and always be with me.

(Reproduced by kind permission of The Middlesex Hospital)